Decision Methodology

Decision Methodology

A formalization of the O R process

D. J. WHITE
Professor of Decision Theory
University of Manchester

A Wiley–Interscience Publication

JOHN WILEY & SONS
London · New York · Sydney · Toronto

Library of Congress Cataloging in Publication Data:

White, Douglas John.
Decision methodology.
'A Wiley–Interscience publication.'
1. Decision-making. I. Title.

BF441.W48 658.4'03 74-1754
ISBN 0 471 94045 3

Printed in Great Britain by William Clowes & Sons Ltd.,
London, Colchester and Beccles.

Preface

Although systematic analyses of decision situations have undoubtedly been part of life for a very long time, it is only in the last three decades that a significant development of structured approaches to solving decision problems has been achieved. Perhaps the main contribution to this development has come from the Operational Research, or Operations Research, developments stimulated by Second World War military studies. Clearly, however, there are numerous people, working under different titles, who are equally well concerned with decision analysis, and this book is addressed to all such people, with certain minimal technical capabilities. It is not a technical book, but it does require an appreciation of the technicalities of Decision Analysis.

In the carrying out of a particular Decision Analysis, many tools and techniques may be brought to bear upon the problem. In applying these tools many decisions will have to be made about the conduct of the analysis. At all stages we are compromising with the economics of application, and the rigour and degree of sophistication of the study. This book deals with these problems.

Such problems are referred to as 'secondary problems', and the problem which the Decision Analysis seeks to resolve is referred to as a 'primary problem'.

Ackoff,[1] writing on implementation of research results and organization of research effort, which clearly generate secondary problems, says:

'When we discuss implementation of research results and organisation of research effort, this (the building of models to facilitate their analysis) is no longer possible. Although an increasing amount of effort is being put into the study of these aspects of research, and even more into writing about them, they are very poorly understood . . . . In the meantime discussions of implementation and organisation of research are more likely to be based on opinion, experience and wishful thinking, than on analysis, experimentation and systematic observation.'

In writing this book, and dealing with the broad spectrum of secondary problems, this statement is always borne in mind. The book attempts to identify the nature of the problems, and, in some instances, to indicate how they might themselves be formalized as higher-level decision problems. It is expected that such approaches will be arguable, but, if we accept the fundamental importance of these problems, we must also accept some attempt to discuss them. By this process we would hope to add more understanding to what is required to answer the questions which, as Ackoff states, are at present largely resolved by hunch. This problem area is discussed specifically in Chapter 3, on Suboptimization, where reference is made to the work of Minas[87] in this context.

It is to be noted that when we face secondary problems, their appropriate resolution depends on the influence of this choice on the primary decisions based on the analysis. This idea is well established in the area of Statistical Decision Theory which, indeed, constitutes part of the secondary decision methodology. One realizes that, even though it is the most formally developed, it has seen little application. Nonetheless the ideas are relevant and it is hoped that the supplementary ideas of this book will be seen to be equally relevant and pursued further in due course, but on a rigorous footing which the Statistical Decision Theory ideas have now gained. Even if formal models are some way off, the setting up of a framework of conflicts in facing such decisions should be of use.

In considering the difficulties and limitations of a scientific treatment of decision situations, one comes face to face with the acceptability of modelling in many cases and with the temptation to accept subjective views. It must however be remembered that any subjective view is either based on some mental model of the situation or is unsupported. As Forrester[46] says:

'But what justification can there be for the apparent assumption that we do not know enough to construct models, but believe we know enough to design new social systems by passing laws and starting new social programs?'

If one wishes to argue that one approach is better than another then the base of the subjective opinion should be established and compared with proposed alternative bases. On the other hand we do include subjective judgements in our models without querying the appropriateness of such judgements (e.g. in value and uncertainty judgements) and if we do this, then why not accept judgements about the models themselves? The answer to this is that it depends on whether one wishes to provide a supporting framework for such judgements and it is the task of this book to suggest, in a very modest way, how this might be tackled.

In doing this we leave ourselves open to the setting off of an infinite regress in our model building. This point is brought out when examining the application of scientific method, but it is not explored further.

Parallel with the professional development of Decision Analysts, under various headings, has been the development of academic teaching programmes. This book has, in particular, been written on the basis of teaching in a postgraduate Operational Research programme.

Clearly, any students in this area must be aware of the broader issues of the analysis process itself, as well as being made competent in the tools and techniques themselves. Such students very often have little organizational contextual decision material, and this makes such teaching difficult and slow. Nonetheless, although their real grasp of the secondary problem issues will only arise after a lengthy, perhaps painful, experience, which they may thereafter use in the manner of Ackoff's statement, familiarity with these issues, even if in an elementary, and somewhat incomplete, manner, can serve to accelerate the learning process and indeed to provide a framework which experience could clothe in a systematic manner in due course.

The aims of this book are therefore modest in simply attempting to provide the above framework.

In adopting this point of view, it might be argued that attempts to predirect the activities of a decision analysis can be harmful in that they become rigid and restrict the creative aspects of the analyst. These dangers are appreciated and, in the end analysis, the usefulness of such directives will depend on intelligent interpretation of the material. Just as traditional techniques have been criticized for misuse, then so will methodological directives, which begin to assume the form of a technique, at a higher level, be open to criticism.

In considering students' needs, the question of full case studies arises. In this book the approach has been to abstract general ideas from many practical studies, using many elementary examples to illustrate particular points. Many of these projects have been projects on which students themselves have worked, and in which guidance was needed on the points mentioned. Just as reliance on personal experience to resolve the particular secondary problems can founder on inappropriate experience, then so can reliance on case studies founder on the limitations of these. It is not contested that one approach is better than the other, but simply that it is arguable. Clearly it would be useful to see one case study through each of its phases and this is possible with suitable material, which exists in many ways.

In putting forward such illustrations, the book also provides a high variety of material for discussion sessions on particular themes. In addition to this source of discussion material, a set of questions appearing in postgraduate examination papers is included. These questions differ significantly in depth and style, arising from different authors, and no attempt has been made to edit them.

Although the book is addressed to students of Decision Analysis, its content is applicable to many others concerned with the subject in theory and in practice. For example the practising manager would find the material on problem formulation relevant and non-technical.

Before commencing with the main work it is, perhaps, appropriate to mention Hollander's[60] characterization of attitudes which may arise in systems studies. He mentions: the 'problem seeker' (seeking problems to fit his technique, a point mentioned later on when discussing Sciorrino's[114] work); the simplifier (reduces everything to a few variables); the scoffer (only 'gut' feeling can solve the problems of major systems); the ostrich (finds a side issue which he can solve, and ignores real problem); the data collector (collects reams of data on everything); the technique refiner (devotes energies to improving algorithms, etc.); the hypothesizer (postulates complex models when data is scarce); the simulator (makes simplifying assumptions to produce neat models, but forgets his simplifying actions); rigor mortician (every notion or idea to be demonstrated rigorously); the sage, about which he says,

'The sage knows how to design a major system. He is ready to share his wisdom freely with approximately the following prescription: Define the problem, establish your criteria, accumulate the data . . . etc. When he comes to specifics he refers to his recently published book on systems analysis, consisting of survey chapters such as probability theory, elements of operations research, and linear and non-linear programming. Applying these techniques to a major system is an exercise left for the student. The sage is usually found in a consulting capacity among university extension lecturers;'

and the saviour, about which he says:

'High on his throne as the head of a university laboratory sits systems scientists' saviour. He has the global answer for all major systems problems, but for the unwashed he cannot bear to write it down or show its application except for trivial examples in tutorials. Whoever challenges him obviously shows his ignorance. You cannot pass his course or get his approving signature on your dissertation unless you accept his divinity. After a student has been fully immersed in his credo and his disdain for contrary views, he may go forth into industry as a disciple blessed with a Ph.D. as imprimatur. All references to his knowledge are "private communications to his disciples".'

In the successful conduct of Decision Analysis, the recognition of diverse attitudes and the ability to take these into account is clearly important. It is particularly important to understand these, for there is likely to be an element of relevance in each. Many of the points raised by Hollander arise in this book. The final two points are particularly relevant, since they relate to the authority and motives for this book. I hope, in due course, to escape the deadly end of being classified either as a sage or as a saviour, but time alone will tell.

In writing this book, the work of Ackoff has been the main guideline and the central phases discussed are his, although the general orientation and details are somewhat different.

Chapter 1 deals with the general origins and nature of Decision Analysis as a serious development, with reference to system components, technical content and analysis procedures in principle.

Chapter 2 deals with the phases of Decision Analysis as defined by Ackoff, *viz.*, formulating the problem, constructing the model, deriving the solution. As distinct from Ackoff, testing and controlling the solutions and models have been included as part of model construction, reflecting the fact that modelling is an ongoing process and that testing and controlling are an integral part of modelling. In this section in particular, due consideration has been given to the methods of testing; in the section on getting the solution, due consideration has been given to the practicalities of life and to what one might term 'quick methods of solution' which, however, must themselves be subject to test as to adequacy.

In Chapter 3 an attempt is made to look at the specific secondary problems arising in the previous chapter and to examine how they might be posed and resolved in the light of the resources and time factors involved and of the effect of the answers to such problems on the degree of suboptimization of primary problems. It is, in fact, the trade-off between such suboptimality and rigour and effort in the process itself which constitutes the central methodological problem.

In this chapter we have concentrated on the modelling and solution technique secondary problems from specific points of view, and have not included factors linking the analysis to its sponsors, advisors, or to any other people associated with the study. Chapter 4 deals with such factors, which, in principle, will influence the suboptimization factor, but are not considered here as such. The chapter discusses general advisory dogma for Decision Analysts, in the context of choice and extent of problem study, communication with and involvement of, affected parties, and implementation of results.

Chapter 5 provides a source of exercises for students.

These exercises are not edited and consequently differ widely in degree of detail. However, since this is a problem with which practitioners have to contend, some advantage is gained from this. Not all questions are answerable on the basis of this text alone and reference to Ackoff[1] is needed for some.

1973

D. J. WHITE

Contents

CHAPTER 1

Decision Analysis Outline

1.1 Introductory Remarks

The growth of effort allocated to the analysis of decision situations is associated with the growth of Operational Research. In fact this text is concerned with the Operational Research process and the words 'Operational Research Methodology' and 'Decision Methodology' are interchangeable. It is therefore appropriate to say a little about Operational Research, its origins and nature, although the title 'Decision Methodology' will be retained, since this text has equal implications for other areas.

The recognition of Operational Research as a cognate subject matter arose, to a large extent, during the Second World War.

Recognition of the need for analysis of tactical and strategic military operations of different complexities gave rise to the evolution of military groups whose task was to carry out such analyses. Hence the name 'Operational Analysis' or, now, 'Operational Research' came into recognized use. These groups were made up of people with mathematical, statistical and scientific backgrounds.

Blackett[12] gives a general account of military Operational Research investigations. Some of the investigations carried out were as follows, as interpreted by this author:

(a) determination of the optimum convoy size, where empirical data suggested that the bigger its size, then the smaller the proportional losses due to submarine attacks;

(b) determination of the correct colour of aircraft, where it was possible to demonstrate the effective increase in submarines sunk as a result of changing from black to white;

(c) determination of the correct setting of depth charges;

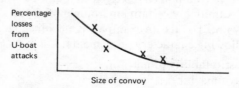

Figure 1. Convoy size problem

(d) determination of the best way to deploy radar units to give maximum coverage of possible enemy attacks.

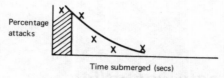

Figure 2. Aircraft colour problem

The essence of much of these initial studies lay in simple mathematical statistical investigations. Even today, much leeway can be made without great sophistication.

Since then there has been an increased attention paid to more complex studies of forms of warfare, of weapons assessment and of general logistics in the military field. The name 'Operational Research' is, therefore, essentially historically justifiable.

Basically Decision Analysis is concerned with formal modelling of decision situations with a view to improving them in some sense. Simon[119] puts it quite simply when he says the basic conflict is between the old, less costly, less reliable, intuitive processes, and the new, more costly, more reliable, formal processes.

In this text the words Decision Analysis, Decision Methodology and Decision Theory are used in specific senses. Decision Analysis is taken to be the actual analysis of a primary problem; Decision Methodology is concerned with a study of the phases involved in such an analysis. Decision Theory is the study of the theoretical foundations of the object and subject system (to be defined later) involving the synthesis of the theory of choice and computational techniques.

1.2 The Subject Matter and the Methodology of Decision Analysis

The basic nature of Decision Analysis has two viewpoints: (A) as a subject; (B) as a methodological approach.

A THE SUBJECT MATTER OF DECISION ANALYSIS

It would be a sterile subject, and indeed, a poor world, if every situation were taken to be unique. Managers are often heard to say, 'but my situation is unique'. But is it? What do we mean by uniqueness?

It is because situations in different areas of an organization, and in different organizations, do have common characteristics that it becomes useful to identify and exploit these. Admittedly certain environmental factors may vary but basic characteristics may not. To take an example, in machine loading many situations will involve the following characteristic elements:

number and substitutability of machines;
processing rates of machines;
arrival patterns of jobs;

value factors for completion times of various jobs;
various cost factors.

The details of these may differ but it is still possible to produce standard procedures for evaluating various classes of this type situation, still allowing for some variation in elements for individual situations. In some cases queueing theory may be used; in others special models are developed; we may have to use simulation.

At present, of course, the proportion of problematic situations for which we have ready-made procedures is small. However, as with other subjects, the process of characterizing such situations is one central aim. The characteristics break into two groups, *viz.*:

(a) those which characterize the problem;
(b) those which characterize the solution procedure.

In group (a) we include the following in Table 1:

Table 1: Problem characterization

Problem situation	Characteristics
Inventory	Supply pattern; replenishment pattern; costs
Queueing	Arrival pattern; service pattern; costs
Maintenance	Deterioration or breakdown pattern; repair/replacement pattern; costs
Critical path analysis	Ordered activities; times; costs
Production overage	Mix of work; wastage characteristics; modifiability of finished product; costs

It is, of course, true that many problems do not fit 'neatly' into compartments like this. They spread into wider connected problems. However, even general problems have focal components and the above characteristics apply to such focal problem components involving judgements on the interface with other components. Thus a simple approach to the overage problem might require a judgement about the value of 'excess production' without providing a method of assessing this, being tied up, as it is, with other decisions on the way excess production may be used.

In group (b) we include the following in Table 2:

Table 2: Solution characterization

Solution procedure	Characteristics
Linear programming	Linear equations and inequalities
Non-linear programming	Non-linear equations and inequalities
Dynamic programming	Sequential decisions and 'Principle of Optimality'
Simulation	Any dynamic situation
Heuristic programming	Any situation

There are also many miscellaneous techniques for tackling production problems, marketing problems, transportation and distribution problems.

Even if we do not have a technique in the bag for every situation, the formal subject matter of Decision Analysis provides a platform on which we can hinge our problem structuring; it stimulates our ability to ask relevant questions, to identify pertinent features of our problem and to put the various factors together.

B THE METHODOLOGY OF DECISION ANALYSIS

We realize that the subject matter, as it now exists in the context of the 'techniques' element described, has limited application as far as (a) goes at least, and to some extent as far as (b) goes. Thus there are problematic situations which we may well have to begin from scratch to study. Out of these studies we will, of course, enlarge our subject matter.

We need therefore to study the Decision Analysis approach, or 'methodology' as it is called, and we will find parallels with other methodologies in work study, method study and systems analysis, for example, to which the subject matter of this text is highly related.

There are two basic elements to our study, *viz.*, (a) subject system; (b) object system.

(a) *Subject System.* This is the collection of decisionmakers for whom the study is being carried out.

(b) *Object System.* This is the system about which decisions are being made, i.e. the system being controlled (see Figure 3).

This model is not comprehensive but is adequate for our purposes for the moment and will be expanded later on.

The three basic features which are emphasized are:

(i) the OBJECT study, which is concerned with relating various alternatives to selected outcomes;

(ii) the SUBJECT study, which is concerned with value judgements of various combinations of outcomes;

(iii) the CALCULATION process, in the diagram identified with the decision process, which calculates the decision to be taken.

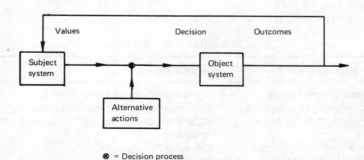

⊗ = Decision process

Figure 3. Subject and object systems

Component (i) is related to our characterization techniques; component (ii) comes under the general heading of theory of choice; component (iii) is related to mathematical optimization techniques.

As we shall see the subjective element enters into our model building in two forms of judgement (see Shelley and Bryan[117]), *viz.*, those judgements involving input processing and those judgements expressing value. Simon's[119] thesis is that management aids play their role in the former type where unreliability of input processing is the human's weak point.

The subjective element will be seen to appear both in the problem formulation stage and in the model construction stage in a very similar way since, ultimately, the empirical premises with which we begin our analysis come from human judgements. Thus the choice of alternatives to consider (problem formulation) has the same subjective bias as the choice of regression model to use (model construction). These phases are separated simply to separate the primary decision specification from its analysis.

1.3 Techniques of Decision Analysis

We have already said that techniques tend to break up into those of problem characterization and those of problem solution. It is worth exploring a little further the basic differences between certain established techniques. This is particularly important for the development of Decision Analysis so that we can avoid this being seen as a miscellaneous collection of techniques and developmental needs can be structured. Consider the following in Table 3 based on White:[153]

Table 3: Decision analysis techniques

Linear programming
Non-linear programming
Dynamic programming
Maintenance theory
Queueing theory
Inventory control
Simulation
Las Vegas
Heuristics
Critical path analysis
Theory of choice
Computers
Statistics.

Quite obviously there are similarities and differences in the content of each of these subject headings as well as interrelations.

First, take linear programming and inventory control. They very often appear together. But a problem in inventory control may be formulated as a linear programme. They are, therefore, radically different with respect to their place in the structure of Decision Analysis.

If we look a little further we see that we consider inventory control analyses in which the idea of prescribing an optimal action simply is not considered, whereas a linear programme is specifically an optimizing technique. Both inventory control and linear programming are 'characterizing' procedures, but in linear programming the 'optimizing' concept is an essential ingredient. In inventory studies quite useful results are obtained of the form 'if this policy is used then this will be the outcome'.

The reason why such an analysis is not complete lies in the characterization of the subject system, i.e. the ultimate decisionmakers. To cater for this we have added, as part of the model-building structure, the theory of choice. This is concerned with the behavioural aspects of a person's selection process in specific situations and encompasses value and uncertainty theories, and the ways in which such theories can be used to obtain a final decision.

A further investigation of critical path analysis leads us to realize that not only are some of the techniques not necessarily optimality oriented but that critical path analysis is not related formally to any action problem. It specifies the critical path and slack activities, but is not of the form 'if act a, then consequence $\theta(a)$'. Yet dynamic programming, as an optimization technique, can provide the critical path.

The interrelation between the concepts, therefore, needs some unravelling. Let us put forward a model of the mathematical modelling processes for this purpose only. The basic concepts needed are:

(A): mathematical characterization of (a) object system; (b) subject system;
(B): solution of mathematical model;
(C): output of mathematical model.

A MATHEMATICAL CHARACTERIZATION

The basic steps are:

(i) define the set of allowable actions;
(ii) determine the 'action–consequence' relation (object system);
(iii) determine the 'consequence–value' relation (subject system).

Let us now look at three of our subject headings, *viz.*: linear programming, non-linear programming and dynamic programming. We see that they have three characteristics, *viz.*:

(a) they are concerned with all three steps and hence are basically optimizing models;
(b) they are applicable, each, to a wide variety of operational situations;
(c) they are abstract models to which an intense mathematical effort has been devoted to getting computational algorithms in a standardized form.

Turning to inventory control and queueing theory we see that these have several characteristics also, *viz.*:

(a) they have basic concepts defining physical operational situations (*viz.*: 'supply–demand' and 'arrival–service' respectively);

(b) they can be usefully analysed, in some cases, without direct consideration of the third (subjective) step, and, in the case where the third step is effective the analysis can be carried out using linear programming, non-linear programming or dynamic programming characterizations;

(c) they apply to a wide variety of differing physical (as distinct from abstract) operations;

(d) the wide variety of differing conditions has led to an intense effort in the analysis of the act–consequence relations for these differing conditions.

One quite rightly asks whether inventory control and queueing theory are the only such areas. One possible candidate is that of allocation operations. The reason why this does not appear separately is that there is a tendency to subsume this within linear programming, as a very frequent application of this model. Items (c) of the first group and (d) of the second group are the real motivating factors for the present emphasis on the groupings above.

What of critical path analysis? There is no phase involving the comparison of alternative acts in this. It simply says 'the consequence will be c'. It provides information on the basis of an action already selected (i.e. selected activities). It fits steps (i) and (ii) only if the set of allowable acts is restricted to the one already chosen. Only by making the activities subject to choice, in some way, does it fall into the usual act–consequence characterization of Decision Analysis. It can, however, be used to suggest decision points in a network.

In all our models we have both deterministic and stochastic (we include adaptive within stochastic) situations and hence statistics (and probability) is an essential subject, governing the rest, relating both to the subjective and objective contents of the models.

Let us now turn to the solution phase.

B SOLUTION OF MATHEMATICAL MODELS

As stressed above a great deal of effort has been put into determining algorithms for getting solutions to optimization problems in the form of linear programmes, non-linear programmes and dynamic programmes. In the more complex cases the computer is essential and hence we have another one of our essential subjects, *viz.*: computers.

There are still many cases in which these standard algorithms are impracticable for reasons of computational time or storage space. To be able to cope with these, numerous, situations, various suboptimizing standard procedures have been developed. Two of these are:

simulation;
heuristics.

Simulation involves a physical analogue of the mathematical model. Its purpose is the evaluation of decision rules. It is characteristically suboptimal.

Heuristics may involve the use of standardized procedures for getting a sub-optimal policy without there being any 'proof' that the final answer is within any specific distance of the true optimal answer. The adequacy of any standardized heuristic procedure is assessed empirically by its performance in cases where the optimal answer is known.

The final stage is the mathematical output.

C   OUTPUT OF MATHEMATICAL MODEL

The three output forms, already mentioned, are:

(i) the consequence will be θ;
(ii) if act a then consequence $\theta(a)$;
(iii) select act a.

At this stage we may now collect together our classifications and find that:

linear programming, non-linear programming and dynamic programming are basically characteristic mathematical optimization formulations depending on the theory of choice, providing standard optimization algorithms and being applicable to a wide variety of operational situations and the output is always of form (iii);

inventory control and queueing theory are basically physical operational characterizations with a wide physical interpretation; where an attempt is made to prescribe an optimal action, any of the three optimization characterizations above may be applicable; much of practical inventory control and queueing theory is not of the optimal action type and results in an output of form (ii);

critical path analysis is not action oriented and results in an output of type (i);

simulation and heuristics are suboptimization procedures designed for use when optimal algorithms stemming from the standard optimization characterizations are impracticable;

computers provide the physical mechanism for getting solutions to complex problems;

statistics (and probability) govern the mathematical characterizations in non-deterministic situations.

Ideally one would wish to separate the optimal characterization models from the operational situations, if the purpose were purely taxonomical. However, from a teaching point of view, and from the manner in which present groupings have arisen, it is preferable to teach, say, linear programming, and refer to operational situations, such as allocation operations, within the same course, and to teach, say, inventory control separately, referring to the appropriate optimization characterization in the course. Doing it this way allows us to appreciate the range (operational-wise) of a specific optimization technique, the range (optimization-wise) of a specific operational situation, and the range even of an operational characterization over different features of such operations.

We shall be discussing a very loose procedure for Decision Analysis (which is called Decision Methodology) within which there is a great deal of freedom of 'choice' for the Decision Analyst. There is also a degree of complexity and interaction between the phases not evident at a first glance. As Kazanowski[66] points out, a generalized approach (of a particularly specific nature) is not, at the moment, available and instruction to graduates in the field of management science (etc.), proceeds largely by identifying pitfalls, fallacies and misconceptions. A lot of this will be in this text. When this approach has developed into an instructional approach, Decision Methodology will have arrived as a subject in its own right.

It is perhaps worth the reader's time to peruse some of the principles of management, work study, method study, and to look at Cole[26] who specifies five steps in analysing decision situations mentioned in the Staff Officer's Field Manual.

1.4 Methodological Formats of Decision Analysis

In Figure 3 we gave a simple format for the logic of Decision Analysis, adequate for our introductory purposes there. In a sense this is a model of the Decision Analysis process and, like all models, is constructed with various purposes in mind. It lacks detail for other purposes; for example it says nothing about the various scientific problems arising in the determination of specific relationships, and it says nothing about the continuing backwards and forwards process which goes on in any practical study. We will now expand on this model in more detail and present several formats, or 'snapshots', of the Decision Analysis process as it is seen by several authors in this area. A totally comprehensive model, allowing for dynamic development, is possible, but would obscure some of the simpler viewpoints so necessary to produce a useful picture on which to hang subsequent discussions. This is not therefore done in this text but the reader may, as a major exercise, attempt such a construction.

Considerable emphasis in this text will be put on the formal science–mathematics structure of the Decision Analysis process. Figure 4 gives one way of depicting this.

To facilitate interpretation of Figure 4, a simple example is given following the same pattern.

Example
Real system
    Objective: Machine;
    Subjective: Works Manager.
Scientific method
    Variables: Decision: machine speeds: s;
               Consequences: output rate: r;
                          quality: q;
                          customer dissatisfaction: d;
              Criterion: profit: θ.
    Measure variables:
       s, r: obvious;
       q: sometimes obvious when items are clearly defective or non-defective; sometimes subjective classification of: very good, good, reasonable, bad, e.g. in surface quality;

10

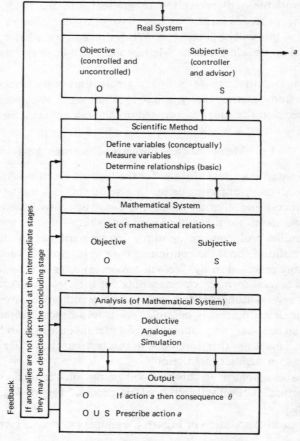

Figure 4. Science–mathematics format

    d: usually not measured but efforts have been made to measure the effect
         of quality on lost orders and hence 'lost orders' represents d;
    θ: profit.

Relate variables: $r = r(s)$;
(basic empirical $q = q(s)$;
relationships) $d = d(q)$.

It will be noted in Figure 4 that the arrows between 'real system' and 'scientific
method' are two way indicating the continual recycling process which can go on
throughout the study.

Mathematical system

    Objective: only one synthesized relation:
$$d = d(q(s)) = D(s)$$
    Subjective: $\theta = \alpha r(s) - \beta D(s)$

It is not possible in principle to separate the mathematical aspect completely from the scientific method aspect, since the very statement of the scientific inputs requires this. The 'mathematical system' phase is really just a formal statement of the scientific output and any relevant conditions together with any clear synthesis which may take place prior to the actual determination of decision output information. It therefore includes some partial synthesis, as the example indicates.

Mathematical analysis—output

If d is not measured, or not related to q, then for each s we present the consequences thus: $s \rightarrow$ (output value, quality) $\equiv (\alpha r(s), q(s))$; if d is measured, and related to q, we find s which maximizes: $\alpha r(s) - \beta D(s)$.

Feedback

If the investigation had been properly carried out in the first place, then there would be no effective feedback. It may arise, however, that the results are absurd. Thus a recommendation of an absurdly low speed. This may then result in a reinvestigation of the relationship between speed and quality.

The results may violate an unthought-of constraint. Thus a high speed may have violated some safety factor.

If nothing is evidently wrong to begin with, then the invalidity of the solution may show up when it is implemented. It is in this case that controlling the solution becomes important.

A different perspective on the mathematical–science model of the decision analysis process is given by S. Bonder.[14] This is shown in Figure 5. It will be seen that the modelling aspect is divided into the qualitative and quantitative stages,

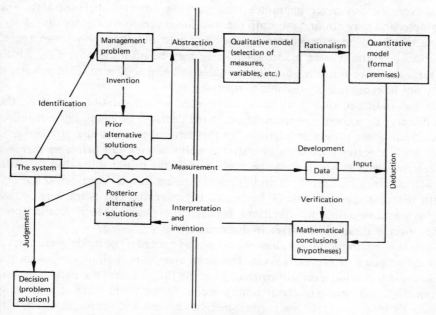

Figure 5. Bonder's format

and that certain other aspects of the scientific content, such as verification and data sources are separated out but are implicit in Figure 4. In addition the 'system' is not separated into its objective and subjective parts.

The most well-known format for Decision Analysis is that of Ackoff.[1] He lists these as six phases as given in Table 4:

Table 4: Ackoff's format

1. Formulating the problem
2. Constructing the model
3. Testing the model
4. Deriving the solution
5. Testing and controlling the solution
6. Implementing the solution

It is seen that Figure 4 and Table 4 emphasize different things, although highly related.

Thus we see that the 'scientific method' phase of Figure 4 contains Ackoff's phases 1, 3, 5 and, together with the 'mathematical system' phase, would contain Ackoff's phase 2.

As we have seen, the model involves both objective and subjective components. For this reason so-called 'objective criteria', or more generally, 'value functions', come within the model construction stage and may involve scientific method, e.g. $v(\theta) = f(\text{cost, delays})$, for some function f, if $\theta \equiv (\text{cost, delays})$.

Also if the model is correct, then there may be no need to test solution. However, we can never guarantee that we have covered all constraints, for example, and may not find out until the solution is presented, e.g. we may determine the 'best' inventory control policy and find out that the storage space, overlooked initially, was inadequate. There may be no finite procedure which ensures that all constraints are determinable initially and, even if there were, it may not be economically feasible to operate.

It was indicated that there 'may' be no need to test solution. However, the model may be a correct representation of the decision problem, but not reflect the effectiveness of implementation. In this sense the test is one of whether it will work effectively from an operational point of view. In principle this is a subjective element which could be made part of the initial study, but scientific limitations may make it more appropriate to assess this at the end of the study, with the consequential risk of having to begin again. The point here is that again we have subtle interrelations between the phases. More detailed consideration of these will be given in due course.

The 'controlling solution' phase would not be needed if the model were correct in the first place. However, it is usual to make assumptions about environmental behaviour following a certain pattern, knowing full well that the parameters are gradually changing, e.g. (i) assuming mean demand $= \mu$, when it is actually gradually increasing each year; (ii) sometimes booms and slumps interfere with the validity of solutions (in a specific case a slump resulted in an accumulation of steel strip because the suggested procedure was followed although conditions changed). We shall deal with this in detail later on.

Clearly the six phases of Ackoff's methodology may give rise to a recycling process in which we may go back to any of the preceding phases dependent on the state of our study. In this sense we cannot say that the phases are ordered. However, certain phases may presuppose output from a previous phase. As we shall see later on, the testing and controlling aspects may take place before and/or after implementation, whereas we cannot build a model until we have formulated the problem; even in some very open form, we cannot obtain a solution until we have built the model, even in a non-final form, and we cannot implement until we have a solution. Figure 6 indicates the directional effects.

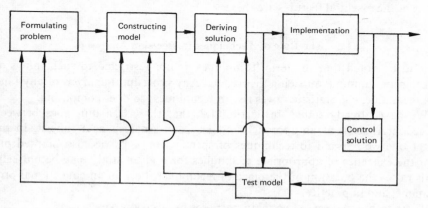

Figure 6. Decision Analysis feedback format

In what follows in the main text we will make use of parts of Ackoff's format, but will group phases 2, 3 and 6 under phase 2, while at the same time remembering that some of the testing and controlling takes place after a particular model has been built. Phase 2 will therefore be spread, inseparably, over the whole process, as indeed will the other phases. We identify these phases not by their chronology but by their nature alone. In doing this the science–mathematics format becomes useful. Tocher[134] identifies eight phases in the investigations, as given in Table 5.

In a further article Tocher[135] discusses some of the phases of the Decision

Table 5: Tocher's format

1. Problem propounded—data collected—talked around—precise problem posed
2. Model building—mathematical—statistical—logical—biological—organizational
3. Model testing
4. Model solution
5. Check solution
6. Sell solution
7. Implement
8. Monitor solution

(6) is an extra phase to Ackoff. (8) and (5) correspond to Ackoff's (5).

Analysis process, in which the emphasis is on changes in problem formulation (alternatives, objectives, constraints) and not on the changes in the mode of analysis and solution, except in as much as the actual behaviour during implementation is used as a feedback to provide better assumptions for the analysis. This is related to testing by implementation and to control of the model, and solution, discussed in the next chapter.

Snodgrass[124] discusses problem formulation and solution along the lines of: definition of historical situation from which problems arise, defining goals, stating the problem, outlining the alternatives, determining the effects, selecting solution and implementing and subsequent control. It is clear that his concept of problem formulation is not identical to the one used in this text. Nonetheless some of the essential features are there.

1.5 The Role of Techniques in Decision Analysis

It is to be noted that the term 'techniques' is not restricted to such things as linear programming, queueing theory, etc. Any procedural analysis of any kind is a technique, e.g. statistics gives rise to techniques; so does computing.

We have already stated, in Section 1.2, that there is a difference between Decision Analysis as an approach and Decision Analysis as a subject. In the latter one we referred to techniques of specific kinds. It was also pointed out that the existence of appropriate techniques for a given study may be unlikely. This raises the question of the place of techniques, both in an educational programme, and in practice.

These techniques serve two main purposes in Decision Analysis, *viz.*:

(i) they are concerned with characterizing situations, and develop, in the student and practitioner, a model-building technical ability or a model-solution technical ability, and when faced with new situations he should be able to set about building the model and getting solution;

(ii) sometimes it is useful to violate the reality of a problem to get an insight into its characteristics which can then be used in refined investigations, e.g. (see Tocher[135]) in queueing theory we may use special distributions to get a 'feel' for the likely solutions and then simulate. We shall discuss this aspect in more detail when we come to the chapter on 'getting the solution'.

In support of this, Tocher[135] puts two values on theories in Operational Research, *viz.*:

(1) 'The role of general theories is to give an insight into problems being studied;'

(2) 'The second great value of these theoretical studies is that they develop the mathematical tools necessary to solve new formalised problems.'

The place of techniques in Decision Analysis is further emphasized by Simon[119] who distinguishes between 'programmed' and 'non-programmed' decisions on the basis of techniques available to handle problems. The more standard and formalizeable a decision situation then the higher likelihood of a technique being available and the decision becoming 'programmed'. The general

Decision Methodology provides the basis for analysing non-programmed decisions.

1.6 Decision Methodology, Theory of Choice and of Object System and Techniques of Solution

We have already discussed, directly and indirectly:

A = decision methodology;
B_1 = theory of choice;
B_2 = theory of object system;
C = techniques of solution.

It is clear that these interact and, as we shall discuss many specific aspects in what follows, it is useful to indicate schematically this interrelationship.

We first of all differentiate between the primary problems, which are the object of the analysis, and the secondary problems, which characterize the process of analysis, i.e. the decision methodology.

Figure 7 indicates the interactive situation.

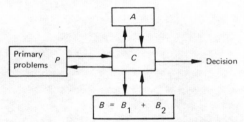

Figure 7. Primary and secondary interactions

$A \rightarrow C$ because C will need techniques of solution;
$C \rightarrow A$ because C dictates the choice in A;
$B \rightarrow C$ because C will need the theory of B as a special area of application of B;
$C \rightarrow B$ because C will dictate the proper theory in B to use on primary problems;
$P \rightarrow C$ since C operates on primary problems;
$C \rightarrow P$ since C dictates choice of primary problems.

It has already been indicated that it is, in some ways, a little illogical to separate problem formulation from model construction, and, in fact, many of the questions raised in the model-construction section apply equally well to problem formulation. In Figure 7 it is seen that the theory of choice (i.e. the theory of the subject system from a point of view of choice) plays a special role since, in the end analysis, the appropriateness of any particular model of the object system has to be assessed in terms of its influence on the extent to which a solution is seen as good or bad by the decisionmaker. We will also see later on, when attempting to formulate the secondary problems of decision methodology, that this plays a central role. Therefore not only have we treated problem formulation as a special aspect of this methodology to be consistent with Ackoff, but its central importance also merits this.

Also in view of the interrelations between Ackoff's six phases, these will be grouped rather differently and 'testing model' and 'testing and controlling solution' will all be taken to be part of 'model construction', leaving 'deriving solution' as a separate, but highly related, phase, and leaving 'implementation' as a special aspect of the final chapter.

CHAPTER 2

Decision Analysis Phases

2.1 Primary Problem Formulation Phase

2.1.1 Definition

Formulating the primary problem can be identified with several steps, *viz.*:
(a) Who are the ultimate decisionmakers?
(b) What types of decision are being considered?
(c) How are the alternatives specified within the chosen class?
(d) What are the variables in terms of which alternatives are to be evaluated?
(e) What is the criterion in terms of which alternatives are evaluated?

Dewey[34] specifies 'problem solving' in a different way to Ackoff, *viz.*:
(a) What is the problem?
(b) What are the alternatives?
(c) Which alternative is the best?

Clearly Dewey's definition is different to that of Ackoff in that his third phase is related more to model construction and solution. However, more important is the fact that his second phase is separate to the problem formulation phase. This is a particularly important point since problem formulation (or 'What is the problem?') means different things to different people. To some people 'What is your problem?' means 'What is wrong with your system?', but this is really only the beginnings of the definition of the problem. We will discuss this later on.

It is also to be noted that, as has already been stated, the problem formulation stage can be seen as a very special, subject system oriented, part of the model construction phase to be discussed later on. Thus, for example, the determination of consequences and criteria form part of the modelling activity, and the scientific approaches so discussed apply equally well to problem formulation, although the difficulties are more serious.

In looking at Ackoff's definition, we note that although, ideally, we would like to determine the criteria for our decision problem, this is not always possible. In Chapter 1 it was pointed out that the forms of output of a Decision Analysis might only indicate the effects of a decision, and that the process may end there. This was referred to as the 'open' or 'information' form of Decision Analysis.

Although Ackoff's steps are lettered as (a), (b), (c), (d), (e), the cycle can be entered at any point and re-entered again at any point, just as the methodological models of Figures 4, 5, 6 can be entered and re-entered at any point. Each stage can be a generator of the next (not necessarily in order (a), (b), (c), (d), (e)). Thus, although we have said that it is not necessary to have a criterion, a criterion may lead to better search for alternatives (steps (b) or (c)).

Decision Analysis is concerned with 'problem solving' where the 'problem' is defined in terms of specific 'primary decisions' which are being investigated (see Ackoff[1]).

Although 'problems of model construction' arise, these are not the 'Decision Analysis problems' in the sense in which we use the word. Thus the choice of what form of model to use is not a Decision Analysis problem, although it is, of course, a problem of scientific method; it is not concerned with a physical decision. We refer to this as a 'secondary decision'. It is the 'Decision Methodology problem'.

In discussing the problem formulation as a distinct entity from the model building, our reason lies in the separation of the decisions being investigated from the methods involved in the analysis and the decisions on these, i.e. separation of 'primary' from 'secondary' decisions.

It is important to realize that the subjective element enters into the problem formulation stage quite significantly (see Reitman[107]). Our problem formulation stage is bound to be undefined to a large degree, and gets more defined as we progress, involving subjective judgements such as follows:

(i) we may never know all of our alternatives, objectives, constraints, even at the end, let alone at the beginning;

(ii) the choice of alternatives is, for example, a decision in itself, (see Churchman[24]), and is, as we have stated, a methodological decision;

(iii) alternatives can be deliberately ignored (see Churchman and Eisenberg[25]), e.g. in considering a problem area, the senior executive, in a case in fact, refused to consider certain alternatives, probably not because they were not worthwhile, but probably because someone else thought they were worthwhile, and he wished the study to emanate from his own ideas;

(iv) objectives are preweighted, e.g. a production manager may have an obsession for machine utilization, or a hospital administrator may have an obsession for bed utilization, irrespective of other considerations, until they are, during the investigation, strongly brought to his attention; the effect of this may be to bias the selection of alternatives to maximize facility utilization.

Selig[115] also discusses the difficulty of defining the problem adequately in the first place. He quotes oversimplified problem statements, such as Steiner's[127] minimal distance tree interconnecting points $A_1, A_2, \ldots, A_n$, where complications such as right of way, cemeteries, etc., provide more constraints than can be readily handled. In general one should not expect to be able to state all the constraints, let alone know them. He states that difficulties in stating the problem give rise to difficulties of knowing in advance what constitutes an acceptable solution. The suggested procedure is to develop a method of study which allows two-way communication between solution process and decisionmaker, so that added definition to the problem can be obtained as part of this interplay. Thus, as we have indicated, although problem formulation is a distinct phase, it interacts in two directions with other aspects of the analysis, as shown in Figure 8.

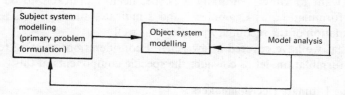

Figure 8. Subject–object system modelling interaction

We shall see later that the manner in which the problem is defined (e.g. intensively (some objective in mind), extensively (alternatives given)) varies considerably from situation to situation. However, Reitman[107] introduces a standard format $(A, B \rightarrow)$ in which all problems are considered to be concerned with the transformation $(\rightarrow)$ from some initial state (A) to some final state (B).

Examples

(1) If the alternatives are given (A), the search may be for a criterion $(\rightarrow)$ which transforms (A) into a final choice (B), e.g. criterion for a time series of cash flows: present worth? payback period? (see White[144]).

(2) Sometimes an objective (B) (design motor car) is stated and (A) is free (we can begin with many kinds of materials, etc.), and the car is to be designed $(\rightarrow)$.

(3) Ruderman[110] mentions several cost benefit methods, *viz.*:

(a) an estimate of the reduction in duration of disability using different drugs (physical approach), where: $(A) \equiv$ drugs; $(\rightarrow) \equiv$ relationship between (A) and (B); $(B) \equiv$ durations of disability; only (A), (B) given;

(b) an estimation of economic returns for a given expenditure (economic approach), where: $(A) \equiv$ expenditure + ways of using it; $(\rightarrow) \equiv$ relationship between (A) and (B); $(B) \equiv$ economic returns; only (A), (B) given.

(c) an estimation of the economic benefits if certain diseases could be reduced to certain levels; in this case the cost of doing this is not, initially, known, where: $(A^*) \equiv$ ways of reducing diseases; $(A) \equiv$ reduction in diseases; $(\rightarrow) \equiv$ study; $(B) \equiv$ economic benefits; only (A), (B) given.

We see that problems are posed in more or less complete forms, the answers to which, in themselves, do not result in decision, but provide a starting point. In case (c), for example, if we find disease D_1 is much more burdensome than D_2, and no discrimination between costs is available, then D_1 is likely to be pursued as a research project.

It is perhaps worth stressing the general nature of $(\rightarrow)$, and that $(\rightarrow)$ is any transformation to be performed on A to achieve B. In some cases it is a 'design'; in some cases it is a 'method of analysis'; in some cases it is a 'relationship'.

20

Reitman's format is not solely a format for the primary decision problem formulation, since it may involve a search for a relationship, as in Example 3 above. Neither is it separated from the object system, as the same example shows. It is rather a general format which enables us to state what we know and what we want to know. Naturally it is specifically applicable to our primary problem formulation, as Examples 1 and 2 indicate, although it is relevant to the formulation of the secondary problems as well.

Now that we have covered a few general considerations relating to primary problem formulation, let us consider the specific components of this.

2.1.2 The Ultimate Decisionmakers

As we have already seen, the subjective part of Decision Analysis centres around characteristics of the ultimate decisionmakers, although subjectivity enters in other ways.

If we intend to prescribe action, particularly in cases of uncertainty, it is essential that we isolate the correct decisionmakers, since decisionmakers with different value systems would prefer different alternatives in general. We may know the sponsors; the question is 'which representatives should make the decision?'

Examples

(1) We may have a production scheduling problem, and alternative policies may result in different costs and different delay distributions for customer delivery time, as shown in Figure 9.

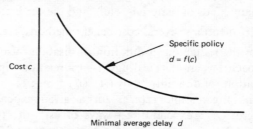

Figure 9. Production costs and delays

Who is going to make the final decision on the production policies? The production controller? The sales manager? The chairman?

If we can put a cost to the delays, then no problem arises, but this has not, in general, been achieved. Some analysis is possible if we may assume that a value function can be ascertained.

Thus in our cost/delay problem above, we may have two different value functions, one for the production controller and one for the sales manager.

$$V_{PC}(c, d) = \alpha - \beta c - \gamma d = \alpha - \beta c - \gamma f(c) = U_{PC}(c)$$
$$V_{SM}(c, d) = \alpha' - \beta' c - \gamma' d = \alpha' - \beta' c - \gamma' f(c) = U_{SM}(c)$$

Usually we will find that $\gamma' > \gamma$, $\beta' < \beta$.

Figure 10 illustrates the situation.

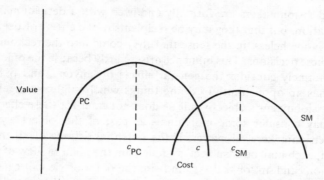

Figure 10. Values of sales manager and production controller

With the aid of Figure 10 it might be possible to resolve the problem with an agreement somewhere in the region between c_{PC} and c_{SM}.

(2) In production scheduling we cannot ignore the operators, since any production schedule has consequences for them as well as the company. They are therefore in a position to make decisions such as to strike. If one takes a company to be an entity in harmony, not in conflict, then the operators may need to be considered as part of the decisionmaking group.

(3) In investment problems one cannot ignore the shareholders, whose dividends depend on capital investment decisions. Thus, in principle, we need to be able to determine what consequences to consider for all shareholders involved, although in practice this is not feasible.

(4) Consider the problem of choosing the best form of central heating for a block of flats. Who are the effective decisionmakers? The builders? The council? The prospective tenants? Who are these anyhow, present or future tenants?

(5) Consider the problem of replacement of a bus. The economic replacement policy may result in running the less modern buses. Who are the decisionmakers? The public? The Transport Department General Manager? The Minister of Transport? Again there are a diversity of value judgements, and the effective decisionmakers have to be determined.

(6) In a certain study, tenants of houses were asked what their preferences were between maintenance services which were mixtures of the time to do a job and the quality of the job.

Now in this instance the tenants were not usually in occupation for long and hence quality of job and the resulting long-term effects were rated low. Unfortunately the effect of this was to be seen for future tenants and not the present tenants. Thus the study produced results which were not realistically oriented towards the total long-term problem and the true population of people concerned.

It is a logical consequence that, if we wish to ascertain, and validate, a correct decision, we must ascertain the effective decisionmakers. It is not always true that such decisionmakers are formally endowed with a decisionmaking role in an organization, but that they may be recipients of the effects of decisions made by others. Nonetheless, in the sense that they come into the reckoning, they do influence these decisions. This influence arises partly because the official decision-makers genuinely consider the general effects on anyone, and partly because everyone has an opportunity of doing things which might adversely affect the official decisionmaker's objectives if he does not cater for these effects. In either case we may consider some individuals as part of the 'object' system of the official decisionmakers. However, if the potential actions of all individuals is considered, each may be a 'subject' system from the point of view of studying his own decisions and an 'object' system from the point of view of catering for the effects on him of others' decisions. We must therefore approach the use of the 'subject' and 'object' system classification with caution. Nonetheless, if we are trying to establish the appropriateness of a decision, or group of decisions, we must establish criteria and this leads us back to the question of whose criteria. Naturally one might consider the open, or informative, approach and simply indicate the effects of alternatives, but this does not really solve our problem, since we still have to know what effects are important, why alternatives are important, and this naturally leads us back to the same question.

It is a dilemma that most of our more important problems involve groups of people with differing value systems and yet we have no satisfactory way of ascertaining what is the appropriate decision on behalf of such a group. The major work in this area is that of Arrow,[2] who establishes an impossibility theorem in the sense that no general solution, meeting intuitive concepts of fairness, exists.

2.1.3 Types of Decision

Before the objective model stage can commence, it is necessary to have alternative actions in mind. This does not preclude additions at a later date if further search is thought desirable.

Example

If we are concerned with client or internal service, do we consider the possible improvements in scheduling or do we consider addition of extra capacity? Do we consider production technique, or do we consider bonus schemes? There are probably other alternatives (see Figure 11).

This problem is a subtle one. Clearly they are all interrelated, but there is a limit to the size of any study we can carry out. It is sensible to limit it, at least in the first stages. This limitation is obtained by an initial judgement that certain

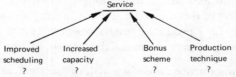

Figure 11. Choice of primary decision type

courses of action are likely to be the most productive, or be more implementable, etc.

Similarly, what are we concerned with in stock re-order rules? Are we concerned with production scheduling? Are we concerned with both? Are we concerned with possible increases in capacity? Should we look at capital replacement, assuming present maintenance policies and their effects? Or is there a better payoff in looking at ways of improving maintenance, assuming present replacement policy? These latter areas illustrate hierarchical dependencies.

Later on we shall discuss the problem of project selection and criteria for such selection. This aspect is part of that general problem. It is clearly worthless to spend time on unproductive alternatives.

There are a wide variety of decisions with which we could concern ourselves, and these interact to a greater or lesser degree. We cannot consider them all. Usually, for some reason, one or two types present themselves, and an analysis of these usually brings in others as is thought appropriate.

Examples

(1) An approach to the Decision Analyst to investigate inventory control may lead on to associated production control, since it may not be solely the demand

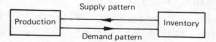

Figure 12. Interaction of alternatives

pattern which determines the correct inventory level, but flexibility of production in bringing forward jobs planned, initially, some time ahead. Thus the production people may look at the inventory and future load and determine production in light of the inventory situation. Figure 12 illustrates the situation.

(2) An approach to the Decision Analyst to look at maintenance problems may lead to a consideration of capital replacement, etc.

(3) Consider a problem in the general area of hospital beds. The possible decisions can be concerned with use of the beds, number of beds, patient scheduling, etc. A brief analysis of the focal consequences may reveal that the real potential for improvement lies in increasing the number of beds, and not in the other alternative types of decision.

(4) An investigation of material allowances may lead to an investigation of customer production reallocation decisions.

(5) An investigation of spares provision may lead to an analysis of replacement decisions.

(6) When asked to look at production delays we might rule out the installation of extra equipment because the capital is not available, although, if the gains to be obtained were large enough, it might well be forthcoming. The emphasis might be on scheduling policies in the first instance, but lead naturally to capital investment.

24

(7) When studying absenteeism and turnover, a study of recruitment policies might lead to a study of ways of influencing absenteeism and turnover rates.

(8) A study began with considering the best ways of using existing resources to cope with hospital emergencies. It is possible that a more profitable study might have been to examine alternative means of cutting down the emergencies in the first place.

(9) The routing of vehicles to deliver and pick up items in varying quantities at various points can be quite difficult. The difficulty arises because the pattern of demand is widely distributed in various quantities. If this pattern could be controlled to suit the vehicles and ideal transport policies (by grouping of similar quantities in compact areas) then the transport costs might be minimized. If the clients were given price discounts, or increases, for varying delivery times, both client and distributors may gain. Thus a routing alternatives study might lead to a price structure study.

(10) The routing of a hospital ambulance fleet to pick up widely distributed patients with varying appointment times created difficulties. If the appointment times could be controlled so that they were similar for patients in compact areas then the transport costs and patient lost time could be both reduced, and the original routing alternatives study simplified.

(11) A decisionmaker may be asked to decide whether to spend money on a particular research and development project. This cannot be seen in isolation and raises the question of what he would do with the money if he decided not to invest in this particular project. We thus see, as will be stressed later on, that the criteria for a specific decision may well involve widening the set of alternatives which have to be considered. In White[144, 146] a model is developed, under specific conditions, in which the value of the decision 'not to invest' can be calculated by looking ahead to future possible decisions. Later on we will stress the way in which suboptimization arises because of failure to look at what is, in effect, a sequential decision situation.

There is a two-way interrelationship between alternatives and criteria, as indicated in Figure 13.

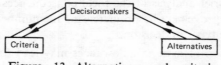

Figure 13. Alternatives and criteria interaction

We can, similarly, represent the interaction between alternatives and consequences as in Figure 14.

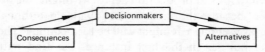

Figure 14. Alternatives and consequences interaction

The complete figure would be as in Figure 15.

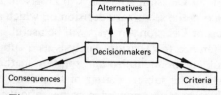

Figure 15. Alternatives, consequences
and criteria interaction

We will return to these figures later on.

It is difficult to see any way of rationalizing the search for alternatives without some idea of the criterion which is being optimized, since we need to know which alternatives are likely to influence the value of the criterion enough for it to be worthwhile studying them. In the previous examples it is likely that this aspect resulted in moving from one area to another. The following examples partly formalize this process. Reference should be made to Figure 15.

Examples

(1) We may have, in maintenance

$$v(c, l, q) = v_0 - (c + 0 \cdot 01 l + 0 \cdot 001 q),$$

where $c \equiv$ cost, $l \equiv$ delay, $q \equiv$ quality.

If we now even have a qualitative estimate of the way in which decisions influence c, l, q we have a way of selecting the decisions to be analysed.

(2) In a recent study of the cost of steel making and the production of steel strip, 75% of the cost was seen to arise in the first few stages. Since the complexity factor was at its lowest here, it seemed a feasible area of study. The remaining stages were bedevilled by the huge increase in variety and would need more elaborate procedures for analysis. There was, of course, no guarantee that the approach taken was the best, since the room for improvement in less complicated situations is correspondingly less.

Sometimes the recognition of desired consequences can help determine novel alternatives.

Example

The following story is reported to be true. During the Second World War, the question of gun armaments for ships was being studied. It was asked why the guns were needed. The obvious answer was 'to sink enemy ships'. It was then asked how this was achieved, to which the answer was that they blew holes in them, which let the water in. It was then suggested that it might be just as effective to remove the water in the first place. This appeared to be absurd but some thought was given to the possibility of spraying the water with some chemical which would alter its properties, thus ensuring that the ships sank.

In actual fact nothing effective was produced, but this does illustrate the worth of searching for novel alternatives, which may be forthcoming when the desired effects are identified.

When we come to the chapter on model construction, some discussion of taxonomy and its role in Decision Analysis will be given. It is useful to note at this stage that, in making the secondary decision on which alternatives to study, a taxonomy of aspects of Decision Analysis will be useful.

We have made reference to Decision Analysis as a subject in which characteristic classes of problem are identified and solution methods developed. There are other ways in which the subject matter of Decision Analysis may develop. One of these is with respect to knowledge gained about the value of different kinds of problem area studies, in relationship not only to the importance of the problem area, but also to the productivity of resources expended in studying it. This leads, as does all scientific method, to a qualitative taxonomy of features of different problem areas. This has a direct bearing on the answer to the main question of this section, *viz.*, selection of alternatives to consider. Let us consider a few possibilities.

A   TAXONOMY WITH RESPECT TO DIFFICULTIES

We might try a taxonomy with respect to the difficulties to be found in investigating certain decisions, e.g. personnel selection is scientifically difficult as distinct from inventory re-ordering, because it is difficult to evaluate the effects of various policies and to measure qualities of employees.

B   TAXONOMY WITH RESPECT TO IMPORTANCE

If we were interested in choosing projects with large returns, we might try a taxonomy with respect to the importance of the decision, e.g. a daily production schedule has less effect on the company than a capital investment decision.

When considering criteria, Hitch,[58] in terms of importance, states 'plant < multiplant < company < nation', where < means 'less important than'.

C   TAXONOMY WITH RESPECT TO FREQUENCY

We might classify them according to frequency (daily production *vs.* capital investment), with a view to the nature of the solution we are looking for. A daily production problem may have a repetitive linear programming solution, with repetitive pay offs (see Ornea;[100] Hitch[58]). A capital investment decision is usually relatively unique, because circumstances change fast enough with respect to the frequency of the decision (e.g. economic climate; competitive position, etc.), and requires a relatively new study each time it arises, hence the nature of the approach is different.

D   TAXONOMY WITH RESPECT TO TIME SPAN

If we were interested in influence over time we would wish to distinguish between those whose time span of influence was small (daily production decision) and those whose span of influence was large (a new production process). This may be important when the opportunity for adjustment is considered in relationship to risk.

E TAXONOMY WITH RESPECT TO OPERATIONAL/TECHNOLOGICAL/INVESTMENT
 CHARACTERISTICS

Ornea[100] discusses a taxonomy in terms of operational/technological/investment which have different characteristics.

An operational decision is concerned with the best way to utilize given resources to operate a specified system, e.g. inventory control; a technological decision is concerned with the design specifications of the system, e.g. design decisions for a lens, or for a transformer, or for a food; an investment decision is concerned with the level and nature of facilities, e.g. how many warehouses and what size.

We see that taxonomies may be correlated, e.g. importance may increase as we move from operational decisions, through technological decisions, to investment decisions.

Ornea's taxonomy is somewhat incomplete. For example, there are policy decisions within which other operational, investment, and even technological decisions, have to be made. Thus, for example, a policy decision which constrains the selection of personnel for certain posts to personnel within the organization is not included in Ornea's taxonomy (see White[143]). Nonetheless the ideas are useful.

The important point is that some cross taxonomy, with respect to attributes of decision situations, is necessary if the full implications of a decision to consider certain types of alternative are to be studied. In general we have all too little quantitative evidence on the effectiveness and efficiency of tackling certain decision areas and any justification may, for some time yet, have to be arrived at from a knowledge of these attributes.

2.1.4 Specification of Alternatives

There appear to be two ways in which the alternatives may be specified, *viz.*:

(i) the allowable set is made explicit, and we have to evaluate each alternative in this set;

(ii) the allowable set is defined via constraints and we have to search for feasible solutions.

(i) *Explicit Definition*

Examples

(1) We might be asked whether or not a given investment opportunity is to be taken up.

(2) We might be asked whether or not to inspect a product.

(ii) *Implicit Definition*

Examples

(1) We might be allowed any production schedule not violating overtime limitations.

(2) We might be allowed any maintenance policy which does not involve more work than the present crews can cope with.

(3) We might be allowed any inventory control policy which does not involve more than a 0·05 chance of run-out.

(4) We may be asked to design equipment to do a certain job at a certain cost, with complete freedom to choose the design, and any solution is as good as another if it achieves this objective.

(5) We might be asked to re-organize the company to cut down operating costs by £c, with all alternatives being admissible.

(6) In the newspaper industry van drivers must not make more than four trips per shift (union rules), and this indirectly defines the allowable schedules.

(7) A maximum time is laid down for police cars to get to a police call, thus constraining possible solutions for force size and routing.

(8) We may ask 'what advertising policies will result in a specific number of enquiries' without saying anything else about the desirability of these policies.

(9) In a recent study of the utilization of a building site the following constraints were used:

(a) minimum number of hours sunlight per day (assumed cloudless);
(b) maximum length of carry for refuse collection personnel.

These constraints influenced the closeness of buildings and the length of blocks (no vehicle access along length of block) and hence influenced the minimum cost per dwelling.

Just as we would find it useful to produce a taxonomy of decision situations, from the point of view of the decision, it is useful to produce a taxonomy of decision situations from the point of view of constraints. Then, in dealing with any specific situation, our knowledge of these taxonomies may reduce the chances of overlooking such constraints.

Eilon[41] classifies constraints as follows:

(α) market constraints;
(β) product constraints;
(γ) technological constraints;
(δ) organizational constraints;
(ε) resource constraints.

For example: the market constraint might be the quantity of a product which can be sold; the product constraint might be a design constraint; the technological constraint might be with respect to production method; the organizational constraint may be with respect to the planning of the production; and the resource constraint may relate to the capacity of the organization to produce the product at a certain rate.

This classification does not refer to a service organization, but can be modified to cover this. The organizational constraints will include all internally generated constraints as a means of carrying out the business effectively, e.g. constraints on availability of equipment imposed on the maintenance department.

The problem of constraints in Decision Analysis is one of fundamental concern. Several important aspects of these will now be dealt with.

A   CONSTRAINT VIOLATION AND SENSITIVITY ANALYSIS

The setting of constraints without a sensitivity analysis is difficult to justify, since the appropriate level of a variable is always relative to other variables. Thus how can we set a run-out level of 0·05 in the absence of knowing how this will change as we change the other costs? How can we set the emergency service level at 0·95 when we do not know the effect of varying this on throughput rates?

We thus see that the setting of constraints is related to the identification of more general criteria and that constraints are not necessarily inviolable.

Let us consider a few examples of violable constraints and the existence of criteria substitutable for such constraints.

Examples

(1) The avoidance of overtime is not that rigid that, if the gains to be made in its violation were high enough, it would not be firmly demanded.

Figure 16 indicates the possible results of a full analysis.

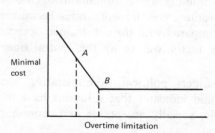

Figure 16.   Cost and overtime constraint level

If the overtime limit is set at A, then this may prevent the achievement of a much lower cost at B. The difference between B and A might be shared between operators and management. To set the limit at A without knowledge of the curve, and, in particular, the variations in the region of A, is only justified if the cost of carrying the study further is high enough.

(2) The non-violation of capacity limitations arises because extra capacity is not thought, *a priori*, desirable, but, if the gains were high enough, there might be a change of mind. Monetary criteria may exist.

(3) In a production problem it was initially stated that only a certain percentage reduction per pass could be acceptably achieved when rolling steel strip. After several months of calculations based on these, the rolling procedures were changed to violate these. The process of enquiry had produced a good effect, although research time was lost. The technological criteria had been examined.

30

(4) In a recent problem, a police force wanted to schedule its holidays in such a way that the policemen had a reasonable chance of beginning their holidays, every few years, at the beginning of the popular holiday period. This would enable accommodation to be booked at popular holiday resorts. There was a constraint that no more than a certain percentage of policemen would be off duty at any specific time. No feasible solution existed within this constraint. A feasible solution did exist if the constraint was slightly modified. However, this was thought so undesirable that they were not prepared to make the change. A study of the reasons for undesirability might uncover substitutable criteria.

(5) In a recent study of hospital beds, the 'cooperation' of units was taken to be not feasible, and hence this alternative was not pursued. Nonetheless, had this been pursued, the other advantages may have outweighed the contributing factors giving rise to the exclusion of this alternative, and substitutable criteria found.

(6) In the fabrication shop of a shipyard, specific types of unit were allocated to specific foremen working in specific areas because it was felt that their experience on specific types would produce speedy throughputs. However, this constraint prevented optimum utilization of facilities and it was possible that the relaxation of this constraint might have also significantly influenced throughput by allowing better programming. The optimum throughput obtained by relaxing this constraint, and assuming specific work rates because of inexperience on some units, could be compared with the constrained optimum as a real test of whether the experience factor was really the central one, and substitutable criteria uncovered.

(7) Snodgrass[124] considers political, administrative, social and economic aspects of a problem and indicates that solutions have to be politically and administratively feasible, socially acceptable and economically sound as per Figure 17.

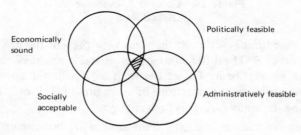

Figure 17. Solution characteristics

The shaded area contains the final feasible set. However, none of the constraints is really binding since a sacrifice in one aspect may lead to more than compensating changes in others. The constraints are only starting conditions. In fact in many cases the constraints have to be changed, otherwise feasible solutions may cease to exist at all.

B IDENTIFYING CONSTRAINTS

There can be delays in identifying constraints, which may not be fully realized until some results have been obtained from the study. As has already been stated, the taxonomy of decision situations, with due reference to constraints, may help reduce the overlooking of such constraints and save valuable research time. Some examples are as follows.

Examples

(1) If we specify the cost of producing an item, we may find that a production time limitation is exceeded, and a re-analysis is needed.

(2) In a production scheduling problem concerned with pre-heaters it took some time to see why there was a problem at all. In the end it turned out that there was a limited space within which finished and semi-finished goods could be stored and this had a significant effect on the maximum run lengths and on the optimum schedule.

The continual adding of constraints when a project is under way is a well-known phenomenon in Decision Analysis and, through a knowledge of past similar studies perhaps, significant loss of effort might be avoided if as many as possible can be anticipated.

C THE HIERARCHICAL NATURE OF CONSTRAINTS

Constraints can exist at various levels because the true consequences at each level are unknown.

Examples

(1) When specifying a building, constraints can exist in terms of:

(a) physical specification: room height 7' 3"; window size 9' 2";
(b) environmental specification: lumens $\geq L$; temperature between 60–65 °F;
(c) activities specification: no-one should need to walk more than 1 mile in a day; intelligibility of speech must be above a certain level;
(d) economics specification: the rate of return on the building must be at least 15%.

It is easily seen that we could begin with (d) and forget (a), (b), (c) since these are important only inasmuch as they influence (d). However, it may not be practicable to try to do it this way and (a), (b), (c) may reflect value judgements.

D NUMBER OF ALTERNATIVES

When the nature of the alternatives are given, there are sometimes far too many discrete alternatives to enumerate. Some subjective valuation of the goodness or badness of a solution, *a priori*, is then needed.

Example

Lampkin and Saalmans[72] discuss a bus-routing problem where the type and number of routes examined were chosen on the basis of undesirability of changes on high-demand routes and wish to avoid using too many routes in the final solution (a 'set of routes' was the required solution).

Thus prior value judgements are used to cut down the number of alternatives, by imposing appropriate constraints.

This also happens in school timetabling and general vehicle routing.

E DEPENDENCE OF CONSTRAINTS ON CONDITIONS

Constraints may be set as a means of ensuring business is carried out within certain regions of performance. Such constraints may be 'policy' constraints and may vary with conditions. Thus any model must reflect the variability of these constraints.

Example

Stark and Mayer[126] discuss controllable and uncontrollable constraints, and mention such things as 'minimum acceptable mark-up on contract' as being modifiable in the light of conditions. This might reduce if competition is severe and increase if competition is not strong. In this sense such constraints are 'decisions' themselves, as has already been stated.

This is related to controlling the solution, which will be discussed later on.

F STARTING POINT FOR ALTERNATIVES WHEN TYPE IS DEFINED

There is a strong tendency to follow the 'evolutionary' process in which the alternatives are selected within a region of the presently operating procedures (see Ornea[100]). This constrains the alternatives considered.

Examples

(1) If we are simulating a production situation we may choose alternatives not too far removed from present rules.

(2) If we are considering new processes we may try not to be too revolutionary.

(3) If we are adding extra capacity we may not make this more than a certain percentage of present capacity.

The reasons for doing this are partly because it might be difficult to implement radically different solutions, partly because the study of alternatives outside the local range of experience may meet validation problems, and partly because the available resources to consider more than minor deviations are not there. The latter possibility needs careful consideration because, for example, financial limits are not real if the savings can offset the outlay. The real danger in improvement by steps is that it may take longer to significantly improve performance than a major change might achieve.

In some instances a good way of arriving at alternatives to be considered is to assume the system will continue to operate as at present and determine the extent to which objectives may or may not be met. Alternatives may then be generated in the form of modifications to existing programmes or policies rather than having to take a completely new look at the system.

Example

Smith[123] is concerned with the personnel training programme needed to meet the demand for various categories of personnel over a time period. He suggests that one should forecast availability of manpower under the existing programme (and even this is complex) and then forecast the demand for manpower. By comparing these two it is possible to see where the deficiencies arise and to consider appropriate modifications to the existing programme to make up these deficiencies.

The quest for statistical experience on which to base decisions tends to inhibit new ideas and may lead towards the system being 'captured' within certain patterns of behaviour.

Example

In research and development a statistical study may indicate that certain areas of activity are the most productive and tends to channel resources in the same direction, thus reducing the chances that new ideas may arise in, at present, less productive areas, and even in areas not yet defined. Even the process of quantification itself, being based on 'what has happened', can retard the generation of new ideas.

2.1.5 Consequences

We now have to identify the consequence variables in terms of which the alternatives are to be evaluated. It is important to stress once again that this phase may be dependent on other phases. Thus we have already explained the interaction between alternatives and criteria, and, in the same way, the interaction between consequences and alternatives. Sometimes the consequence variables are established and this then gives rise to a search for actions which will influence them in the right direction. We represented the situation in Figure 14.

In Figure 14, we see that we can begin with selected consequences, search for alternatives which will influence these, recognize that the alternatives have other consequences and begin the process all over again. Alternatively we can begin with the alternatives and produce a series of similar steps. Also involved in this process is the process of establishing relevance of consequences, a point to which we will shortly turn.

Let us consider a few examples.

Examples

(1) In the case of investment analysis, we may need to look at: cash flows in general; initial capital in particular; payback period, if future is uncertain beyond some point.

(2) In production scheduling, we may see the problem in terms of: lateness of delivery; costs; organizational difficulties (manpower usage, etc.).

(3) In the medical field 'patient service' is one consequence variable, and this has various realizations, e.g.

(a) time taken for an ambulance to reach accident;
(b) time spent by patient in outpatient department when on an appointment;
(c) survival, or added life.

(4) Ruderman[110] mentions some difficulties of finding true consequences. He mentions: prolongation of life; added resources; consumed resources; reduced physicians time (prevention value).

(5) Dodson[37] states that the objectives of urban planning are 'improvement of quality of urban living'. When it comes to defining quality the following variables are listed: investment costs; congestion; air pollution; service; intrusion of automobiles into streets; travel times; accidents; physical discomfort; safety hazards; space required; service to special groups (poor, aged).

This just indicates the complexity of grappling with the measures of performance in terms of which planners have to think, let alone determining ultimate criteria.

Forrester[46] faces the same problem involving quality of life in terms of crowding, pollution, food.

In the above examples it may be fairly obvious that certain variables are consequences, even if they are not ultimate. There are some situations in which attributes of a decision may not be seen as consequences, but in reality they are, and they certainly influence the decision taken.

Examples

(1) When deciding which of several control procedures to install, we might feel that 'simplicity' of operation is important. It then becomes a consequence of putting in a particular form of control.

(2) When choosing between applicants for a job, one might think in terms of qualities of various kinds. These then become consequences of the decision taken.

We will quickly run through several aspects of consequences via an example in an organization which does work for itself and for external clients. The aspects we will discuss are: relevance, definition and aggregation, the latter two of which are treated in detail later on.

Example

The first step is to identify the outcomes or performance variables which they are trying to control. In Figure 18 we list a few possibilities which might be pertinent.

The second step is to determine whether these are appropriate.

Is utilization a suitable effect in terms of which to evaluate a production policy? It may just be a correlated symptom, when cost and service are what are really sought. Utilization could, for example, be improved by having a large number of jobs waiting to be done at any given time and this may be undesirable.

Production downtime may be emphasized, but if capacity is in excess of demand to some extent, there may be no real significance for sufficiently small quantities of lost time.

The third step is to find ways of defining these, if possible.

The problem of defining the correct costs is well known, but let us look at some of the other pertinent variables.

How would we define safety? In terms of hours of work lost? In terms of medical assessments of physical injury? In terms of insurance premiums and

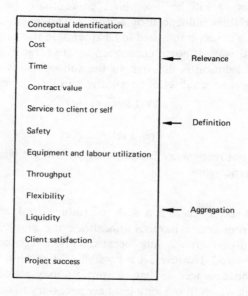

Figure 18. Consequence attributes

payouts? How would we define flexibility? In terms of costs and time needed to adapt to one of a variety of contingencies? Which contingencies? How do we define the success of a project?

We raise these questions because they are pertinent and they are difficult. It is sometimes precisely because people cannot see answers to obvious difficulties that they tend to rule out Decision Analysis from the beginning. However, these are important enough to think about, because until we can define these, we cannot say whether we are improving or getting worse.

The fourth step is to determine which combinations of the various outcomes are sought. Each will have a different significance. We will consider this under the heading of criteria. We shall consider the third step (definition) when we get on to model building. For the moment we shall concentrate on identifying the consequences and on their relevance, the latter point being considered under the heading of 'ultimate consequences'.

Let us consider two special aspects of consequences.

A   SPECTRUM OF CONSEQUENCES

Every action results in changes in many variables which can conceptually be identified as being part of the description of a company's behaviour, e.g. 'personnel satisfaction', p; 'customer satisfaction', c; 'quality', q; 'continuity of employment', e; 'shareholder dividends', s. Given their operational definition the consequence of an action is then a vector:

$$\theta = [p, c, q, e]$$

Usually, in fact, θ will be incomplete conceptually because of failure to recognize the variables influenced by action a. This phenomenon is related to suboptimization, a concept discussed in Chapter 3. In this case the suboptimality arises in a special way. If some consequences are forgotten, then the ensuing suboptimality of solution is different to the suboptimality of solution arising when we only consider a subset of alternatives. In the former case we may have

$$a \text{ Pref } b \text{ rel}(p, c, q)$$

but

$$b \text{ Pref } a \text{ rel}(p, c, q, e)$$

Thus if we do not recognize e initially then we can get alternatives the wrong way round preference-wise.

Examples
(1) In modern society there is a wish to produce drink and food which is as free as possible from known hazards to health. For example, pasteurized milk is preferred to non-pasteurized milk because certain consequences, *viz.*, virus infections, are reduced. However, it is possible that pasteurizing has harmful, as yet unknown, consequences in that the process may also interfere with other properties of milk which in the long term are necessary to our general health.

(2) In a study of a freighter terminal operations the effect on service of customers, arising through limited public road access, was completely overlooked in the initial phases. Without consideration of ways of alleviating this, it might have been preferable not to have such terminals. This of course led more naturally to a search for corrective action and hence influenced the alternatives envisaged (see Figure 13).

(3) A study was carried out on maintenance incentive schemes. It was stated that using a specific scheme, productivity, defined in terms of time to do a certain work mix, increased 81%. This was achieved by a selective grouping process. However, in doing this there would be some effect on delays incurred in some jobs since grouping implies this in general. It would be important from a Decision Analysis point of view to see that this consequence was not ignored.

(4) Jennings[64] discusses the problem of controlling the supply of blood. Variables used were: shortages and outdating. He mentioned 'average blood age' in stock, but said he could not incorporate this. What is the effect of 'blood age'? Is 'average blood age' adequate, or do we need the distribution of blood ages, bearing in mind the likely bias of new and old blood in its effects?

In this latter example we have touched upon the multidimensional nature of consequence variables, a point we will consider further in the context of measurement and definition. It may not be appropriate to reduce a distribution function to a single measurement on this function.

It must be borne in mind that it is not always easy to identify variables to which the decisionmaker should attach importance when making his decision. Some variables may be outside the experience of the decisionmaker and he may find it difficult to make judgements on them. Hole[59] says, in the context of house design:

'. . . simple preference survey in which people are asked their opinion of a number of alternatives . . . not all of which they know equally well, is virtually meaningless. A more useful approach is to obtain the informant's views concerning the features of the dwellings they occupy and their reasons for likes and dislikes; this approach can provide feedback on a particular design.'†

The problem here is intimately tied up with the problem of determining ultimate consequences, on the basis of which any design should be possible. Thus, to ask someone if they prefer sliding doors or conventional doors has, ultimately, to rest upon the effects of each alternative which can be related to existing experiences.

B NON-ULTIMATE CONSEQUENCES

Some of these so-called consequences are not ultimate consequences. Thus, returning to the first paragraph of A, p may have importance only as a generator of high production, and hence of money. Similarly with the others except s. s may itself be the ultimate consequence of money. On the other hand, future inflow of cash to the firm may depend on s. Added to this, some variables may have value in themselves and as producers of other variables, e.g. p.

The big difficulty lies in relating producer variables to product variables. Sometimes, because of severe difficulties in getting these relations, it is left to a subjective valuation. This gives rise to the need to consider prior *vs.* posterior suboptimization. Clearly a subjective valuation approach can result in a non-optimal decision in retrospect, but it can still be optimal on a prior basis. We shall deal with this later on in Chapter 3. Consequence variables should be 'end' or 'product' variables, in principle, but this is not always possible in practice, and there is some doubt as to whether there are such things as end variables. Let us consider a few examples which highlight the difficulties.

Examples

(1) 'Lateness of delivery' may be important because of an intrinsic value to the manufacturer in that he is proud of his service. In this case it might be a product variable. It may be that it is the loss in sales due to this which is the true consequence variable, in which case 'lateness of delivery' becomes an intermediate, or producer, variable.

† W. V. Hole, *User Needs and the Design of Houses*, Building Research Station Current Paper 51/68, 1968. Reprinted by permission of the Director of the Building Research Establishment.

38

It is possible that only one true consequence variable exists (*viz.*, profit), but that difficulties may arise in relating, say, delay time, to such profit, in which case they may, effectively, be treated as ultimate consequences, with the necessity of a subjective valuation concerning its influence on profit.

(2) Similar situations arise when 'run-outs' occur in stock needed for production, and these are difficult to evaluate in many cases. In some cases we have emergency premiums; in others overdrafts; in others it simply results in a delay and some unknown penalty.

(3) In some capital investment problems, 'flexibility' is a key attribute (e.g. production equipment, school buildings, etc.). But what is flexibility? It has to be interpreted in terms of actual consequences to the sponsor. We can seldom do this.

In this case the question of 'ultimacy' has led to the question of 'definition'.

(4) Let us consider an example taken from Kazanowski[66] who writes on weapons effectiveness.

When an assessment is made, certain primary factors are taken into consideration. Some of these are: armour thickness and shape, a; firepower, f; weapon range, w; crew comfort, c; maintainability, m; cost, k.

Now the final assessment of a weapon is on the basis of its social effects, l. The weapon influences this by the security it produces, s, and by its cost of making and maintaining, k. The security is obtained by the effectiveness of the weapon, e, and maintainability, m.

Let us now consider the influences between the variables as shown in Figure 19.

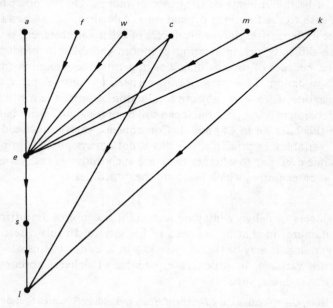

Figure 19. Weapons effectiveness consequence influences

Ideally we should evaluate the weapon in terms of a suitable variable, l, but, not only is it difficult to think of a suitable variable, but finding the relations between the variables is not yet possible. We are thus left with a subjective evaluation at the lower level, in terms of variables which are not ultimate consequences.

Stratton[128] refers to the inability of reducing defence investment effects to a single variable for effectiveness, and, emphasizes the highly subjective nature of this by stating that:

'like beauty, effectiveness lies in the eye of the beholder.'

(5) A police problem arises in the determination of the number of, and routing of, police cars. The central objective is to minimize the delay in getting to police calls. However, what are the real consequences of such delays?

(6) A similar situation arises in the case of hospital ambulances, where delays in getting to accidents are concerned.

(7) Ackoff[1] gives an example of a mail-order firm in which the consequences of delays were measured in terms of returned orders. This did not prohibit the possibility that, even if the order were not returned, no further orders would arise from that source.

(8) What are the consequences of restoring a man to health? Some economists traditionally do this in terms of wages. Is it right to maximize net effect of equivalent wage benefits and costs?

In trying to improve the working conditions of people, it has been suggested that we should do it in terms of 'probabilities of keeping staff × the respective salaries', the salary representing the consequence to a firm of keeping the man. But what is the consequence of not having the man?

(9) The following quotation is taken from Hansmann:[54]

'In the commercial area it is frequently impossible to forecast the economic benefits of an investment decision. The thing to do is to backtrack in the causal chain of events until something measurable is reached.'

The following two examples are given:

(a) military: probability of winning war replaced by ability to inflict damage in the event of war;
(b) commercial: probability of marketable product replaced by physical and cost characteristics of product.

(10) Weingartner[141] states that, for some people, no investment must have a payback period greater than P, for some P, fixed in advance. Thus payback period is a consequence from this point of view. However, one ought to ask what the consequences of a varying payback period are, perhaps probabilistically, if uncertainty is a relevant factor.

(11) Internal personnel training may require departmental staff to spend time with trainees. A schedule may be required to minimize the effect of total time lost by all departments. But how do we compare time lost by, say, a decision

40

analysis department, with that lost by a personnel department? What are the true consequences of a minute of time of any specific department?

(12) In a study of production in a steel company, because of the possibilities of defective production, a fixed overage has to be allowed in the production programme. The effects of the overage may be excess or deficit in production. Prior to the study no calculations of these effects were made. During the study the question was raised as to what were the further consequences of excess or deficit production. This was complicated because of the difficulty of determining the policy for handling such contingencies. For example, in the event of a deficit, either a new production run may be initiated or part of another customer's order modified to make up the deficiency. In this case this then raised the question of the consequences for the other customer's order. If an excess arises this may go into stock, thus raising the question of how this influences future production consequences. Alternatively the customer may accept the excess.

(13) Dick[35] mentions the evaluation of safety arising through improved design of structures. He mentions the social benefit and also the direct economic benefit arising from reduced accident rates.

The following examples express diagrammatically the ultimate/non-ultimate relationship in terms of interrelated levels of objective in organizations.

(14) See Figure 20.

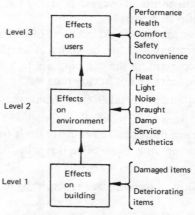

Figure 20.   Levels of objective
(owner/user) in building industry

(15) See Figure 21.

(16) Steiner[127] discusses different levels of assessment in the military field (see Figure 22).

Judgements about 'weapons' features should ideally be related to the effect of that weapon in use as part of: (a) a sortie, (b) a mission, (c) a scenario.

See Example 4 for comparison.

(17) In assessing the effectiveness of a maintenance policy on a fleet operation, the reliability of the fleet is often considered. However, a failure of a vehicle may

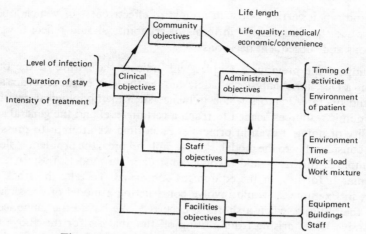

Figure 21. Levels of objective in health service

have different direct consequences depending on the circumstances. Thus the failure may prevent the vehicle proceeding further and emergency action involving transfer of goods to another vehicle sent out, if one is available, may be needed. Alternatively the delivery may be simply delayed until the vehicle can be repaired on the road. If the failure is serious and happens at a crucial time, the vehicle and goods may be lost. If the failure is minor, delivery may be com-

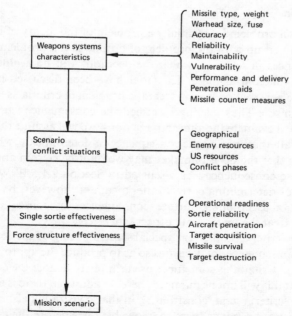

Figure 22. Levels of objective in the military services

pleted and repair carried out with no loss of effectiveness of vehicle operation. Thus we see that judgements in terms of reliability should reflect a variety of conditions and subsequent decisions.

A study of the previous examples will indicate the nature of the problems besetting a Decision Analyst when determining the level of consequence at which he should operate. Factors which influence such methodological decisions are the economic resources needed to reach a certain level and the general scientific possibility of doing it even in principle. Each time we attempt to press further we add considerably to the model. For example, to press the problem of flexibility, in Example 3, further would involve constructing a model of alternative uses, and demands for use, of the equipment concerned. To take the stock run-out further, in Example 2, would involve constructing a model of decisions made, and of their effects, when a shortage occurred. We have little guidance on the quantitative losses arising from cutting off the analysis for the above reasons. We can, however, be aware of the nature of the chain effects set up and, as with the taxonomical aspects of decisions and constraints, a formal identification of the related networks in a given situation can help.

The purpose of this section has been to indicate the nature of the problems met when we try to ascertain the consequences in terms of which we should evaluate our decisions. This has led to a network picture which extends throughout the total set of variables included in the model. We will discuss this later on in the modelling chapter.

2.1.6 Criteria

The criterion problem is essentially a problem of the theory of choice.

Very much tied up with the problem of criteria is the problem of identifying the consequences in terms of which the decisions will be evaluated, since the criterion is a function of these. The latter have been discussed in the previous section. In the next section we will treat the problem of criteria as if the situations were deterministic. Thus, having identified the consequence variables in terms of which we will evaluate the alternative actions, we will assume that the relationship between alternatives and the consequences is deterministic, while at the same time realizing that the decisionmaker may well not be certain about the further effects of these consequences, as discussed in Section 2.1.5.B. We will see that the problem of determining correct criteria cannot, however, be divorced from the problem of ascertaining further consequences of consequences. We will subsequently treat the uncertainty aspect separately.

We will use 'criteria' in the very special sense of a single function operating on the space of consequences of decisions so as to produce the appropriate decisions (see White[144]). 'Criteria' is sometimes used simply to denote the consequences of a decision, but this will not be our usage here. In addition, there is a clear relationship between 'criteria' and 'constraints', in that constraints also operate on the space of decisions to reduce them to allowable ones before the criterion, in our sense, is further applied to choose between the allowable ones. We have already noted that the validity of constraint statements is related to the determination of appropriate criteria (see Section 2.1.4) via the implied trade-off of consequences against each other in the context of some criterion.

2.1.6.1 CRITERIA FOR DIFFERENT PROBLEM AREAS

Let us take a few examples of the criterion problem from various areas:
A. transport criteria;
B. educational criteria;
C. marketing criteria;
D. wealth criteria;
E. buildings criteria;
F. production criteria;
G. smoothing criteria;
H. nutritional criteria;
I. public authority criteria;
J. general economic criteria.

In the examples which follow we will treat some a little more fully than others, and the reader can explore them more fully. No suggestion as to the correct criterion is given. We simply point to some of the features involved in each case. The determination of the appropriate criterion, whether subjectively at a non-ultimate level, or by further tracing of effects, culminating in a final subjective assessment, must depend upon the circumstances. In the end analysis all criteria are subjective.

A TRANSPORT CRITERIA

Examples

(1) A recent investigation into the effect of fare increases on revenue resulted in the determination of the number of passengers, x_i, who would travel an i miles journey if the fares were changed in a certain way. The suggested criterion was $C \equiv \sum_i ix_i$ which was to be maximized subject to equality of revenue and costs. However, in what sense is C an appropriate criterion function? The transport department may, effectively, take this to be so, and this might be then a very subjective type of criterion. Thus we may take the view that we are simply attempting to produce a decision which is best in relationship to this subjective criterion and not examine in what sense such subjectivity is representative of further aspects of reality.

If $x_i = x_i(f_i), f_i$ is fare, we then maximize $\sum_i ix_i(f_i)$ subject to $\sum_i f_i x_i(f_i) = $ costs, if costs are fixed.

On the other hand if $\sum_i ix_i \equiv \sum_i ix_i'$, the solutions may be different in terms of their influence on the community. Is $[10, 0, 0, 0, \ldots] \equiv [0, 0, \ldots, 1]$? The effect of fare changes is to induce people to walk, or take a bus, or buy a car, etc., and if we are simply given $x_1, x_2, \ldots, x_{10}$, we know nothing about the real consequences to the community. Thus our fare changes may induce all long-distance people to buy a car and all short-distance people to use the bus, and then we have traffic problems.

Hence we see that, although $\sum_i ix_i$ could be taken as a criterion, it may be a poor correlate with any true criterion, in terms of further consequences.

Thus we also see that the correctness of the criterion in this instance is related to the problem of correct consequences mentioned previously.

(2) In distribution problems one often comes across the 'ton–mile' criterion. If vehicles are assumed fully loaded, and have a specific tonnage, then the criterion reduces to minimizing $\sum$ journeys × distance. However, this is not necessarily representative of actual costs. For example, in long journeys vehicle utilization may fall off because there may not be quite enough time left in a given day or week to get in another run. For short journeys the amount of time spent loading and unloading per mile is greater. The real criterion may be one of minimizing total variable costs.

The use of a 'ton–mile' criterion arises from its simplicity where the calculation of an optimal cost-oriented solution may be difficult and where the calculation may have to be made very often, say every day. If such a surrogate criterion is to be used then it should be corrected for a vehicle time and load utilization factor over each journey.

(3) A car owner might instruct a garage to minimize his fuel consumption and the garage could simply disconnect his petrol tank. The car owner might then have to say that he wished his car to move at a certain speed in which case the garage might carry out road tests and adjust the car until it gave minimal petrol consumption at that speed. However, the car would then be tuned up in a 'warmed up' condition, whereas fuel costs can be important in starting up a car from cold depending on whether the owner does many short journeys in relationship to long journeys. The concern with costs might then raise the question of whether public transport might not have been cheaper. Thus from some rather simple criterion has emerged the need to consider a much wider oriented criterion, which reflects not only costs but other aspects of car ownership. The garage is being asked to do its best without really knowing what constitutes 'best' for the car owner.

(4) In studying the optimal location and structure of a fire service the problem of valuing the time taken to get to a fire arises. In the absence of objective measurement of the influence of time on progress and effects of fire, subjective value judgements of combined costs and service were needed.

B EDUCATIONAL CRITERIA

Examples

(1) We are often faced with the problem of choosing between different educational systems. Thus we may use closed-circuit television and large classes, or more teachers and smaller classes. A suggested criterion might be, for a given outlay, the number of people who pass their examinations. Thus in the first instance we may have a larger intake and proportionally less passes, and poorer overall quality, but in the latter we may have less intake, but proportionally more passes, and better overall quality.

If x is the decision, $N(x)$ is the intake, $p(x)$ is the passes proportion, $f(x)$ is the failures proportion, then the criterion might be $N(x)p(x)$.

However, perhaps we ought to consider $p(x,z)$, equal to the proportion with level z, and then use $(\sum_z zp(x,z))N(x)$? But we then have the same problem as with the transport problem. What are the consequences to the nation of people passing/failing examinations at any level z? We have no clear indication of this, but, in view of the large amounts of money involved, surely this should be considered? What about the value of the future time, spent by failures on various activities, to themselves or to the community?

(2) In assessing a dissertation on a practical project several factors are taken into account: enterprise, presentation, technical analysis, and originality. The procedure is to award a mark for each aspect up to a maximum specified for each aspect. However, it needs to be pointed out that if the probability of being original is small, its value is high. The difficulty is caused by the fact that a maximal number of points is to be allocated. The procedure of putting a maximal number of points on each factor does not seem realistic.

C MARKETING CRITERIA

Example

One objective which a company may believe in is that of 'share of market', in the belief that this is highly correlated with 'profits'. However, this need not be so, since an effort to increase market share may increase costs, increase competition and hence, indirectly, further increase costs or reduce income.

We assume here that prices are fixed and that our decision concerns sales effort only. The cost of getting a specific market share may be prohibitive and hence lose profit.

If m is proportion of market, this may be a function of sales effort, s, say $m = m(s)$. However, the cost of achieving sales effort s may be a function $c(s)$. The total profit is then, as a function of s, given by $p(s) = \alpha m(s) - c(s)$.

We may have something like the following in Figure 23.

As with the other problems, it is a problem which needs a clear analysis of the consequences ensuing from a pursuance of a policy based on this criterion.

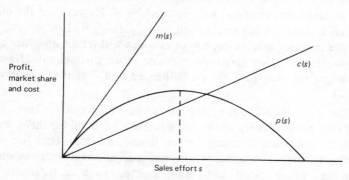

Figure 23. Market performance as a function of sales effort

46

D HEALTH CRITERIA

Examples

(1) In a study of the layout of a hospital the criterion was taken to be a weighted average of the time spent by various categories of staff in travelling between units during their daily routine. It may be argued that one should find the real effects on patient care and optimize patient care. On the other hand one presumably has to consider the demands on the staff as distinct from the effects of these demands on such care, and a compromise between the two is needed. Even if we accepted this approach, it must be noted that an additive scale is doubtful since there is a limit to which each category can contribute if the other categories are not available in the appropriate proportions. Thus the patient care arising from one unit of a surgeon's time becoming available, depends on how many units of other people's time simultaneously becomes available.

(2) In a study of setting aside a special emergency unit, the criterion was taken to be some function of the total throughput and a measure of inconvenience in

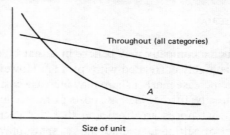

Figure 24. Throughput and excess emergencies. A = average number of emergencies per day for which extra provision has to be made

having to handle excess emergencies. We assume that throughput is not increased by separating off the emergencies; if it is, then there is no real problem (see Figure 24).

As with the other problems, one might determine the relative weightings of throughput and inconvenience, as measured by A. However, if the effect of A can be seen as contributing to throughput (negatively if A increases), as it will do since the energies used to cope with excesses will reflect on other aspects of the hospital, the criterion may reduce to one of net throughput. However, it is likely that patient care will also be influenced and that the former viewpoint will prevail.

(3) In the medical field, bed utilization can be improved by asking all waiting-list patients to come in every week until a bed can be found for them, with a high chance of one not being found on the first few attendances. Thus bed utilization is suspect as a criterion function. It is even suspect as a relevant consequence (see Figure 18 for a similar point) and yet much emphasis is put on maximizing bed utilization.

(4) Suppose we could either reduce the number of emergencies or improve the service to present emergencies. What would be our criterion for this sort of problem? This would involve some concept of quality of life and relative comparisons with life length and would ultimately rest on subjective judgements of relative value.

(5) In an ambulance problem, by varying the number allocated to emergencies the consequences can be expressed in terms of:

(a) time spent in vehicles by outpatients;
(b) time spent waiting by outpatients;
(c) time taken to get to emergency patient.

In each aspect we are concerned with aspects of patient care and service. Again the subjective view at this level may be taken, although each consequence has further, traceable consequences, and such judgements may not reflect reality at another level.

(6) Baligh[4] discusses the problem of criteria when scheduling patients through hospitals. Patient days/day is inadequate, since all we need to do is to keep patients in as long as possible. A 'weighted utilization of resources' is inadequate since it is not a terminal output and may not reflect the values of patients. The suggestion is to weight classes of patients and to maximize the weighted sum of throughputs, again a highly questionable approach.

E BUILDINGS CRITERIA

Example

When designing a school or any other building where we can vary space, noise, light, heat, etc., how do we do this in a way which is best for individuals as a whole? Keighley[67] discusses the criterion which should be used when designing a building. He states this should be 'the specific proportion of population which find the noise "acceptable" '. However, what do we mean by 'acceptable'? Do we just ask them? Or should we determine what they will do, or what will happen, as a result of various noise conditions? Will they strike? Will they go deaf? Will they perform badly? What are the real effects?

F PRODUCTION CRITERIA

Example

Often, production people are concerned with improving machine utilization. However, this can be achieved by having a lot of work in progress and is likely to result in delays in fulfilling some customers' orders. Not only this but utilization is really a surrogate of throughput and it is some combination of service and the latter which may be more relevant.

G SMOOTHING CRITERIA

Example

In a problem in forecasting the load in an electricity supply company the load was initially forecast in discrete form as per Figure 25.

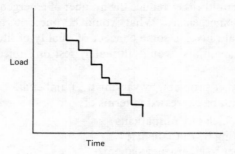

Figure 25. Load as a function of time

It was required to find a 'smooth' fit to the discrete curve, but it was difficult to get the criterion of fit.

It could have been:

(i) sum of squares of deviations;
(ii) sum of moduli of deviations;
(iii) sum of moduli of ratio of deviations to actual;
(iv) maximum modulus of deviations.

Until the decisions and consequential effects of errors could be studied there was no right criterion which could be used.

H NUTRITIONAL CRITERIA

Example

Simon[120] discusses the nutritional problem. This reduces to a criterion problem of cost and nutritional value. By fixing the minimal nutritional levels, we can find the minimal cost solution. However, the problem arises when we wish to get the optimal compromise between nutritional values and cost. This may be subjectively approached at this level, or, alternatively, the effects of nutritional levels could be examined.

I PUBLIC SERVICE CRITERIA

Example

The failure of bulbs and neon tubes between repairs will have different values depending on the areas concerned, e.g. main roads, housing estates, public places, etc. If P_i is the proportion of time in an area i, in a failed state, we might try to minimize $\sum_i \alpha_i P_i$ subject to total cost being no greater than C. However, how do we get the α_i? Can we relate a failure in a given area to other consequences such as accidents, robbery, inconvenience? We can tackle it subjectively at this level, or try to determine these effects.

J GENERAL ECONOMIC CRITERIA

Problems often arise in which the costs, or incomes, arise over a time period as distinct from at a particular point in time. Because of the general importance of this we treat this as a separate section, although it is clearly related to the other sections.

Examples

(1) The following example arose in the field of provision of water supplies in which there were two proposals, *viz.*: S, to operate the present system; S', a further installation. Table 6 gives the formal cost picture.

Table 6: Operating and capital costs

S:	Operating costs
	$c_1 c_2 c_3 \ldots c_n$
S':	Capital costs
	$K \quad 0 \quad 0$
	Operating costs
	$c_1' c_2' \ldots c_n$

We are required to produce a criterion for comparing S and S'.

We could take the subjective view at this level. We could, for example, simply determine a value function for vectors of the form $[x_1, x_2, \ldots, x_n]$, e.g.

$$V[x_1, x_2, \ldots, x_n] = V_0 - \sum_{s=1}^{n} \alpha^s x_s$$

where the summation expression is the present worth of cash flows.

However, a further decomposition of the alternatives may be worthwhile since the decisionmaker may not be aware of the true implications of each x_s.

The first thing we need to ask is, are the cash flows, given above, the real cash flows? In this respect, the capital cost, K, is not the true cash flow in cases where this has to be borrowed. The same applies to c_s if this has to be borrowed, but we assume that this is not the case. Let us assume K is paid back at a fixed level, k, over 40 years, where the interest rate is i. Then $k = iK/(1 - (1 + i)^{-40})$. The new alternative is now represented by the net cash flows,

$$c_1' + k, \, c_2' + k, \, \ldots, \, c_{40}' + k, \, \ldots, \, c_{41}', \, \ldots,$$

providing c_i' is not borrowed. c_i' could, for example, be negative.

The second thing to note is that even these cash flows are not, in themselves, final cash consequences. If a positive cost arises, then this may subtract from resources available (especially if we have to borrow) and hence influence other decisions. We thus have the usual 'opportunity loss' cost. If we borrow £100,000 now to build a new pumping station, this may preclude the borrowing of cash next year to extend a reservoir. Since each decision influences cash flows directly associated with it, we thus see that the pumping station decision influences costs associated with any reservoir decision. The future use of reservoirs depends on pumping capacity.

Strauss[129] says, 'One decision always affects another cause of action.'

This is, of course, part of the general theme already discussed that 'consequences have consequences have consequences . . .'.

Thus we see that, in looking at one financial decision, one should be aware of other financial decisions influenced by it, and hence the awareness of the spectrum of alternatives is important, both now and in the future. The total cash flow within the organization should be considered, in order to get the appropriate effects.

If we wish to evaluate the single decision, while allowing for its influence on other decisions and cash flows, a suggested approach is to allow for the productivity of cash by the discounted cash flow or present worth method. By this means, the series $[x_1, x_2, \ldots, x_n, \ldots]$ becomes, on a common effective scale, $[(1 + r)^N x_1, (1 + r)^{N-1} x_2, \ldots]$ and this becomes proportional to

$$[\alpha x_1, \alpha^2 x_2, \alpha^2 x_3, \ldots] \quad \text{with} \quad \alpha = (1 + r)^{-1}$$

to avoid difficulty of time horizon.

Although the idea looks intuitively appealing the derivation of α can only be properly done by an extensive analysis of cash flows and decisions mentioned above, even if it were valid.

It must be realized that the value of cash depends not only on external factors (like borrowing) but also on internal factors (like investment opportunities and their cost behaviour). For an organization on a perpetual overdraft the answer may be radically different to that when the organization has large cash reserves.

There are two other reasons why a discount factor may be valid, *viz.*:

(a) £1 today will purchase less than £1 ten years later, for certain commodities, but not all; thus the costs of buildings are going up, but equipment costs (for the Water Department) may not, since technological progress is an important factor;

(b) the future events, although they may be the same as now, do not occupy the same attention as immediate events; thus providing 10,000 gallons of water for a community now is not viewed, value-wise, as the same as providing those same 10,000 gallons for the next generation. This is a purely psychological factor that the decisionmaker may insist on. The derivation of any α is then dependent on an appropriate theory of value.

As a special situation, if we are concerned with periods of time over which the interest aspect is small (i.e. effect on other cash flows is small), then $\Delta x_1 + \Delta x_2 + \cdots + \Delta x_n$ gives the value of a decision, where Δx_i is a small quantity of money. Suppose it costs us £10 per week, to save £20 per week in scrap output. Then, assuming this decision has no strong interaction with other decisions, $\alpha \simeq 1 \cdot 0$ (per week). For a given year, $x_i = -£10$ per week and, whatever the interest factor, if it is small, it is simply the net cost which influences the decision.

As has been indicated earlier, the illustrations given have not been examined with a view to determining what the criterion should be, but rather to indicate the sorts of problem raised in determining criteria. The problem cannot be separated from the problem of identifying consequences at the appropriate level. In the end analysis the problem becomes a subjective aggregation one at some level. Figure 26 depicts the situation.

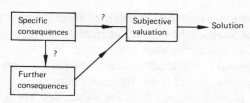

Figure 26. The criterion problem

In the previous examples we have seen that:

(a) if we rely on subjective criteria at a level at which one might in principle pursue in terms of further consequences, then one's solution is no more than compatible with these, that it is possible that such valuations may not reflect the true combined effect of further consequences, and that even the structure of the valuation function may be invalid (see Examples B(2), D(1));
(b) some of the consequences depicted in Figure 26 are intertwined with other decisions (see Example J(1) in particular, although this applies equally well to all the examples in which a certain consequence sets into motion a further decision process).

Our basic methodological problem is one of deciding whether to accept subjectivity at one level of consequence, or to expend further effort to analyse subsequent effects. If the latter course of action is taken, a rather more complex model can arise, particularly where the subsequently generated decision processes have to be examined.

In the light of these remarks we see that the problem formulation criterion aspect is highly related to the modelling of the objective system and is very often a surrogate representation of this.

It is, of course, no easy thing to determine criteria and yet the Decision Analyst must believe that the decisionmaker can be persuaded to exhibit such criteria, since otherwise one has no way of judging whether the analysis process itself is worthwhile.

Ideally one would like to find the appropriate criteria early on in the study, since this would help identify the appropriate objective system model. However, in practice this is not generally the case, although more knowledge of the formal nature of decision situations of particular kinds might lead to an agreed approach to criteria in those situations, e.g., in inventory control.

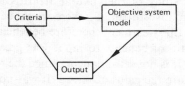

Figure 27. Interaction of criteria
and objective system models

The general situation is that there is feedback from the objective system model output which helps identify the criteria adequately enough for the purposes of the study. Figure 27 depicts this situation.

Monarchi, Kisiel and Duckstein[90] indicate how such an interactive procedure might work in a specific area of water resource planning.

The theoretical foundation of subjective value, and allied theories, has not been pursued (see White[143]).

In addition to the points which have arisen in the previous examples, several special points related to the criterion problem will now be discussed.

2.1.6.2 SOME SPECIAL POINTS ON CRITERIA

A RATIO CRITERIA

Hitch[58] stresses the dangers of using ratios for criteria. Let us consider a few examples illustrating this point.

Examples

(1) Consider the following problem.

Alternative I: Capital cost £400, return (after cost) £100 at end of year;
Alternative II: Capital cost £1000, return (after cost) £200 at end of year.

I gives better rate of return (25%) against that of II (20%) but II gives better profit (£200) against that of I (£100).

The error in the rate of return approach is that of ignoring other decisions, a point we have recently stressed.

Suppose we have £1000 capital. In the first case we have £600 to invest and some, perhaps unknown, rate of return r, giving a total return £100 + £600r. In the latter case we have £200. The answer then depends on the expected value of r. The real criterion in this case might be the expected return at end of period. It does not matter whether we begin with a fixed amount of money, whether the cost is borne out of income, or whether we borrow money to finance the ventures.

Note that if every investment is self-financing, then, if it produces profit at all, it should be accepted.

(2) As another example we refer to Hitch's[58] convoy problem with the criterion of 'number of U-boats sunk/convoy ships sunk', leading to maximum convoy size which was not in the interests of winning war, since the deployment of ships has a wider objective than simply sinking U-boats.

(3) In a cost-benefit study of rheumatoid arthritis it was estimated that, in some areas, for a present investment of x there would be a net discounted return, over time, of $16x$. Was this treatment therefore beneficial?

The fact that the ratio of benefits to input was greater than unity does not mean it was beneficial. It is not self-financing since the resources needed initially had to be provided before the gains occurred. It was not necessarily good, since if these (equivalent physical) resources were not used they would, with some probability, be used for some other purpose, the relative benefits of which would be unknown. In principle, the decision to invest must be based on probabilities of benefits from all potential competitors for cash.

We would need to consider a variety of other avenues of investment and, even if we could accept the 'rate of return' as a valid measure of investment value, we still have to produce a probability distribution as follows before we can assume a given rate of return is worthwhile (see Figure 28).

This would undoubtedly be difficult, but a decision without something like this is speculative.

Figure 28. Probability distribution of rate of return

It is worth noting that a policy to invest in alternatives with the highest expected return rates, in the Health Services, might produce a highly specialized Health Service.

B PLAUSIBLE CRITERIA

Hitch also states that people tend to accept the first plausible criterion they perceive. The U-boat criterion appears plausible but fails to represent the true situation since it does not adequately represent the true consequences of a decision. This is why the criterion function is tied up with the determination of proper consequences.

We note that Hitch[58] and Kazanowski[66] condemn the tendency to maximize physical quantities, whose relation to true consequences is obscure.

Example

Consider the criterion of 'cost'. 'Cost' depends on 'price' per unit of each input. Why should 'cost minimization' be valid? It can result in 'inappropriate consumption of resources'. Why not 'total man hours' for all inputs? Thus so many hours of a machine is equivalent to so many hours of labour required to make the machine, bearing in mind the life of the machine, etc. (see R. Baylis[7]).

C LONG-TERM AND SHORT-TERM CRITERIA

It has to be realized that the interrelationship between the short-term and long-term decisions is very important and that the best decision for the short term is not the best for the long term. There can be two different criteria.

54

Examples

(1) In a recent case study there arose the problem of optimal crew size for a refuse collection team. There were two possible criteria.

First of all, on the assumption that the resources (manpower, vehicles) remained the same for, say, the next year, then there was a question of providing a feasible schedule and crew size so that all the scheduled work could be done with a minimization of variable costs, like overtime costs.

However, manpower levels and vehicle numbers are long-term decisions. During the passage of time the volume of refuse will increase, forcing decisions on the above levels of resources. This is a cost-oriented decision and hence the long-term criterion might be to minimize annual (discounted) cost. Thus if the respective operating costs were available, a minimal total cost solution, using costs like man wages per hour, vehicle costs per hour (once lifetime has been fixed) would lead to a minimal total cost schedule.

(2) The same sort of situation arises in production problems, *viz.*, finding a feasible production schedule to minimize variable costs, and finding a minimal total cost solution, given unit production costs (man wages/hr., etc.).

The argument that 'given resources should not contribute to costs' depends solely on which decision one is considering. If one did the latter and then adjusted one's resources, in due course, to meet the demand, this would give the minimal total cost.

(3) In the traditional routing problem, involving utilization of vehicle fleets to pick up and deliver, there arises the problem of the daily criteria used to schedule fleet.

In the long run the criterion is made up of total costs, service and equity of workload for employees.

In the short term the daily criterion is equivalent to a decision rule, which may, however, not really coincide with the long-term criterion. There are, for example, arguments as to whether the daily criterion should be:

(a) total quantity picked up and/or delivered;
(b) the total mileage involved (we can make this zero, and this is clearly not correct);
(c) the number of trucks used.

These criteria are all short term and it is necessary to use Hitch's argument that they should be consistent with the long-term criteria.

D CONSISTENCY OF CRITERIA

We refer to Hitch[58] on the point of required consistency between high- and low-level criteria.

Examples

(1) In example C(3) it would be essential to see that the selected short-term criteria were compatible with the long-term criteria.

(2) Hitch quotes example A(2) in terms of the ships lost/U-boats sunk, which was not consistent with the higher-level criterion of probability of winning the war.

(3) Laut[73] gives the following criterion for measuring overall systems effectiveness in the design of equipment:

OSE = performance × reliability × availability × cost effectiveness

Naturally, everything else being equal, the value of a piece of equipment will increase if each of the first three variables increase. Cost effectiveness is a ratio (= net worth/total cost) and we have already discussed the dangers of these. However, apart from this, what higher-level considerations give rise to the above criterion? Other criteria retain the monotonicity aspects, e.g. addition rather than multiplication. If the equipment were producing a product, then performance × reliability would give a measure of output, since, in this case, reliability refers to length of time equipment can maintain performance; but why multiply by availability, which is probability of being available when wanted? Surely this influences penalties for a late start, and may have a negative, additive, effect on total behaviour? Thus we see that such a criterion could be at variance with higher-level considerations. If such valuations are to be used they should at least have a proper structure, even if the final weights are intuitive.

(4) When ascertaining the value of an investment opportunity, very often the 'present worth' criterion is used. A single investment opportunity can be one of many and can arise in a dynamic stream of investment opportunities. To know the value of a single investment presupposes some model of its relationship with its total environment and must also presuppose some higher-level criterion related to total system performance. In White[144, 146] a simple total model was used to establish the validity of the present worth criterion under special circumstances. It is not valid under all circumstances.

E   CRITERIA UNDER UNCERTAINTY

So far we have dealt only with the aggregation of outcomes in deterministic situations. We also have to face the problem of uncertain situations. Much of this is related to the manner in which we handle the construction of the model dealt with in the next chapter. However, there still remains the question of representing the uncertainty factor in some formal manner and the determination of relevant criteria for assessing alternatives under different conditions. Such conditions are often broken into three classes (see White[143]), viz., certainty, risk, strict uncertainty. The first case is self-explanatory. The risk situation is one in which consequences are probabilistically expressed. The strict uncertainty class contains the residual situations. The case of subjective probability can legitimately be included in either of the last two classes from a logical point of view. The various forms of game theory can likewise be included in the third class.

Extensive literature exists on the problem of criteria under uncertainty (see White,[143] Fishburn,[44] Luce and Raiffa[77]). Much of this is technical and deals with the axiomatic foundations. The most commonly discussed approaches are those of von Neumann and Morgenstern[138] and of Savage.[111] These both result in the expected utility theory of the form:

$$v(\mathbf{x}) = \sum_s p(s) v(\theta(\mathbf{x}, s))$$

where v is the value (criterion function), $\mathbf{x}$ is an alternative, $\theta(\mathbf{x}, s)$ is the consequence vector if $\mathbf{x}$ is taken and state (event) s arises, and $p(s)$ is the probability of state (event) s.

The difference between the two approaches is that in the former case the probabilities are specified, whereas in the latter case they are subjectively derived from the decisionmaker.

Although considerable attention has been given in this book to the problem of criteria for given consequence vectors, since this has not been adequately explored in alternative literature, no special attention is given, in this book, to the uncertainty criteria problem, since considerable alternative literature exists.

F   THE ROLE AND WORTH OF ESTABLISHING CRITERIA

Three basic difficulties in getting criteria arise, *viz.*:

(a) in trying to amalgamate the desires of different decisionmakers to produce a representative desire;
(b) in trying to amalgamate the consequences of a decision into a criterion for a single decisionmaker;
(c) in trying to formally incorporate the uncertainty factors.

The role of formal criteria is that they enable the model to take a closed, rather than open form, as explained in Chapter 1. Figure 3 depicts this ideal situation. The open form severely restricts the comprehensiveness of the analysis.

In addition, as has been pointed out in Sections 2.1.3 and 2.1.5, the knowledge of criteria may usefully lead us to the determination of appropriate alternatives and consequences. Nonetheless the difficulties mentioned above do constitute real ones.

There is no satisfactory solution to (a). In Section 2.1.6, examples A(1), A(4), B(1), B(2), D(1), D(2), D(3), D(4), D(5), D(6), E, I, all suffer from the possibilities that decisions may be made by, or on behalf of, a group of individuals with different values, although in some areas a closer identity may exist than in others. See Arrow[2] for a discussion of some aspects of these problems.

The acceptance of the value theory approach to (b) depends on the acceptance that the judgements are 'good' in some sense, unless one takes the view that the final solution is acceptable if it is compatible with these judgements, and that one can go no further.

Case (c) has its theoretical development, as do (a) and (b), but it raises the question of prior and posterior validation of alternatives, a point to which we will return in Chapter 3.

Irrespective of the difficulties, it is a fact that, even with the open informative form of analysis, judgements have to be imposed and that if we have reason to suppose that these judgements are poor, in some sense, then we equally well have reason not to undertake any analysis at all, since all analysis presupposes some justifiable net increase in value.

As with our other methodological problems, we face a clear choice of whether we deal with open models, of a limited kind, and then let the decisionmaker choose, or whether we attempt to use a closed model, with the increased coherence, and end up with prescribed solutions. If we may assume that, eventually, we can properly identify the criteria, then the methodological problem reduces to the choice of technique of analysis, which we will discuss later on. In arriving at these criteria we may make use of the open form of the model in an attempt to converge on the appropriate criterion, as illustrated in Figure 29.

Initially we begin with an open form of analysis and, on the basis of stated choices, model the criterion. This is then used to produce a closed form and

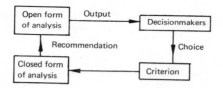

Figure 29. Open and closed models

recommend a solution. This solution is then used in the open context and the decisionmaker again makes his choice. The process continues until agreement is reached, aided by discussions such as have arisen in situations A–J.

Needless to say, we still have to make a judgement that this process is worthwhile, raising a further methodological issue.

As has been indicated, the uncertainty aspect poses a special problem with respect to the prior–posterior validation dilemma. It poses a particular problem for the analyst in that if he incorporates the uncertainty formally and recommends an action, although this may be, from a prior point of view, valid, the end result may be failure. He may be criticized for this, even though the decisionmaker would have taken the same decision in an appropriate open form of analysis. As will be mentioned in the final chapter, the understanding between the analyst and the decisionmaker is important in these situations in particular.

G EFFICIENT SOLUTIONS

Hitch[58] states that, bearing in mind the difficulties in getting such criteria, Operational Research workers should concentrate on getting 'efficient solutions', i.e. solutions for which no other solution exists which is better in some component and at least as good in other components.

Examples

(1) Markowitz[79] discusses efficient sets in portfolio analysis. Suppose we have a quantity of cash x to be divided among n investment opportunities in quantities $x_1, x_2, x_3, \ldots, x_n$.

If μ_i is the mean return, and σ_{ij} is the covariance of return, for opportunity i

58

and pairs of opportunities i, j respectively, then if μ, σ^2 are the mean and variance of total return respectively, we have

$$\mu = \sum x_i \mu_i$$
$$\sigma^2 = \sum_i \sum_j x_i x_j \sigma_{ij}$$

For a given mean μ, a decisionmaker may prefer alternatives with the smallest variance. The set of pairs $(\mu, \sigma^2_{\min}(\mu))$ thus generated contains the efficient set. See Figure 30, where AB gives the efficient set.

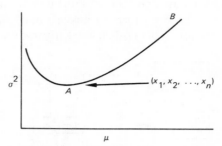

Figure 30. Efficient solutions in portfolio analysis

(2) In problems concerning community benefits, if the benefits to every member of the community offset his contribution then this would be an efficient solution. When considering investment in defence, those who had more to lose might not mind paying more taxes.

(3) A company was concerned with forecasting demand for spares. The forecasting system allowed them both to reduce stocks and to maintain the service level by improved production planning based on the forecasts. This solution 'dominated' the previous solution and there was no need to 'weight' service level to achieve this improvement. This is, of course, only immediately true if the forecasting is costless.

In brief, Hitch's philosophy amounts to improving the components of a criterion, without adversely influencing the other components, as much as we can. Industrial engineering is typically oriented this way, being concerned with the cost-improvement aspect without adversely influencing personnel, etc.

It must be noted that when several decisionmakers are involved the reduction of the problem to an efficient set may not remove all the difficulties.

Example

During the building of a large hospital for a client, work stopped because of a disagreement on stage payments. One possibility was to put the matter to arbitration, to which both parties agreed to accept the verdict. However, there were clear dangers for both parties in doing this. It was calculated that the expected net return to the builder was $\underline{c}$, and that the expected net cost to the client was $\bar{c}$, with $\bar{c} > \underline{c}$. Clearly the only acceptable actions were to settle in this range or arbitration. In principle, within this set, any immediate settlement in the range $\underline{c} \leqslant s \leqslant \bar{c}$ would provide an efficient solution for both parties. However, there remains the problem of deciding exactly where to settle.

H PARTIAL CRITERIA

In any realistic analysis we may come up against the so-called tangible *vs.* intangible variables.

Example

'Cost' is relatively easy to measure. But measuring 'personnel resistance' to certain things is difficult. What one does, providing an outright rejection is not likely, is to concentrate on a partial criterion and maximize this. Thus if we have $x = [x_1, x_2]$, $x_1 \equiv$ cost, $x_2 \equiv$ overtime, then we might minimize x_1. Once we know what x_1 (minimum) is, then we have a basis on which to negotiate in a concrete fashion. If the gain over the present costs is large then resistance may decrease because: (a) of the formidable loss it may force on the company; (b) part of this gain can be passed over. Until this gain has been established then 'persuasion' is not easy.

I CHANGING CRITERIA

In discussing criteria, the view has been taken that a problem cannot be solved unless the criterion has been established. However, in an evolving world criteria are changing and sometimes these are deliberately changed.

Example

Michael[85] points to the active manipulation of expectations of operating personnel.

In essence their values are being deliberately influenced and the appropriateness of their decisions will change in accordance with their change in values. However, this influence is being exerted in accordance with some higher-level criterion of other decisionmakers. Without this base line the whole problem of criteria, and subsequent Decision Analysis, becomes meaningless if values can be freely changed in an undirected manner.

Flagle[45] points out the changing criteria in the Health Services arising from an ongoing concern with the rights of men to medical care.

2.1.7 Forms of Primary Problem Statement

As we have already said in Chapter 1, we can, in principle, model the subject system, in the sense that we can determine the preferences for various combinations of effects of decisions, in situations of varying degrees of uncertainty.

Figure 31 restates what has been said in the introductory chapter with respect to the subject system.

As we have already said, basically there are two types of solution output, *viz.*:

(a) informative: specifies some of the effects of an alternative;
(b) prescriptive: prescribes which action ought to be taken.

The latter situation is ideal and, with the advent of powerful computational techniques, considerably expands the powers of analysis. Unfortunately there are many circumstances in which it is not possible to get the decision criterion needed to close the decision process, and much of what we have already said in this chapter illustrates the difficulties.

The form of solution will depend on the form of statement of the problem, which depends on the way in which the previous phases were carried out.

The following examples indicate the sorts of solution which may arise.

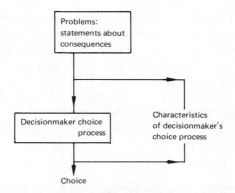

Figure 31. Subject system characteristics

One must, of course, take a broad view on prescription. Thus a specification of alternatives which are feasible in meeting certain constraints prescribes that the selected alternative must be in the given set. The following examples are all prescriptive in this broad sense, although only in certain circumstances will a single solution be prescribed.

Naturally, there are situations of the informative type, which are of an exploratory nature, in which the decisionmakers wish to explore the effects of various alternatives without being anywhere near as explicit as Figures 32–34 would require in the first instance, but in which this explicitness would evolve as a result of the output of the study.

Examples

(1) In Figure 32 we see that we have three progressively more sophisticated formats. In the first one we simply look for feasible solutions. In doing so we face the prospect of having to handle a very large number. In the second one we optimize on one variable, subject to constraints on others. This reduces the number of solutions. The third one arises when all constraints are converted into some criterion. This is divided into two possibilities referred to as the 'reduced' and 'non-reduced' possibilities. In the former case, which is equivalent to tracing through consequences until a single variable expression is possible, the cost effects of infection are determined and added to the costs of control. In the latter case this is not done and a weighting factor approach is used. It is possible to **combine** both methods. If the effects of infection are seen not only as subsequent

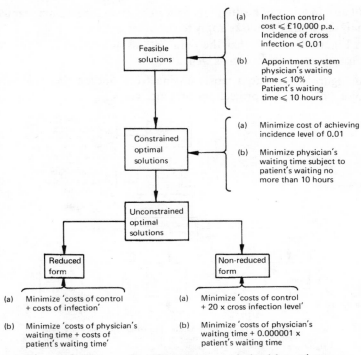

Figure 32. Forms of problem statement in health services

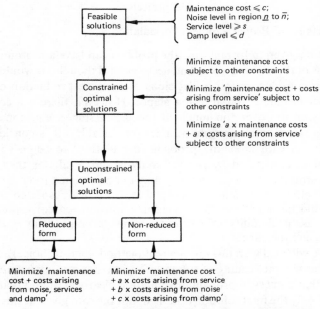

Figure 33. Forms of problem statement for buildings

62

costs, but also in terms of health in its own right, then the latter case must figure in the analysis. Similar remarks apply to the other examples.

(2) In Figure 33 we see that the reduced and non-reduced forms can arise in the constrained optimization as well.

(3) In Figure 34 note that 'costs arising from' means the 'cost effects of'. Thus noise will influence project performance costs.

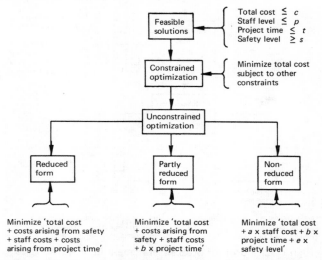

Figure 34. Forms of problem statement for special industrial projects

2.1.8 Importance of Proper Problem Formulation

The attention given to formulating the problem can have a profound effect on the usefulness of the ensuing work, and needs careful thought. It would obviously be chaotic to consider inventory decisions and ignore production decisions if there is sufficient interaction at a first glance. However, there is a considerable danger in trying to cover too much in the initial stages, e.g. considering all possible constraints or bringing in all relevant variables. It is considered good practice to begin with moderate problem formulations to begin with, and to enlarge them as is dictated by further analysis and results as they arise, e.g. (i) ignore constraints (if you suspect they may not be violated too much) and test afterwards whether the violation is acceptable; (ii) if it is suspected that certain variables would be impracticable to measure, introduce a corresponding constraint such as 'probability of run out $= \alpha$' or 'average delay $= d$', without trying to measure the effects.

Later on we will deal with this problem (of methodological choice) a little more fully under the general heading of suboptimization, but it is important to realize at this stage that choices in problem formulation clearly exist and that they may influence not only the final solution obtained, but the care given at this stage may significantly influence the efficiency of the analysis as a whole.

Perhaps the most significant point arising from these discussions is that we can never state a problem fully in terms of the effects eventually emanating from a decision (see Kazanowski[66]).

The big problem of Decision Analysis is to achieve a workable and useful degree of isolation. What we must ask is that the problem be a 'proper problem' (see Strauss[129]). Hitch defines a 'proper problem' as one that 'covers all important aspects and yet is specific enough to be meaningful'.

Strauss[129] points out, quite rightly, that if we knew, in this sense, that the problem was proper, we would know enough to take the correct decision ourselves. The implication of this is that it is only the improper problems with which the Decision Analyst can usefully help. By this statement Strauss probably means that we need to know what the influence on the final solution is, and if we know this we know the answer to our problem.

Example

In the example of Figure 24 both 'throughput' and 'emergency service' were taken to be important. Presumably it was anticipated that the interaction between the two was of sufficient importance to necessitate the inclusion of both.

Naturally, outside the context of the study, these variables are important, but importance in Hitch's sense relates to their part in the proposed study.

It is worthwhile here mentioning the interrelation between what has been discussed and the statement of an organization's objectives. The statement of objectives of a company will often involve reference to consequences and alternatives, and will often involve conflicts. Such statements serve as no more than a guide to problem formulation in its early stages and, on deeper examination, indicate no more than the directive to consider certain aspects. Much more work is needed to make them operational.

Example

Olsen[98] discusses the statement of objectives in an insurance company in the following form:

(i) to seek new and renewal policies (alternatives);
(ii) to increase policy sales (consequences);
(iii) to solicit policies from various prospects and areas (alternatives);
(iv) to restrict revenue to less than a specific share of the market in order to avoid effort in getting undesirable policies with loss histories (alternatives).

In (i), (iii), (iv) the company directs the selection of alternatives, which are selected because of their influence on cash consequences and risk involved. In (ii) direct reference is made to cash income (of a kind) which is not the final income and will influence this income. There is also, for example, conflict between (ii) and (iv), because if (ii) were taken to be true, we would not consider the risk involved in policies. Similarly in (ii) and (iii) policy sales would be a maximum if (iii) were relaxed. White[143] discusses further the problem of criteria and objectives.

Finally, let us mention one very important decision to which we shall return later on. We have the option of not only how to carry out a study, but whether to carry it out at all. As Strauss[129] states, every problem should be viewed in the light of the resources it will command in its solution (and implementation of). This problem is the superproblem of Decision Methodology.

2.2 Object System Model Phase

2.2.1 Introductory Remarks

It has already been pointed out that problem formulation is no less a model construction activity than is a study of the object system. In studying problem formulation separately, however, no attention was given to the scientific problems. Although in this section we will concentrate on the scientific problems involved in studying the object system, many of the points apply equally well to the subject system and hence to problem formulation. It is hoped that the reader will recognize that the bias in treatment is not a bias in fact. Perhaps the central reason for this bias is that we are, in general, happier with our ability to handle the object system, except where this contains human aspects, than we are with the subject system.

Decision Analysis is concerned extensively with model building. Ideally we would like to produce generalized models which have a variety wide enough to cater for all variations of classes of problems, e.g. a generalized inventory model. However, from an analytic point of view, no compatible general models exist for wide general classes of problems, but they do exist for specific classes of problem. We touched upon this subject matter when outlining Decision Analysis in Chapter 1.

Examples

(1) No general inventory control model exists, although specific inventory control models do exist. Pictorially we have Figure 35. It must be stressed that Figure 35 is purely a conceptual figure.

Thus we have analytic solutions for the case of uniform demand and costs of the form: stockholding, ordering, quantity discounts. Similarly we have solutions for the case of probabilistic, independently distributed from period to period,

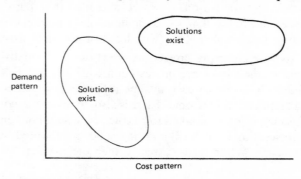

Figure 35. Solutions for inventory control problems

demand. But we have no analytic solutions when demand is autocorrelated over several periods.

There always exist solution methods in principle of course, but we are here referring to analytic methods for the class concerned. We can probably solve the problem using dynamic programming, but it would be very expensive computationally.

(2) In queueing theory we have Figure 36.

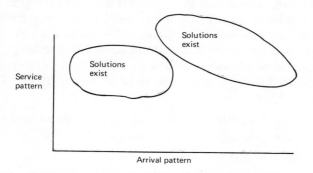

Figure 36. Solutions for queueing problems

In a spare beds problem the true service mechanism allowed for early discharge, but this was difficult to formulate, and even more so to solve. Two extreme service mechanisms could be solved: (a) all excess turned away; (b) a 'queue' allowed to form. The true solution was deemed to be near to these if they gave similar results, which they did, *viz.*, small potential queues and small early discharges.

In general, in characteristic problem areas, a finite set of specific, overlapping models exist, but a large area, with more than a few characterizing aspects, is not touched.

The formal modelling of problem areas has been restricted severely by the search for problem areas which are analytically tractable. Even where algorithmic approaches are sought, we still have limitations. As a result of this we are usually in the position of having to construct new specific models from scratch, and hence need to understand fully what model building amounts to.

In addition to this we still have to ensure, even when off-the-peg models apparently exist, that such models do fit our situation.

At the same time, although in many cases we have to construct models from scratch, there are also many circumstances in which the existence of models which are in some sense close to the situation existing may facilitate the development of the appropriate model. Morris[92] stresses this point.

Camp[20] suggests that it might be possible to cover a complex model by solving simplified models which totally overlap the real model. Thus if the real model is $M(\alpha, \beta, \gamma)$ we may be able to solve $M(\alpha, \beta, 0)$, $M(0, \beta, \gamma)$ and $M(\alpha, 0, \gamma)$, where α, β, γ are features characterizing the model. Thus, for example, in inventory

66

control α might relate to storage aspects, β to discount structures, and γ to run-out penalties. This idea is intuitively appealing but has to be developed further.

It is important to realize that such models may be nothing more than logical models, in the sense that they can always exist in theory without having practical realizations. However, most will have their origins in recognizable problem areas characterized by various features. We then have the task of validating and interpreting the models and, in particular, of carrying out the measurements implicit in the models. This latter activity is not a minor one, and the logical approach to models may not concern itself with this activity. Thus it may assume a cost of run out, but not indicate how to get this cost. This again is a very strong reason why we should concern ourselves with the principles of modelling.

We have used the words 'model' and 'theory' without examining their relationship. Braithwaite[16] discusses the concepts of model and theory. He defines a scientific theory, T, as

'a deductive system consisting of certain initial hypotheses at the summit and empirically testable generalisations at the base'

and a model, M, of a theory, T,

'is a mapping of the theory, T, so that some concepts and relations in T hold in a mapped form in M'.

Suppes[131] further states

'... tendency to amalgamate what logicians would call the model and the theory of the model. It is very widespread practice in mathematical statistics and in the behavioural sciences to use the word "model" to mean the set of quantitative assumptions of the theory, that is the set of sentences which, in a precise treatment would be taken as axioms, or if they themselves are adequately exact, would constitute the intuitive basis for formulating a set of axioms.'†

In the practice of Decision Analysis, one is therefore working with models if a problem is being studied for which no theory exists, and with theories if, for example, one is simply determining inputs into existing theories, models of which fit the existing circumstances.

In queueing theory, we not only have all the behavioural postulates but the deductions which can be made on the basis of the postulates. A model, based on T, would simply represent some of the postulates. Suppes gives, as an example, the construction of a computer stat-rat model, based on axioms describing some aspects of an actual rat's behaviour. This model is to be separated from conclusions based on the postulates, but a test of the model is whether the conclusions fit actuality.

He also lists four ways in which theories can gain from models, which he calls nth order predictive novelty, $n = 1, 2, 3, 4$. We will not deal with these here and simply point out that there is a need to logically separate a model and a theory

† P. Suppes, 'A comparison of the meaning and uses of models', in *The Concept and Role of the Model in Mathematics and the Natural and Social Sciences*, Eds. B. Hazemier and D. Vuysje, 1961. Reprinted by permission of D. Reidel Publishing Co., Dordrecht, Holland.

and that they play supporting roles in Decision Analysis, *viz.*, some theory is needed so that aspects of models can be tested and that some model is needed so that the effects of changes can be examined. In particular, validation of a model needs a theory. Thus, for example, even the demonstration that a certain pattern of demand model is valid requires a theory of consequential behaviour which can be compared with actual behaviour. However, we will discuss validation separately later on.

It is worth noting that Mehlberg[83] discusses the functions of a theory.

One of these is the summarizing function, whereby a number of consequences can be deduced from a theory. He quotes the 'Principle of Least Action' from which many physical laws can be derived. As has been indicated in the opening paragraphs, it seems unlikely that we will be able to see many of our models as being realizable mappings of a single, comprehensive theory, at least for some time.

The second is its predictive function and, in Decision Analysis, this is precisely what we wish to do when considering alternative policies.

The third is its controlling and explanatory function, an aspect with which we will deal later on in the context of model validation.

The final one is its information function, relating to observable variables and their role in model validation.

Margenau[78] also discusses the hierarchical structure of theories.

Oportel[99] discusses the roles of models, both physical and symbolic, under the headings: theory formation (given facts, no theory, replace facts with theory which overlaps, e.g. neurology or organizational behaviour studied by analog computer model); simplification (given facts and theory, computationally too difficult, simplify, e.g. theory of harmonic oscillator in study of heat conduction; modifying relations in Decision Analysis to allow analysis); reduction (two theories without contact, construct a common model, e.g. some queueing theory and inventory theory situations may have a common model); extension (theory incomplete, construct model to achieve completeness, e.g. quantification of a qualitative model, involving development of quantification procedure); adequation (relating new theories to old ones as new information becomes available, e.g. relating theories of behaviour in one class of circumstances to theories of behaviour in a wider class of circumstances); explanation (theory exists about facts, but does not explain facts, e.g. models for theories of light and statistical mechanics; the influence of environmental conditions on effectiveness of implementation is theorized but not explained and a model might help); causetization (theories exist about items too big or too small to observe directly, model constructed so that experiments can be done, e.g. particle velocities in some problems; or in business it is not possible to record every single activity of a person and any theory of his behaviour will need a model whose behaviour will relate to the theory about these activities); globalization (model used for visualization and realization of closed structure, e.g. an inventory control model); experimentation (when theories contain non-observables, a model helps experimentation, e.g. probabilities cannot be observed in principle and models are needed to allow relevant measurements to be made).

We will, later on, be concerned with some of these aspects, e.g. use of analogues, simplification, extension, explanation, experimentation, although all aspects are relevant, to a greater or less extent, to Decision Analysis.

In addition to these points, he concerns himself with the relevance of the purposes of a model to the choice of a model, and the problem of determining from these purposes the features of an appropriate model. As we shall see later on, different models, based on a common theory, may serve different purposes. In addition, different models, based on a common theory, may give rise to different computational requirements, which must be considered as part of the analysis problem.

Having discussed the concepts of model and theory, and their roles, it is important to reflect upon attitudes towards modelling. Sciorrino,[114] writing on Operational Research, says:

(a) Operational Research is not mathematical mechanics. The notion that any situation can be better understood by a model has one fundamental risk, *viz.*, finding the right solution to the wrong problem.

   Thus the search for a model should not blind one to the necessity to validate it somehow, even if approximations are being sought.

(b) Operational Research is not intuition and common sense. Tendency to follow intuition, gather data, get complex, fall back on intuition; runs the risk of getting the wrong solution to the right problem.

   There is thus a need for a model because complexity defeats reliable calculation without formal aids.

(c) Operational Research is not a specific technique(s). Viewing Operational Research as a set of techniques (or models) may lead to no solution to a given problem or to the right solution to few problems.

   Thus the place of techniques in Decision Analysis should be appreciated.

The basic purpose of the model building phase is ultimately to provide the relationships between the various alternative actions and the outcomes of these actions. Such relationships are the combined effects of various component inputs, outputs and relationships which make up the system. The identification of all the relevant factors, and basic constraints and interrelationships, is then the essence of this phase.

We can represent this thus in Figure 37.

We will illustrate this, and, as a very simple example, consider the recruitment of labour in the tth period of a planning period, which decision may arise in the control of some project.

Let X_t be the size of labour force at the beginning of the period t (Outcome Controlled Variable).

Let R_t be the quantity of labour recruited in addition at this point in time (Control Variable).

Let L_t be the number who leave at the end of the tth period (Free Environmental Variable).

Let T_t be the total cost in period t.

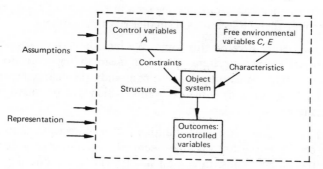

Figure 37. A model of modelling

Let S_t be the state of project at beginning of period t.

Let $P_t(F, S)$ be the project progress in the period t with labour force F (Outcome Controlled Variable).

Let $C_t(R)$ be the cost of recruiting extra labour force R at time t (Outcome Controlled Variable).

Let $K_t(F)$ be the direct labour cost plus other costs during period t (Outcome Controlled Variable).

Then we have:

$$S_{t+1} = S_t + P_t(X_t + R_t, S_t)$$
$$X_{t+1} = X_t + R_t - L_t$$
$$T_t = K_t(X_t + R_t) + C_t(R_t)$$

We build up our model as a set of relationships of this kind. This is the 'synthetic' approach to modelling. We shall be going into detail on the model-building aspect, but, just now, let us stress two aspects of modelling which might serve as a platform for the more thorough treatment to come: (a) assumptions; (b) representation.

(a) *Assumptions*. We have deliberately separated the assumptions input to emphasize it. One value of the logical modelling is that we can examine the influence of assumptions of various kinds in a routine manner. We know that, within the scope of the present knowledge, certain things are uncertain, but we should not neglect consideration of the fact that certain policies may be better than others in the face of possible patterns which can arise. Models will thus be a mixture of accepted premises and possible premises.

Whether or not the model is adequate in treating uncertainty must rest with the subject system and is related to the problem formulation aspect.

Example

In the previous example the operation of a continuous recruitment policy, in an effort to reduce labour force to a minimum, runs the risk of lost productivity because of the higher inexperienced element proportion and possibility of poor quality of work. It may well be that this particular feature is unknown. However, by postulating the various assumptions which seem reasonable, the total cost and project performance behaviour may be seen in the light of each possibility. Certain policies may then be seen to run smaller risks than others.

We will go no further here on this topic. We include it simply to stress that because we do not know everything does not mean that we can do nothing. Providing we can state the assumptions we can study the characteristics of the policies. We do, however, face some problems, which will be raised under the heading of sensitivity analysis later on.

(b) *Representation.* Sometimes an inhibiting factor in decision rationalization arises because certain important variables seem difficult to incorporate as formal statements in the model. Thus, in capital investment, the economic climate is important; in production scheduling, operator reactions to new schemes are important; safety factors present such difficulties; client reactions to company policies may be difficult to state.

However, the fact that these variables may not be included in the model itself need not remove the value of the study. It means that part of the process will be rationalized and the other factors will 'be viewed' against this background. We do not always aim for 'complete' models, but rather for 'useful' models.

Figure 38. Interdependence of environment and decision

Ellis and Greene[42] discuss the problem of representing political aspects in an analysis, when they are difficult to measure. In discussing these problems, they apply the concepts of 'relevance' and 'credibility'.

Later on we shall discuss the problem of control as a one-way relationship in which the environment is independent of the decisions taken and the decisions have to change in relationship to this environment. In fact, by normal definition, the environment is taken to be just so independent as indicated in Figure 37. However, it is likely that all variables interact, even if over some lengthy chain of influence, and that, in particular, the system is closed, as in Figure 38. Hollander[60] stresses this point.

Examples

(1) In inventory control, environmental demand patterns are assumed to determine service levels and operational costs. However, service levels will influence demand patterns.

(2) In production control, environmental cost factors are assumed to determine working programmes and production costs. However, these latter variables will influence working attitudes and hence the input cost factors used.

There are many similar situations. In principle one should construct a comprehensive model, which may be closed and have no free environmental variables. It is, however, a matter of judgement as to the degree and timing of such interactive influences when deciding on the extent of the model, and 'environmental' variables may be left to the control mechanism to handle.

Little[75] emphasizes the role of a model for the manager. Models are not always correct but provide a framework on the basis of which the issues at stake can be discussed, leading to modified, agreed models in due course. He says that models should be simple, robust, easy to control, adaptive, complete on important issues, easy to communicate with, and he gives a marketing example. Certainly they should be adaptive and complete on important issues. However, it may not be possible to have a robust model, and the other factors are matters of expediency which may not be valid in specific situations.

In the first chapter we differentiated between the primary decisions (the object of the analysis) and the secondary decisions (those in the analysis itself). Since we are discussing the problems arising in model construction and the acceptability of models, it is important to stress this secondary decision aspect here particularly.

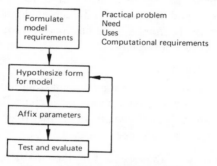

Figure 39. A model of modelling

Smallwood[122] discusses the ways in which modelling may be done, ranging from clairvoyance to complete analysis, as shown in Figure 39.

Figure 39 is clearly related to Figure 4 of Chapter 1, and to Figure 37 of this chapter. Figure 37 corresponds broadly to 'form of model' in Figure 39. However, in Figure 39, the need to consider the uses, computational requirements, etc., of the model is specifically recognized, and these will influence the manner in which subsequent parts of the modelling process will be carried out.

He stresses the need for a trade-off between 'fidelity' and 'computational' complexity and stresses the decisions made in the selection and resolution of the models. He also stresses the need to orient oneself toward solving the practical problem as distinct from determining the parameters of the model which is only incidental to the primary problem. One should also be concerned as much with possible models as with possible parameters.

We shall discuss this later when we come to suboptimality, but it is worth making these points now so that the problems in, and purposes of, modelling can be in one's mind while going through this section.

In dealing with modelling processes, the emphasis is on the ability to logically arrive at the implications of the models. This ability in many cases depends significantly on an ability to handle the mathematical aspects, a point to which we now turn. In taking this point of view, it is realized that many solutions to problems can be obtained without sophisticated mathematics, but, nonetheless, elements of mathematical representation and analysis exist even in these instances. Thus, for example, the building of analogue, or simulation, models still requires precise descriptions of the underlying models before they can be said to represent the system being studied or their operations can be programmed.

2.2.2 Mathematical Models, Quantification and Measurement

2.2.2.1 MATHEMATICS

Simon[118] quotes Fourier:

'Mathematical analysis is as extensive as nature itself; it defines all perceptible relations; measure time, space, force, temperature. Its chief attribute is its clearness; it has no marks to express confused notions; it brings together phenomena the most diverse and discovers the hidden analogues which unite them; it seems to be a faculty of the human mind destined to supplement the shortness of life and the imperfections of the senses.'

Baylis[7] quotes McNamara[82]:

'It is true enough that not every complex human situation can be fully reduced to lines on a graph, or to percentage points on a chart. But all reality can be reasoned about, and not to quantify what can be quantified is only to be content with something less than the full range of reason.'

Fourier's quotation sets the scene for the mathematical aspects, and McNamara's for the related quantitative aspects.

Schwartz[113] is counter mathematics in outlook, stating:

'. . .an argument which is only convincing if it is precise loses all its force if the assumptions on which it is based are slightly changed, while an argument which is convincing but imprecise may well be stable under small perturbations of its underlying axioms.'

It may be a question of what is mathematics, but if an argument is to follow logically, it must have its axioms stated in a manner which allows this. It is part of the problem to allow for uncertainties in such a manner that the results reflect these. We cannot get away from the deductive content unless we do not wish to justify each step in the argument stemming from whatever premises we have assumed. In addition, whether or not a deviation is small presupposes some mechanism for demonstrating this.

Schwartz goes further and indicates that mathematics is simple minded in that it is unable to draw for its argument from many disparate sources. This is not the fault of mathematics, but rather the fault of not being able to state the inputs to the argument in a manner which can be examined. Similarly Schwartz refers to the simple mindedness of mathematics, in which assumptions are made to facilitate analysis. But if the mathematical process cannot produce the correct deductions for a given, albeit complex, set of conditions, how is the unaided process of argument able to do better?

A mathematical model is a collection of statements about a set of variables from which the truth or falsity of other statements can be deduced. We include 'logical' models (e.g. orderings) in 'mathematical'.

It is very important to draw a distinction between 'mathematics' and 'quantification'. Quantification is part, but only part, of mathematics. As we shall find out later on, there is a mathematical theory of relations preceding any quantification, and, although the power of subsequent mathematical processing is diminished without quantification, it is not powerless. Much in the area of mathematics, such as in ring and field theory, has no origins in quantification.

Much of the criticism about overplaying mathematics in the social sciences is really a criticism of quantification and not of mathematics.

A good basis for the mathematical foundations of strict measurement can be found in Pfanzagl.[102] A discussion of mathematics and quantification in business research can be found in White.[148]

Examples of non-'quantified' mathematical statements are:

Examples

(1) In critical-path analysis if we write '$a < b$', we mean 'a precedes b', and this is a mathematical statement without quantification, since $a < b$, $b < c \rightarrow a < c$.

(2) In the theory of choice if we say 'aPb', we mean 'a is preferred to b', and this is a mathematical statement without quantification, since, usually, aPb, $bPc \rightarrow aPc$.

We will be confronted with the problem of deciding when a statement is or is not a mathematical statement. Thus if we say 'the staff are happy', is this a mathematical statement? When we enquire into its meaning we find that we may require to define 'happy'. Why should we wish to define 'happy'? Does it matter if the statement is wrong or right? How much does it matter? When we ask questions of this kind we find that we need to measure 'happiness', h. Not only this, we need to evaluate the consequences of happiness of different degrees, $c = f(h)$, and hence we enter into a mathematical model. Whenever we wish to measure and use the measures we enter into mathematics. If we do not do this, then the statement is relatively ambiguous and non-deductive in content, unless happiness is defined clearly in terms of its effect, e.g. 'to be happy' means 'not to strike'. But then, by defining happiness in terms of its one effect, we destroy its general usage. Also we then have the problem of interpreting 'to strike', and this can be defined as 'to withhold labour for x days'. This is no less mathematical in its content for deductive purposes.

Brand[17] states:

'there is no idea or proposition in the field which cannot be put into mathematical language, although the utility of doing so can very well be doubted'.

In considering the fecundity of mathematics he considers intellectual labour, clarity of expression and accuracy and puts the point that one has to consider the net benefits in these terms when considering mathematical usage. In considering accuracy (i.e. logical synthesizing deductive accuracy) he points to the fact that errors of input can be turned into larger errors of output, thus putting mathematical representation in question. However, this is not a criticism of mathematics itself. In addition we should be concerned with knowing errors of output which can arise from errors of input, which requires mathematical presentation and deduction.

The need to evaluate the worth of mathematical presentation and analysis is not disputed and, indeed, it constitutes one of our secondary problems. As Michael[85] says:

'. . . belief in the virtue of logic is itself a non-logical belief rather unique to western civilisations.'

We will not deal with the secondary problem posed by this issue but simply point out that the answer must depend upon the circumstances.

The accent on mathematical models arises because of their deductive content. Coleman[27] states:

'. . . the power of a theory to provide precise and numerous deductions lies in its ability to carry out transformations—in fact classes of transformations—upon the input data.'

Thus the very ability to develop theories depends on the existence of a formal structure and its logical calculus, which we might term 'mathematics'.

However, if we concern ourselves with the concept of 'deductive' systems, we need not worry too much whether people interpret them as 'mathematical' or not.

The following material is fairly abstract, but the ways in which problems are defined and solved are so varied that a full understanding of the formal content of model building is useful.

The power of Decision Analysis is its ability to deal with premises of various kinds and use its most powerful deductive abilities. These premises can arise in many forms. In particular they may or may not be quantitative in a strict sense; also the mathematical power may take various forms. In the latter case we can quote an instance of someone who said they were doing some 'non-mathematical' model building, which eventually turned out to be a logical exercise, which is still mathematics. Problems of this kind must be understood if we are going to be able to intercommunicate effectively and if we are to understand fully the nature of the studies which we can carry out.

Let us take one example, *viz.*, 'statements'. The types of statement which can appear in any formal analysis of a problem are several and play different roles in model building. A close examination of these statements will reveal exactly what their role is, and, most important, will reveal hidden assumptions. Thus to say '$x \in X$' is tantamount to the acceptance of a rule for determining whether $x \in X$ or $x \notin X$. This arises in modelling if X is set of Normal distributions.

Statements are inputs to our models, as has already been mentioned. Let us now consider them further.

2.2.2.2 STATEMENTS AND EXPRESSIONS

The nature of mathematical models used depends on the nature of statements used. Ackoff[1] gives three characteristics of statements, *viz.*,

(A) form of statement;
(B) form of expression;
(C) scope of statements.

A FORM OF STATEMENTS

These are defined as:

(i) taxonomical (classificatory);
(ii) relational;
(iii) functional.

(*i*) *Taxonomical*

This is simply a statement of the form $x \in *$, where $*$ is defined by its properties.

Examples

$*$: set of all policies x for which probability of run-out $\leqslant 0.05$;

$*$: set of all Normal distributions;

$*$: set of all x for which $x = x^*$ (x is a constant x^*);

$*$: set of all environments of pure conflict type (thus $x \in *$ means that we can expect nature to be antagonistic);

$*$: set of all decisions, $x, 0 \leqslant x \leqslant X$.

A taxonomy is equivalent to segregating elements into sets according to whether they do or do not have a certain property. This is how any scientific endeavour begins, i.e. by examination of properties.

Until recently we have divided areas of study into the physical and non-physical sciences, but we now come to realize that this classification arises because of the properties we observe and not because of any essential distinction; thus a human being is a physical element. We must expect the same feature will arise within the specific area of Decision Analysis. For example, we have already divided our system components into 'subject' and 'object' and yet, in principle, the 'subject' system is no different scientifically, but the properties we observe are different.

Science, in looking for generalities in life, looks for ways of classifying things so that everything fits nicely into one of the classes.

Sells[116] discusses the uses of taxonomies in the social sciences. He states:

'A useful taxonomy should be a theoretical model which orders empirical observations and also permits predictions guiding new observations based on the developed network of relationships.'

In Decision Analysis the coverage of different models has this purpose in mind; Decision Analysis as a subject has a central aim of generalization.

76

In models, the applicability of the model depends on the way it is characterized and we have a taxonomy of models by way of its components.

Examples

(a) Certain inventory control models assume Normality of demand; we then have to ascertain whether the demand is in a given set, i.e. the set of Normal distributions;

(b) similarly for queueing models;

(c) certain heuristic procedures rely on 'similarity of situations'; thus a procedure for solving a travelling salesman problem is meant to apply only in certain circumstances; we need to be able to determine whether our model belongs to the appropriate set;

(d) in the opening chapter, when considering Decision Analysis as a subject, we produced a taxonomy of decision models and solution procedures, which enable problems to be cast into rough framework, even if further development is needed, and such a taxonomy is useful;

(e) the taxonomy of operational, technological and investment decisions is useful because it builds a more general framework within which to develop specific decision models in these areas, e.g. what variables to consider, how to handle these, and what the interaction is between decision areas.

There is a danger in producing taxonomies of the above kind in that some effects and interactions may be ignored. However, if such a taxonomy considers the interface between areas, acceptable solutions may be obtained. With no taxonomy, every problem becomes a new one.

Related to the last taxonomy are the questions of who are the decisionmakers and such a taxonomy should consider this aspect as an integral part of its structure.

As a special part of decision characterization, the statement of problems assumes considerable importance. In Figure 31 it was indicated that the choice process, with respect to particular statements about outcomes, played an important role in the theory of choice. Statements can be made in several languages. For example, 'the cost of activity x will be $c(x)$'; 'the probability distribution of the cost of activity x is $f(c,x)$'; 'if event e happens and activity x is engaged in, the cost will be $c(e,x)$'. Problems can involve statements of various forms and different criteria can be relevant. Thus a taxonomy of statement forms is necessary for a generalized theory of decision. White[150] discusses this in detail.

A taxonomy is useful by virtue of the properties which define the class. Previously we discussed a taxonomy of decision situations, so that models appropriate to each class may be developed and the relationship between each class can be developed. We may also be able to classify problems as to their worth of being studied. Thus we might be able to say it is not worthwhile studying problems in class X, and it is worthwhile studying problems in class Y. X, Y can be general or specific.

Example

In a specific inventory control problem an assumed property of a solution is that it will not give rise to a run-out probability greater than a specified level. It may be believed that it is not worthwhile to consider solutions not in this class.

We shall see later on that there is a relationship between taxonomy and measurement. In some instances, although measurement may be not only possible, but exist, the appropriate decision may only depend on whether a parameter lies in a given range. The division of an interval into ranges is equivalent to producing a taxonomy. However, it might be easier to determine whether the parameter lies in a given range than to determine exactly what its value is.

Example

In an investment problem choosing between alternative investments A, B, we may get A preferred to B if $\alpha < 0.99$, where α is the discount factor. We need only determine whether α is in the set 0–0.99 and this may be accepted without prior analysis. See Blackett,[12] where some conclusions could be drawn for a range of values. All we need to know is whether certain elements are, or are not, in certain sets.

From a Decision Analysis point of view, difficulties may arise in determining whether $x \in X$. What we are concerned with is the effects of errors, if we cannot be positive if $x \in X$ or $x \notin X$.

Thus if $x \notin X$, it may not mean that we would go far wrong in assuming $x \in X$, and it might be expensive to determine the truth. In general, therefore, we need to know the degree with which $x \in X$ or $x \notin X$ and this leads us back to a basic measure on X and hence to a relation between X and R, the real line, a point to which we turn our attention later on.

Example

If x is not exponentially distributed, we may yet get a good solution by assuming it is so. This means we need to be able to measure the extent to which a distribution deviates from exponential and to be able to evaluate the effects of this deviation on the decision.

It is sometimes required that simplifications be made, and this can create problems of definition and identification, to be resolved only by recognizing the way in which the results are to be used.

Examples

(1) In a refuse collection problem attempts were made to divide property into 'tenemental' and 'private'. It became difficult to identify each type precisely in data collected. There was also the problem as to whether two categories were adequate. The reason for separation was that collection times per unit of refuse were thought to be different, because of different access problems. The seriousness of the problem was dependent on the degree of error introduced into calculations by saying a property was in one or other of the classes (defined now by estimated

parameters), when it may be in neither. The problem was eventually shown to be not serious.

(2) A company decided it was going to make synthetic 'oils'. They were then faced with the problem of what constituted an oil. This was a taxonomical problem, although one of degree. An oil can be seen to contain elements of a certain kind, in certain proportions, and excluding others, or it can be seen to be something with certain properties.

The important point here really arises through the consequences of producing something which does not meet certain specifications normally taken to characterize an oil.

(3) There are various 'small business' associations and it is also stated that there are thousands of small businesses in the United Kingdom. However, what is a 'small business'?

In order to answer this we must enquire as to the ways in which a definition of a small business may be used. What is the purpose of a 'small business' association and why should it work for a small business and not for a large business. Perhaps small businesses have problems which a large business does not have and the association has, as its purpose, the generation of ways of solving these. A particular study was concerned with the justification of using Decision Analysis in small businesses. One definition of a small business stemming from this might be one which could not justify having its own Decision Analyst.

The essential point of a taxonomy is that it is the first step in a process leading to measurement, and, in some instances, such a taxonomy can be made use of, without proceeding so far in circumstances where the property concerned is, in principle, measurable in the strict sense.

(ii) Relational

This is simply a statement of the form xRy (or $R(x,y,z,...)$ in the case of more than two elements) where R is a relation existing or not existing between x and y. R is a property of at least a pair of elements. We restrict ourselves to binary relations for our purposes. See Pfanzagl[102] for general relations.

Examples
$xRy \equiv y = f(x)$;
$xRy \equiv x$ 'better than' y;
$xRy \equiv x$ 'has authority over' y;
$xRy \equiv x$ 'causes' y;
$xRy \equiv x$ 'comes before' y.

As we shall see, the common type of relation used in Decision Analysis is the functional relation. However, it is by no means the only one.

Examples
(1) In critical-path analysis, we use the relation xRy, where $R \equiv$ 'comes

'before'. This enables an ordering of activities to be determined, either partial or total.

(2) In the theory of choice, we use a relation xPy, where $P \equiv$ 'better than'.

Both of these appear in the list above.

(3) When we classify items, we may have xRy, when $R \equiv$ 'belongs to same group as'; thus a taxonomy induces a relationship.

(4) When considering variables in a problem, we might have xRy, where $R =$ 'more important than'.

As with our discussion of a taxonomy and mathematics, the reason for stressing these relations is that we often hear the statement that 'mathematics is not essential in Decision Analysis'. What people have in mind is some form of deductive relational structure, including relations of the above kind, and since, as has already been said, relational structures are the basis of all mathematics, the argument arises from a misunderstanding. No deductive study can proceed without some relational, and hence mathematical, structure.

(iii) Functional (Specific or General)

This is simply a correspondence between $x \in X$ and $y \in Y$. The correspondence can be one–one or many–one.

Examples

   (a) $y = 2x$ ($y =$ demand; $x =$ time) (one–one);

   (b) $y =$ age of x ($x =$ person) (many–one);

   (c) $y =$ number of elements in x ($x =$ a set) (many–one);

   (d) y is the father of x ($x, y =$ humans) (many–one);

   (e) y is the vehicle which serves location x (many–one).

Pictorially we have the following in Figure 40.

We can have $X \equiv Y$. Examples (a), (d) are of this kind, where $X = Y =$ real line in (a), and $X = Y =$ human race in (d).

It is quite obvious that (i) and (iii) are of the same type as (ii), *viz.*, relational, although they have special characteristics. Thus $x \in X$ can be put as xRy where $y \equiv X$. In this case xRy is identical with $x \in X$. In case (iii) we can write xRy if $y = f(x)$, where f is the functional relationship between X and Y.

Although, logically speaking, (i), (iii) are equivalent to (ii), the specific nature

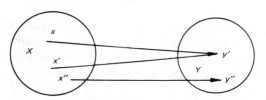

Figure 40. Functional statements

of the statements as given by (i), (ii), (iii) are more meaningful. In (i) the essential feature is one of dividing a universe into a set X and its negation $\tilde{X}$, and all that matters is whether $x \in X$ or $x \notin X$; in (ii) the essential feature is that of identifying pairs of elements, $x \in X$, $y \in Y$, such that x and y have a specific property with respect to each other; in (iii) the essential feature is that of a clear correspondence between $x \in X$ and some y, or set of y, in Y, this being much more restrictive than a general relationship, which might exist between any $x \in X$ and any $y \in Y$. We are saying that for each $x \in X$ there is only one corresponding $y \in Y$.

It is normally assumed that a functional statement is not one–many. However, this is purely a matter of definition, depending on the purposes of the exercise, and one could include a one–many statement in the class of functional statements. This difficulty could be avoided if we considered the correspondence as one between points and subsets, but we will not pursue this here.

All statements are equivalently taxonomic. Thus $y = t(x) \equiv (x,y) \in R$, for some region R.

All mathematics is concerned, fundamentally, with relations of one kind or another.

General relations can be as 'mathematical' as our functional relations.

Example

In a sequencing problem, orderings between elements can be given equivalent mathematical expression in algebraic form.

Let us set $x_{ir} = 1$ if i is in the rth position,
$\quad\quad\quad\quad = 0$ if i is not in the rth position.

Then 'j precedes i' may be expressed mathematically as:

$$\text{if } x_{ir} = 1, \quad \text{then} \quad x_{js} = 0, \quad s \geqslant r;$$
$$\sum_r x_{ir} = 1 = \sum_s x_{js}.$$

We will not deal in general with the various properties of relations important to the development of Decision Analysis models; these are dealt with extensively in Ackoff[1] and Pfanzagl.[102]

It is, however, worth drawing attention to the relevance of one property of relations to the concept of 'best', which is central in Decision Analysis.

We need relations to be 'transitive' if this is to be meaningful, and this can give rise to difficulties. A relation is transitive if $x\text{R}y$, $y\text{R}z \rightarrow x\text{R}z$. However, sometimes intransitivities arise.

Example

A football team A may be better than (able to beat) team B may be better than (able to beat) team C may be better than (able to beat) team A.

Hence the relation 'better' has a specific meaning and is not transitive. It is meaningless, in the context of this relation, to talk about a 'best' team.

Although this 'pathological' example is in no way to be thought unimportant, if we are to be able to talk about 'better' decisions or 'improved' decisions, the transitivity property is necessary, and where intransitivities do arise we should search for reasons as to why this is so.

One reason for this is that if R means 'preferred to' and if x, y, z are alternatives with xRy, yRz, zRx, then our solution will depend on where we start. Thus if we compare x and y, and compare the better of these two (*viz.*, x) with z we end up with z. If we begin with x and z, and compare the better of these two (*viz.*, z) with y, we end up with y. If we begin with y and z and compare the better of these two (*viz.*, y) with x, we end up with x. Thus the whole philosophy of discarding poor alternatives and comparing the residual ones with new alternatives becomes questionable as a decision improvement procedure, and yet this occurs in practice.

Example

May[80] gives an example in which pilots were given a choice between pairs of features of an aircraft. If $R \equiv$ red hot metal, $F \equiv$ falling, and $Fl \equiv$ flames, it was found that:

Fl was preferred to R;

R was preferred to F;

F was preferred to Fl.

Further investigation indicated that the basis of the preferences was changing with each pair. In the first case the choice was made on the basis of 'heat', in the second case it was made on the basis of 'support'; and in the last case the choice was made on the basis of 'probability of death'. Had the basis of comparison been consistent (e.g. probability of death) then no intransitivities would have arisen.

It is also worth noting that we can have partial statements, which are still useful in Decision Analysis.

Example

If X is a set of alternatives with $0.2 < c(x) < 0.5$ we may still be able to eliminate some alternatives for $x \in X$; and if we only know whether xRy or $x \sim Ry$ for some x, $y \in X$ (partial order) where xRy is equivalent to '$c(x) \leqslant c(y)$', we may be similarly able to eliminate some alternatives. The effect of such an elimination is to create an equivalent taxonomy.

Such partial statements still have great value in eliminating certain possibilities in our analysis. An example of this, in the form of 'efficient solution' sets, was discussed in Section 2.1.6.2.

B FORM OF EXPRESSION

Ackoff[1] divides the forms of expression into:

(i) quantitative;

(ii) qualitative.

(i) Quantitative Statements

A quantitative expression is one which gives a correspondence between $x \in X$ and the real line, R.

Example

$$\text{`}c(x) = 3\text{'} \equiv \text{`the cost of operation } x \text{ is 3 units'}$$

Measurement is a form of quantification of a property of an element $x \in X$, or the extent to which a relation (property) exists between a pair x, y, and can extend beyond binary properties.

Hayward[55] who quotes Pfanzagl,[101] on measurement, states:

'The general aim of measurement is to map a set M on the set of real numbers in such a way that, to the greatest possible extent, conclusions concerning the relations between elements of M can be drawn from corresponding relations between their assigned numbers.'

Thus we may draw a distinction between the processes of 'quantification' and 'measurement' if we do not ask that the quantification process satisfies Pfanzagl's requirement. However, quantification without these requirements is sterile. In mathematical terms, quantification may be no more than a 'mapping' whereas measurement implies some 'homomorphism'.

It is important to note that the original mathematical origin of 'measurement' (see, for example, Rogosinski[108]) relates to the content of sets, whereas our point of view, at least in Decision Analysis, is that of Pfanzagl. Even a counting operation is strictly a set-theoretic operation. However, it is easily seen that if X is a set of sets, and x is a set in X, then measuring the content of x is a special case of Pfanzagl's situation. The set-theoretic measurement is identical with 'interval' measurement in principle when we can conceive of two points as being the extreme points of a joining set of points.

If the property is dichotomous, either it exists or not, then we can give any two distinct numbers to represent its presence or absence.

If the property has different levels we can again give it any distinct set of numbers, from a straight quantification point of view.

It does not matter what these numbers are unless we wish to draw different inferences from the use of them, or draw on special properties of the numbers.

Basically we are concerned with three aspects:

(a) definitional property;
(b) combinatorial property;
(c) predictive property.

Example

Let us consider the statement: xAy where $A \equiv$ has authority over. Why should we want to attach a number to x such that it represents this property with respect to y?

This example has been deliberately chosen as one not normally arising in Decision Analysis but also as one which could arise. The suggested measurement is only a suggestion and much more thought is needed to provide a correct one, if, indeed, one exists at all.

Basically, the concept of A centres around the fact that in certain circumstances x can tell y what to do.

Naturally the 'wider' the circumstances the 'higher' the authority. Let C be the total set of circumstances. Then we might have the following.

(a) *Definitional Property*

$$m_{C,y}(x) = \sum_{c \in C} \delta^x_{y,c}$$

where $\delta^x_{y,c} = 1$ if x can tell y what to do in circumstance c; $\delta^x_{y,c} = 0$ otherwise.

(b) *Combinatorial Property*.

$$m_{C,y}(x) = \sum_i m_{C_i,y}(x), \quad C = \bigcup_i C_i, \quad C_i \cap C_j = \varnothing, \quad i \neq j$$

(c) *Predictive Property*. If l is life length of any person, x, we might find

$$l(x) = \phi(m_C(x))$$

where $m_C(x) = \sum_y m_{C,y}(x)$ and C is the total set of conditions relevant to x's authority.

We could put any number to x if we only wished to identify the different authority levels, but we may not be able to use them outside their definitional property with which they are equivalent. Thus if we can rank $x, y, z, \ldots$ according to some subjective authority level assessment, we could put any numbers to the authorities providing the rank order was maintained. We might not then have a combinatorial property nor may the predictive property be good.

Other examples of the combinatorial property are as follows:

(1) In the probability area we have:
$$\text{prob}(A \cup B) = \text{prob}(A) + \text{prob}(B) - \text{prob}(A \cap B)$$

(2) In the value area we may have:
$$v(A \oplus B) = v(A) + v(B)$$

(3) In the entropy area we have:
$$E(A.B) = E(A) + \exp_A E(B/A)$$

Each of these calculi are of considerable use in complex computational situations. Each ensures that the quantification process becomes a measurement process in Pfanzagl's sense.

We need to distinguish between quantified relations and quantified variables.

$V(x) = \alpha$ is a quantified variable, where V represents a property of x.

$U(y) = \alpha V(x)$ is a quantified relation between two variables x and y,

where U, V represent properties of y and x and 'α' represents a property of these properties.

Example

Let x be a company policy. Let y be a customer. Let $V(x)$ be a measure of service resulting from x. Let $U(y)$ be a measure of customer satisfaction on y.

Then we, in principle, may have:

$$U(y) = f(V(x))$$

In the above example our methodological problem becomes very clear. The measurements of 'service' and 'satisfaction' may be carried out in various ways. The only restriction at this stage is that as service increases conceptually then so should its measure increase; similarly with 'satisfaction'. However, we have absolutely no *a priori* reason to believe that one specific measure of service is related to one specific measure of satisfaction. In fact we have no reason to believe that the measures are single-dimensional. Thus service, as has already been stated, is a 'distribution', and a single parameter such as the mean level may not be at all adequate. The client may be as much concerned with the tail of the distribution as with mean and variance. The important point is that the establishing of relationships between properties requires a much more fundamental understanding of the measurement problem.

From the above, it is important to note that a quantified variable depends on the method by which it is obtained. It stems from a specific functional relationship between X and the real line R.

Examples

(1) c (activity x) = method (x) = c (cost)

(2) s (customer x) = method (x) = s (satisfaction)

(3) p (event x) = method (x) = p (probability)

To interpret what c, s, p mean we need to know what method was used. Different methods can give different results. Each number may then have a different meaning.

Thus, as we shall see later on, there can be different ways of costing an activity and each has different implications.

Customer satisfaction might be measured by assessing the number of complaints, or by weighting complaints, or by cancelled orders, or by future orders not placed. Each will produce different measures and hence may have different implications.

In subjective probability we may measure such probabilities by asking the person concerned to state his estimates. On the other hand we may set up a gambling situation and use Savage's[111] method to estimate them. Even though the two measures may exhibit a correlation, it may be weak and hence the measures may have different implications.

It is important to differentiate between the inappropriateness of a measure and the non-uniqueness of a measure. Even measures which do exhibit a structural stability in some of the contexts already mentioned may be transformed into other measures which exhibit no structural stability.

Example

In the measurement of value, any monotonic increasing transformation may suffice unless specific constraints are placed, for special reasons, on the form.

However, if $m(x)$ is additive, and $M(x) = f(m(x))$ is a transformed measure, although it will still represent preferences, it may have no simple combinatorial structure.

However, in principle, there is no real difference between two measurement procedures providing the functional relationship between them is known. Such transformations simply change the structure of the models in which the variables figure.

(ii) Qualitative Statements

This is a statement which makes no direct appeal to real numbers.

Examples

(1) x 'has authority over' y;

(2) x 'precedes' y;

(3) x 'is better than' y. 'Better' may have been assessed on a quantitative basis, but in the form stated it becomes purely qualitative.

(4) x 'is the father of' y.

A qualitative statement may contain quantitative variables of course.

Example

$$[x_1, \ldots, x_n] \ R \ [x'_1, x'_2, \ldots, x'_n]$$

We may try to distinguish between statements which are, in principle, quantifiable, and those which are not.

Thus, under certain circumstances 'x is better than y' may possibly be put in the form:

$$v(x) - v(y) = \varepsilon > 0$$

However, we should query whether qualitative statements mean anything without being, in principle, quantifiable. This will depend on how the statements are to be used, which we will discuss later.

It seems implicit in any useful statement that, at the very least, a counting process underlies its meaning.

Examples

(1) 'How much authority' is equivalent to 'under certain circumstances y must do what x asks'.

(2) 'x causes y' is equivalent to 'if x arises, then y arises every time'.

These are both essentially counting operations.

As a counter to the principle of quantification we quote Kazanowski:[66]

'... there is no rational reason why every adjective by which a system may be described (i.e. maintainable, flexible, ...) should be capable of quantification.'

The answer to this must be that it all depends on the power of reasoning we wish to introduce into our analysis. We have already mentioned the combinatorial and predictive aspects of measurement. Some of the power of our analysis depends on these. We have also mentioned the concept of error representation in the context of taxonomies. We will now consider these points a little further as a counter to Kazanowski's statement. In addition, because a less than complete understanding of the process of quantification can lead to a misuse of the process, and hence possibly give further fuel to the anti-quantification group, some mention of misuses is made. It is also important to stress the multidimensional aspects of measurement, the communication aspects and the information aspects.

Although it may add some power of analysis to the study to provide quantitative measurements it is a judgement as to whether the cost of doing so, if possible, would justify the gains. We do not explore this further but refer to White[143] where this is discussed. In addition it must be noted that there are circumstances in which the difficult to measure variables are seen to have the same level in principle whatever the alternative being considered, or in which the difficult to measure variables are seen to dominate in some alternatives.

Example

In a study of possible changes in a spares distribution system some costs were measurable in principle, but clearly created problems in the actual measurement. For the alternatives being considered it was judged that these would not change. A decision was possible on the basis of the readily measurable variables. However, it must be noted that such a procedure implicitly assumes an independence axiom, and may not always work.

(*a*) *Combinatorial Requirements.* Ranking of elements allows no general combination with other factors.

Examples

(1) What does it mean to say 'E is more uncertain than F'? If $E = £10$, $F = £1$, it does not enable a decision to be made between alternatives involving E and F.

(2) Blackett[12] states that 'increased effort implies reduction in % losses' has little or no value in reaching a decision.

(3) In choosing between computers, cost and flexibility are important considerations. Even if we knew the costs of two computers, if all we knew was that one was more flexible than another, we could make no decision between them unless the cheaper one was also more flexible.

(4) In a recent study[133] the qualitative arguments opposite were given for different building maintenance contractual arrangements. They make it impossible to make a 'decision' as they stand (although a 'choice' may be made (see White[143] for the distinction)).

(5) To say 'A is more important than B' and 'C is more important than D' allows us to make no comparison between A and C and between B and D.

(6) Let us turn to the problem of Figure 44 of Section 2.2.3 and the associated equations. Let us, for our purposes, use nominal equations **NE, 3′** and **4′**, which we will accept in principle as being representative of the situation.

1. *Directly Employed Labour*

Advantages	Disadvantages
(i) Direct control of men	(i) Difficult to supervise
(ii) Control of stores buying	(ii) Low pay attracts poor quality men
(iii) Simplification of paperwork	(iii) No bonus, so no extra reward for best men
(iv) Always available	(iv) Require detailed work, planning by FOT
(v) Stable, and able to establish a working relationship with tenants	(v) Difficult to justify in cost/effectiveness terms

2. *Term Contract*

Advantages	Disadvantages
(i) Requires detailed accounting for jobs completed	(i) Too many pieces of paper required for each job
(ii) By only paying for completed works orders, it provides an incentive for the contractor to complete all work on an order	(ii) Same contractor deals with other client agents for the rest of the base
(iii) Shows detailed maintenance costs to be assigned to particular properties	(iii) Low profitability of work for the contractor
(iv) Pricing of jobs is fixed in advance	(iv) Contract negotiated by region and consequent lack of sanctions at depot level

3. *Day-work Term Contract*

Advantages	Disadvantages
(i) Reduction of clerical work for contractor	(i) Difficult to establish whether value for money is being obtained
(ii) Guaranteed income from married quarters—therefore, able to assign specific resources in terms of manpower and equipment to ensure a profit	(ii) Lack of sanctions because of no precise definition of level of output
(iii) Organization of other work can be kept entirely separate	(iii) Weakening of MPBW powers of supervision
(iv) RAF could place orders directly on contractor	(iv) Tenants' short-term requirements will tend to predominate over long-term structural needs of the property
(v) Possible for the contractor to pay craftsmen the 'going rate'	

88

Clearly, if we do not measure variables (3) and (4) numerically, expressions **NE**, **3'** and **4'** will be very weak, if meaningful at all.

It is possible to argue qualitatively. Thus if, given two bonus parameters (1) and (1)', we have qualitative relations of the kind

$$(1) > (1)'$$
$$(3) < (3)'$$
$$(4) < (4)' \qquad\qquad \mathbf{D}$$

then clearly we would prefer (1)' to (1).

What would we do if we had

$$(1) > (1)'$$
$$(3) < (3)'$$
$$(4) > (4)'? \qquad\qquad \mathbf{ND}$$

In **D** we are better off from all points of view. In **ND** we are better off in two aspects and worse in another. Because we have no numerical measure we can proceed no further. It is possible to have a different example of **ND** which, however, we could not distinguish from **ND**, *viz.*,

$$(1) < (1)''$$
$$(3) < (3)''$$
$$(4) > (4)''$$

(7) Coleman[27] gives an example in which the prestige of various professions is ranked, some of which are doctor 70th (high), salesman 40th, bookkeeper 30th (low). It is not necessarily correct to say that 'prestige (doctor) = prestige (salesman) + prestige (bookkeeper)'. There are many cardinal scales which are compatible with the rankings given but something more is needed to identify the appropriate scale.

(8) Thomson[137] discusses the problem of determining the effect of certain changes on traffic flow. Some steady state relationships which are pertinent to this are $\mathbf{q} = f(\mathbf{c}, t)$, $\mathbf{c} = \mathbf{q}(v)$, $v = h(\mathbf{q})$, where $\mathbf{q}$, $\mathbf{c}$, t, v are, respectively; traffic flow rates, costs, tax and average speed. This involves a feedback model as given in Figure 41, which is a further example of Figure 48 appearing later on.

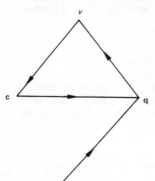

Figure 41. Traffic flow causal model

It is readily seen that even if the component relationships were qualitatively meaningful, it would not be possible to reason out the effects of change in t on the other variables.

(b) *Predictive Requirements.* Science proceeds by relating properties of a single individual x, or several individuals $x, y, \ldots$.

In some cases it is useful to be able to predict one property from others. In such cases the procedures by which the numbers are assigned may be critical.

Examples

(1) If we wish to find the profit generating capacity, P, of a system x, we might see that it is dependent on 'flexibility', y, and we would wish to know how to determine 'flexibility', since some measures may be poor correlates.

(2) We might suspect a relationship between 'poverty' and 'disease' of individuals, and hence we need to consider appropriate procedures of measurement.

(3) Job success may be predictable in terms of 'intelligence', 'personality', etc., and appropriate procedures of measurement need to be considered.

(c) *Error Requirements.* Qualitative statements permit no assessment of errors in taking wrong decisions.

Example

In the maintenance contract problem, we may choose an alternative, but have no idea of size of the errors arising from this choice; to be able to do so, we need to have a scale of division compatible with magnitude of errors to be examined.

(d) *Misuse of Quantification.* It is dangerous to put numbers to elements without careful thought.

Examples

(1) In a hospital study people were asked to give numbers 1–10 to represent importance of certain activities. These numbers were for the purpose of decision-making and may not be the correct ones, which should be obtained using the appropriate value theory.

(2) In a study of maintenance depots, foremen were asked to give numbers to represent the importance of activities. These numbers were used for decision-making, and again there was no guarantee they were the correct ones, which should be obtained using the appropriate value theory.

(3) Northropp, Jenkins and Thomasell[96] are concerned with various factors used in assessing the effectiveness of data buoys. One of these factors is 'capability'. There are 20 parameters and each is given a score on each of 11 counts, and then these are added to give a measure of capability for the data buoy. There is no guarantee that such a measurement process would be consistent with the preferences of the decisionmakers, even if the decisionmakers did the scoring. In addition the score on its own would be of no use unless the decisionmakers knew the measurement procedure. Finally most scores were 0 and 1,

whereas parameters might be continuous, and the conversion of a continuous factor into a 0–1 factor must be suspect.

(e) *Multidimensional Requirements.* It is important to stress that a concept may need several properties necessary to describe it for decision purposes and that a single measurement may not suffice. Sometimes it is difficult to determine the necessary and sufficient measurements to be made.

Examples

(1) 'Noise' is very often considered to be a single-dimensional quantity. However, when trying to describe noise for the purpose of being able to control it, and its effect, in the context of acceptability by occupants of buildings, E. C. Keighley[67] found two attributes necessary to describe noise for their purposes: (a) average Db.A; (b) the number of impact sounds per minute rising substantially above background level.

(2) In forestry management, consideration is given to the 'quality' of a tree. Presumably this has not only an 'aesthetic' content but also a 'performance' content in the context of the use to which the tree is to be put. Thus a poor quality tree may result in large waste when processed to produce a specific item.

(3) When measuring customer service, is it to be measured by 'mean delay', 'variance of delay', or the 'probability that delay will exceed T'? Do we need to specify the whole distribution?

(f) *Communication Requirements.* Measurement plays a vital role in communication.

Mellen[84] quotes Lord Kelvin as follows:

'When you cannot measure what you are speaking of and express it in numbers your knowledge is of a very meagre and unsatisfactory kind.'

In this sense Lord Kelvin is clearly stressing the extent of ambiguity of communication inherent in more qualitative statements.

(g) *Information Requirements.* When the consequences are measurable, but the relationship between alternatives and consequences are difficult to determine, an attempt to specify the consequences in a quantitative manner may ignore information which exists in a subjective sense, but which is difficult to determine.

Example

A sales manager may not accept a solution which attempts to include estimates of lost profit due to poor service; nor a solution which attempts to include, quantitatively, customers' reactions to his policies.

C SCOPE OF STATEMENTS

Here we distinguish between the specific and the general.

(a) *Specific Statements.* For the specific x and y, $x \mathrm{R} y$.

Example
$$x > y, \quad x = 2y, \quad c(x) = 0{\cdot}5$$

(b) *General Statements.* For all $(x, y) \in *$, $x \mathrm{R} y$.

Example

$$y = \alpha x, \quad \text{all} \quad (x,y) \in *$$

A specific fact still depends on a general theory (Churchman[24]). The truth or falsity of a specific statement depends on a theory of errors, which states, in this case, that under the conditions arising the errors are small.

Thus a measurement necessitates a theory of the way it is obtained under certain conditions, and the way in which it can be used.

Examples

(1) If $c =$ cost, then it will be used for some purpose, such as indicating something is wrong; but what theory tells us when a particular value of c is or is not wrong?

If c is to be used as a basis for decisionmaking, what theory tells us whether the procedure c is the correct c?

If c is calculated by a certain mechanism, what theory tells us what the errors are?

(2) Stratton[128] discusses certain physical measurements, such as the measurement of the mass of the earth, which requires certain instrument measurements plus Newton's law (model) of gravitation. However, even the instrument measurements presuppose some theory.

(3) Lacey[71] suggests an index of 'exposure' equal to 'annual rainfall × mean wind speed' as a variable influencing deterioration in buildings. However, to suspect that a relationship would exist, presupposes a knowledge of some theory, unless, initially, this is experimental. Intuitively the quantity of rain and speed of impact would seem to influence deterioration monotonically, but why multiplicatively? Even if multiplicatively, why not other functions of rainfall and wind speed?

(4) In studying the performance of a building it is anticipated that some concept of 'intensity of use' would be important. This might be 'number of persons per year per square foot'. However, what leads us to believe that this measurement is appropriate for any particular purpose, e.g. floor maintenance cost prediction? Again, any initial measurement is either an experimental guess or some explanatory model is held in mind when settling on such a measurement.

(5) Freudenthal[47] points out that the measurement of resistance, R, originates from the recognition of a law that V/I is constant, and that, without this, the concept might never have been established.

As we shall see in the context of Decision Analysis, just as much as decisions depend upon measurements, then so also do measurements depend upon some decision model in some instances.

(6) In a study of ways of improving maintenance activities, some of the data needed related to the failure rate of equipment. However, it was known that not all failures were reported. Hence, if reported failure rate data was to be used to modify maintenance policies on a continuing basis, some theory for modifying the data was needed.

(7) Blalock[13] discusses the theoretical relationship between the level of protestantism and suicide rates and points to the existence of factors which distort the measurements of these two variables in an unknown manner. In principle the original theory requires a theory of data modification if it is to acquire full confidence.

It is a logical consequence of the recognition of a theory of measurement that, if observations conflict with the main theory, we do not know, without the theory of adjustment, whether the main theory is or is not being supported.

When considering measurement errors reference must be made to Heisenberg's Principle of Uncertainty, which indicates that the process of measurement can influence the actual measurement itself. In principle, therefore, we need a theory of measurement adjustment to cater for this interaction.

Examples

(1) Within the area of the theory of choice we are concerned with the measurement of values and subjective probabilities. Contemporary experiments to obtain these introduce an artificiality to the situation which will be reflected in measurement errors.

(2) The knowledge that production performance is being measured may influence the measurements. If the measurements are for bonus purposes, then they may appear low; if they are for promotion purposes they may appear high.

The truth or falsity of a general empirical statement is not provable, if it is infinite. This is particularly important in model building since it means we can never be sure such general premises are true and can only have evidence supporting or refuting them. Observations may be compatible with many possible hypotheses.

It must be stressed, at this stage, that although the specific or general statement is concerned with the 'objective' aspect of the analysis it can contain subjective judgements.

Example

The general statement, lost sales $= f$ (delay), may be derived subjectively.

2.2.3 Constructing the Model

Having cleared the ground for the basis of mathematical models, we need to concern ourselves with the questions relevant to operational construction of such models in a given problematic situation, *viz.*:

(a) how do we identify and represent the variables to be used in the model?
(b) how do we identify and represent the relations to be used in the model?

In this section we will be concerned with the central principles at stake in model construction. It should be stressed once again that even if we are concerned with the use of some established theory we still have to ensure that our model is appropriate for the theory and, hence, the points which follow will still be relevant.

Later on we will concern ourselves with some special approaches to modelling aimed at facilitating the solution procedure.

2.2.3.1 IDENTIFICATION AND DEFINITION OF VARIABLES

We have already stressed in Section 2.1 that we need first of all to isolate our decision (or control) variables (A) and the consequence variables $(\mathscr{C})$ in terms of which $a \in A$ is to be evaluated.

These will be linked by other variables, which may be split into variables which are purely chance (C) variables, and those in the control of decisionmakers external to the system (E). Figure 37 illustrates this.

Note also that the establishment of particular relationships and measurements will add theory to the model.

In presenting this simplified picture, as has been pointed out in the previous section, the process by which some of these variables are measured has to be examined, a point to which we will again turn our attention later on. Such a process is tantamount to making a decision since various procedures are available to us for measuring, for example, costs. Different procedures will have different implications for the analysis. We thus have a, sometimes hidden, secondary decision process to contend with.

The aspects of the variables with which we wish to deal are their conceptual identification, their definition and with subjective measurements.

A CONCEPTUAL IDENTIFICATION

There are two directions in which we can proceed, *viz.*: (i) forward or (ii) backward.

(i) *Forward Identification*

In the forward case, we simply ask, given, in concept, a certain variable, what other variables can it influence?

Examples

(1) If $g \equiv$ 'customer goodwill', we may realize that g influences future 'orders', o, and hence o may become a consequence variable and g relegated to an intermediate variable.

(2) If a is a 'bonus scheme' action, we may see that a influences 'personnel behaviour', p.

(ii) *Backward Identification*

In the backward case, we simply ask what variables influence a given variable?

Example

If l is 'lateness of delivery', we may see that 'equipment availability', e, influences l.

(iii) *Combined Forward and Backward Identification*

This way we build up a network of variables as in Figure 42.

Examples

(1) See Figure 42.

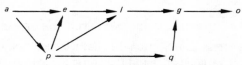

Figure 42. Network of variables

Of course, all our problems will not exhibit, effectively, this complexity.

(2) In inventory control, we may have Figure 43.

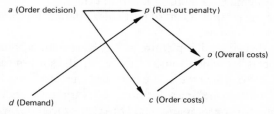

Figure 43. Network of variables for inventory control

This is a generalization of the consequence chain problem discussed in the section on formulating the problem. However, not all variables are consequences from the point of view of the model. Thus, for example, certain variables external to the decisionmaker's system may not be treated as consequence variables in the model.

The purpose of discussing the chain effect in the special case of consequence variables was to emphasize the ultimacy–non-ultimacy problem arising in identifying ultimate consequences.

Although the network approach is simple, it does have considerable value in ensuring that potential influences between variables are recognized and treated as such.

Example

Bettman[11] constructs a list of 8 variables as follows:

1. Air pollution.
2. Medical case services.
3. Rate of population growth.
4. Aid for education.
5. Crime levels.
6. Defence spending.
7. Rate of inflation.
8. Minority relations.

His study is concerned with the values of changes in each of these variables. However, they are treated as independent variables for this purpose, whereas they clearly are not. Figure 44 gives some idea of possible influences, but not all.

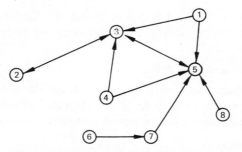

Figure 44. Network of variables for national
goals

Figure 44 shows that values of unit changes in variables are not only relative to each other but may also be derivative from each other. The model is clearly incomplete, but any valuation procedure would benefit from such a presentation.

This discussion does raise the question of whether all variables are consequences of some other variables.

Descartes takes the view that this is so and that each phenomenon has a cause. This would naturally lead either to a closed-loop feedback system or to an infinite model. Descartes probably had the latter view in mind. Blalock[13] also discusses this point. It is clearly possible, in theory, to have a closed system in which every variable influences, and is influenced by, every other variable, but our Decision Analysis models are likely to be 'cuts' in such systems, either accepting inputs and/or not tracing outputs beyond a certain point. Figure 45 illustrates this.

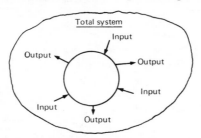

Figure 45. System cuts

At this stage it is useful to see what is involved in such a cutting process, and to this end we will consider an elementary example.

Example

Consider a problem involving the selection of a bonus scheme. Let us assume that the form of the bonus scheme has been chosen, but that a single parameter has yet to be selected, e.g. the rate of payment for unit output in excess of some standard output at a specified quality level.

Figure 46 gives a partial specification of a set of factors, on the lines of Figure 45, emanating from the initial decision factor (1), *viz.*, bonus scheme parameter. It does not include many other factors also at work. Figure 46 is thus an incomplete or partial figure. Let us now discuss this figure under the headings of output (or consequence) variables, decision variables, intermediate variables, and other variables.

(i) Output Variables and Final Effects

In selecting any bonus parameter, its effect on certain basic output, or final, variables, will determine the choice. In this problem such variables are represented by wages (8), revenue (9) and material costs (10). Other variables may be included.

(ii) Decision Variables

Only one decision variable, bonus scheme parameter, is included, which is numbered (1). Other decision variables can be included.

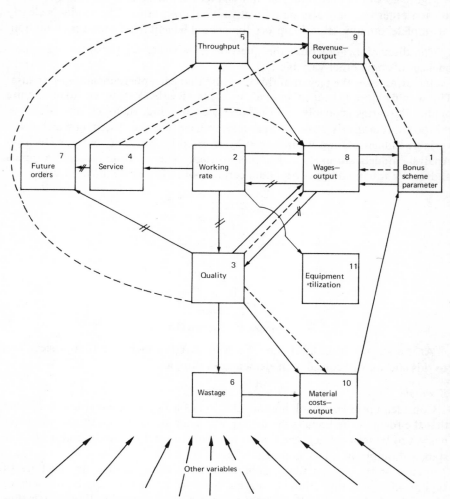

Figure 46. Bonus system network. Full lines: original connections. Broken lines: equivalent connections for cut network

(iii) Intermediate Variables

Variables influenced by (1), or influencing (8), (9) or (10) are called inter-mediate variables. They are part of a network of causal factors relating a decision to its final effects. In Figure 46 they are variables (2), (3), (4), (5), (6), (7), (11).

(iv) Other Variables

Other internal variables are at work; other internal decisions may be taken; external factors are also at play.

In its simplest form, we can conceive of relationships between the variables. We will deal separately with the problem of determining relationships later, but make conceptual use of them now.

We assume that the bonus scheme achieves its impact on the final variables by influencing wages (8).

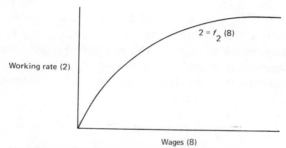

Figure 47. Working rate/wages relationship

We can see that wages (8) will influence working rate (2), but that also working rate (2) will influence wages (8).

In the former case we might represent this as the rate at which an operator is prepared to work to achieve a given wage level. See Figure 47.

In the latter case we also see that wages are influenced by bonus parameter (1), working rate (2), quality (3) and throughput (5). We write this as

$$(8) = f_8(1, 2, 3, 5)$$

Pursuing the same line of reasoning, we can write the relationships in Figure 46 in general formally as follows:

Decision	$(1) = f_1(8, 9, 10)$	**1**
Intermediate effects	$(2) = f_2(8)$	**2**
	$(3) = f_3(8, 2)$	**3**
	$(4) = f_4(2)$	**4**
	$(5) = f_5(2, 7)$	**5**
	$(6) = f_6(3)$	**6**
	$(7) = f_7(4, 3)$	**7**
	$(11) = f_{11}(2)$	**8**
Final effects	$(8) = f_8(1, 2, 3, 5)$	**9**
	$(9) = f_9(5)$	**10**
	$(10) = f_{10}(6, 3)$	**11**

Note that we are assuming steady-state relationships here.

We are now in a position to discuss certain aspects of the analysis, which will have their counterpart in other decision areas, whether they be simpler or more difficult, and will result in a cut being imposed in Figure 46 as per Figure 48.

It will be noted that variable (11) has not played any part in the discussion so far. It has been put in since it is often used in the assessment of efficiency of operation of production systems. However, although it is correlated with (8), (9), (10), it is, in fact, irrelevant to the argument and does not influence (8), (9) or (10) but is influenced by the same variable (2) which influences these latter variables. One can, by being selective in machine loading, improve the utilization of equipment, but run the risk of reducing (5) and (7), and hence (9).

Variable (11) is therefore an irrelevant symptom. One of the problems in Decision Analysis is to remove such irrelevant symptoms and a network such as given in Figure 46 is useful.

Clearly the network, even in Figure 46, may be too much to handle. Even though it is itself a 'cut-off' from the real picture, we may have to 'cut' even further into the network to produce a manageable analysis. Such cuts will give rise to value judgements, which we will now discuss.

Let us suppose that the following relationships are not determinable, *viz.*,

$$(2) = f_2(8) \hspace{4cm} \textbf{2}$$
$$(3) = f_3(8, 2) \hspace{3.6cm} \textbf{3}$$
$$(7) = f_7(4, 3) \hspace{3.6cm} \textbf{7}$$

In principle, if we trace through the relationships we see that

$$(2) = f_2'(1, 2, 3, 4) \hspace{3cm} \textbf{2}'$$

leading to

$$(2) = f_2''(1, 3, 4) \hspace{3.2cm} \textbf{2}''$$

In addition we have:

$$(5) = f_5'(1, 3, 4) \hspace{3.2cm} \textbf{5}'$$
$$(6) = f_6(3) \hspace{3.6cm} \textbf{6}$$

We then have:

$$(8) = f_8'(1, 3, 4)\text{—not known} \hspace{1.6cm} \textbf{8}'$$
$$(9) = f_9'(1, 3, 4)\text{—not known} \hspace{1.6cm} \textbf{9}'$$
$$(10) = f_{10}'(3)\text{—known} \hspace{2.4cm} \textbf{10}'$$

The net effect of **8'**, **9'** and **10'** is not known, although something may be known by virtue of **10'**.

In principle we can write it thus

$$\text{NE} = f_{\text{NE}}(1, 3, 4) \hspace{3cm} \textbf{NE}$$

If we trace through the relationships, we get, in principle, the following relationships:

$$(3) = f_3'(1)\text{—unknown} \hspace{2.6cm} \textbf{3}'$$
$$(4) = f_4'(1)\text{—unknown} \hspace{2.6cm} \textbf{4}'$$

The problem is to choose (1) and hence (3) and (4), to optimize NE. However, we do not know the net-effects function, although we may think that it decreases with (1) (since this tends to increase wages) and increases with (3) and (4) (since these tend to increase future orders). We may make a value judgement on NE by, for example, valuing subjectively NE according to the value function:

$$V_{NE} = (\alpha(3) + \beta(4))(a - b(1)) \qquad\qquad \mathbf{NE'}$$

To solve the problem we still have to estimate $f_3'(1)$ and $f_4'(1)$ on a subjective basis, conditioned by any partial knowledge we have on known relationships in some cases, but, in the extreme, with no consideration of these.

Let these be:

$$(3) = \lambda + \mu(1) \qquad\qquad \mathbf{3''}$$
$$(4) = u + v(1) \qquad\qquad \mathbf{4''}$$

Our problem is then one of finding (1) to maximize

$$V_{NE} = (\alpha\lambda + \beta u + (\alpha\mu + \beta v)(1))(a - b(1)) \qquad\qquad \mathbf{NE''}$$

This looks highly abstract, but it does represent a possible mode of reasoning on which relationships in principle are identified, but in which subjective judgements are incorporated.

In Figure 46 this is brought about simply by severing the links marked.

The effect is to cut out all variables except (1), (3) and (4) and to set up an equivalent linkage indicated by the dotted lines.

In considering Figures 42 and 43 it must be appreciated that the relationships between variables may contain time and delay factors, and may take the form of difference or differential equations. In addition, the directions of influence are not always to the right.

Examples

(1) Thus we might replace Figure 43 by Figure 48.

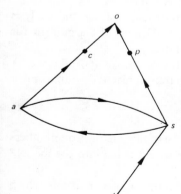

Figure 48. Network of variables with time factor

We have:

$$s_{t+1} = s_t + a_t - d_t$$
$$a_t = 0 \quad \text{if } s_t \geqslant \underline{s}$$
$$\quad = \theta \quad \text{if } s_t < \underline{s}$$
$$c_t = 0 \quad \text{if } a_t = 0$$
$$\quad = \alpha + \beta a_t \quad \text{if } a_t > 0$$
$$p_t = \gamma \max[0, -s_t]$$
$$o_t = c_t + p_t$$

s_t is inventory level at beginning of period t.

a_t, c_t, p_t, d_t are as defined for Figure 43 but specific to period t.

This set of equations is a variant of that given for the example following Figure 37, but set against the background of the pictorial 'feedback' representation of Figure 48. Feedback (or 'feedforward') are simply relationships representing influences between variables, although the nature of this is often hidden by equations without the network representation.

(2) Forrester[46] develops a similar model representing the influences between five major world factors, *viz.*, investment (agriculture and other), population, pollution, resources. In this model, which contains feedback loops, the variables have a high degree of aggregation. Thus, for example, 'resources' amalgamates all world resources as if they were homogeneous. Had resources been separated into different sorts of resources, then the model would have been different. However, bearing in mind the problems of handling completely (if this is at all possible) disaggregated variables, some form of aggregation is probably necessary from a practical point of view. This raises the question of what variables should have been represented.

Bartee[6] discusses the problem of 'closing off' complex social models in which inputs and outputs are eventually modified by the analysis process itself. No 'model' of the closed system is used, but outputs are used, via a process of social discussion, to modify the inputs, and appropriate values are introduced.

The efficiency of variable identification (in concept) depends to some extent on the perception abilities of the analysts.

It is, of course, enhanced by knowledge of similar or related Decision Analysis studies which have been carried out, once again reinforcing the argument for recognition of the subject matter of Decision Analysis.

Whether a variable is important depends on the degree of its influence. A variable may thus be ruled out or introduced on purely subjective grounds prior to the derivation of the relations.

Examples

(1) Suppose one were asked to assess the influence of fare changes on numbers of travelling passengers on buses. What variables would come into the model? How would one decide which ones to incorporate?

Historical statistical analysis may include any number of conditions which may be thought to influence the number of passengers. Initially some are chosen subjectively; a later statistical analysis may indicate the need to search for more variables.

In Figure 49, given below, it is important to note that, from a statistical point of view, the adequacy of the set of variables is not independent of the adequacy of the possible functional forms used. What might turn out to be inadequate on the basis of a linear form, may turn out to be adequate on the basis of a quadratic form. We shall turn to this latter problem in due course, but for the moment use Figure 49 at this stage to show the dependence of one aspect of the analysis on the other. Figure 49 is an expansion of one part of Figure 39.

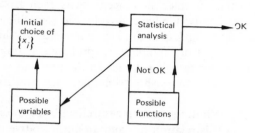

Figure 49. Interaction of selection of variables and of statistical analysis

(2) In a study of vehicle performance there was an initial choice of the variables in terms of which a replacement decision should be made. It was thought that operating and maintenance cost was a function of age. However, it was also thought that it was more dependent on mileage. Statistical tests indicated a correlation between the two, so that either may be used. However, it was possible that the costs depended on the previous history of mileage and/or costs. Therefore, in principle, the governing variables could be multidimensional.

(3) In studying vehicle diagnostics, various variables can be measured. Thus certain characteristics of engine performance could be measured and decisions based on these. Alternatively, measures on engine wear might be taken, and decisions based on these. There are many possible variables which might figure in a diagnostic scheme. Associated with such a system we would have a chain diagram similar to that of Figure 42 in terms of appropriate variables. The ultimate objective is to establish the initial causes, but very often these can only, economically, be inferred with some probability before a major check is made. Thus, as has been indicated, poor engine performance may arise from some engine fault. However, it may equally well be due to the manner of driving the vehicle, or to the strains put on the engine by faulty connections with other parts of the vehicle. It is equally possible that there is nothing wrong with the vehicle and that the conditions under which it is operating are responsible for changes in performance.

In principle, each measurement can be associated probabilistically with the causes, and a model accordingly built, but we have a clear choice of which variables to measure.

(4) 'Operability' and 'flexibility' of solutions may be felt to be important in a given study, but some qualitative subjective measurement would be needed before precise measurements were made and importance established.

(5) In assessing the value of a project in the building industry such things as 'client's standing', and 'expertise in type of building concerned', may be felt to be important when tendering, but the proper establishment of importance presupposes operational definition and measurement.

B DEFINITION

Having identified the variables, in concept, there then arises the question of their definition operationally. We have already said something related to this in the context of qualitative and quantitative statements. In this section we will consider in detail, via a set of examples, the problems arising in practice when it comes to defining and measuring things. In the previous section our interest in measurement lay in its relationship to mathematics and its role in Decision Analysis.

The processes of 'definition' and 'measurement' are intertwined. One can probably argue about this relationship and an authoritative discussion may be found in Ackoff.[1] We take 'measurement' to be a special aspect of 'definition'. One might take the view that measurement is the actual procedure for assigning the real numbers which constitute the measure. However, as pointed out in the previous section, this is the quantification process, and in itself does not constitute a measure unless it is a homomorphism. The homomorphism then defines the measure.

A general definition of an object or event is equivalent to a classification of objects or events, plus a procedure for determining the relevant class, plus a statement of how such a definition may be used. When the taxonomy has an equivalent quantitative expression we then have a measurement of the property to which the taxonomy is equivalent.

Implicit in these definitions is the knowledge of some property of the procedures used. It is not enough to define a variable without knowing some of its properties. It is not enough to put a numerical value to some conceptual variable without knowing some of the properties of these numbers. In the latter case, Pfanzagl's[101] view on measurement requires that the properties of the numbers reflect some property of the event or objects concerned, otherwise the measurement becomes meaningless.

It is the belief of the Operationalists that a statement has no 'meaning' without an operational method of validating it, and hence, for a variable to have 'meaning', it must be operationally definable.

It is important to note that operationalism may refer to operationalism in principle, and that all we need to know is that some procedure exists to determine the applicability of the definition, and that we do not have to apply this to be able to say a sentence is meaningful.

Examples

(1) Hempel[57] discusses the case of medical diagnostics in which we can meaningfully talk of a patient having a certain disease without having con-

clusively demonstrated it, since otherwise we might have to wait for all diseases to take their course before knowing, and this is clearly not possible.

(2) In the definition of a probability distribution one can conceive of an infinite procedure for verifying a particular distribution, but in practice our observations are finite and our meaning of probability may rest in the infinite. Nevertheless we make use of such definitions.

Without the definition (operational) we cannot proceed with deductive models, and, indeed our definition of 'definition' implies a deductive content.

This, however, does not mean that an undefined variable is irrelevant. Clearly the decisionmaker may superimpose his judgements, on this variable, on the other factors, and make a choice. But this is radically different from being able to decide, which is a logical process which cannot proceed without operational definitions (see White[143]).

Clearly, in many instances the object of the exercise may be to determine the precise properties of the definition, and one may have to select some 'intuitive' definition. However, this cannot be completely arbitrary and the 'intuitive' approach really depends on a subjective perception of the properties sought.

Examples
(1) When defining 'quality' one would automatically think of the purpose of the exercise and think in terms of the features of a product, the uses of the product, and the relationships between the two. Thus when thinking of the quality of paper, one might think of the features of the paper which might influence the readability of the writing using different inks, pens and pencils. Or one might think of the features of the paper which influence the acceptability of the noise generated when it is folded.

We see from this case that definition is, in itself, equivalent to a cause and effect analysis. It may happen that a few, or even one, carefully defined variables might be adequate to be able to describe quality as a cause of the effects one has in mind. Thus some measure of 'absorption' or some measure of 'rigidity' may (or may not) suffice.

(2) We talk about 'profit', but there are considerable difficulties in defining it.

Suppose we buy a piece of equipment and measure, using specific procedures:

(a) income $= I$;
(b) direct costs $= C$.

Suppose, relative to some time period, we have a nominal reduction in value, ΔV.

We might define Profit $= I - C - \Delta V$.

But how do we get ΔV? The 'depreciation' approach is not geared to future decisions concerning the equipment.

We cannot deduce anything unless we know what the equivalent financial consequences are for ΔV and this must depend on future decisions. If the equipment were depreciated at the rate of 10% per annum, then for ΔV to be meaningful, the equipment would have to be scrapped after 10 years, and the cash effects arising from tax concessions and any actual setting aside of money for repurchase would be incorporated in ΔV. The purpose of a profit definition is to be able to determine which are the more effective ventures in terms of cash production and the appropriate definition must stem from this requirement. Nothing else is meaningful if this is the real requirement.

(3) Other examples are 'penalty costs', 'interest costs', 'storage costs' and 'costs of lost production time'. In these latter cases an operational definition lies in determining precisely what it is that a company pays out in such circumstances, e.g. exactly how does a cost of storage arise directly associated with holding a specific unit of stock; sometimes there really is no cost incurred at the specific point in time.

(3A) Take, for example, the costing of the production of a specific item, in which we can bring in or leave out overhead costs. Apart from the difficulty of allocating such overheads, should we include them at all?

In a certain situation the problem of whether to manufacture certain items, or subcontract them, arose. One of the overheads allocated was that due to depreciation on buildings and equipment. However, whether we do or do not subcontract, we will still have these buildings and equipment and, hence, putting in overheads on this basis will not be pertinent, directly, to the decision problem on hand.

They are not completely irrelevant since, if we decide not to manufacture, then, when the time comes to rebuild, we may be able to build a smaller workshop. Or, alternatively, we may be able to take on other work. It depends on what other actions we wish to consider. If we do intend, if we decide to subcontract, to reduce the size of building at time T, then the effect of subcontracting quantity Q will be to reduce building outlay by λQ at time T in the future, giving a discounted cost reduction of $\alpha^T \lambda$ per unit manufactured.

Note that, even here, we are using 'discounted cost' measurements without justifying their relevance, but we will accept this for our purposes.

If s is the subcontracting price and c the manufacturing price, we subcontract if

$$s \sum_{k=0}^{\infty} \alpha^k - \alpha^T \lambda \sum_{k=0}^{\infty} \alpha^k < c\left(\sum_{k=0}^{\infty} \alpha^k \right), \quad \text{i.e. } s < c + \alpha^T \lambda$$

We assume the same amount is subcontracted per unit time, and neglect many other factors, of course, such as maintenance. This is a steady-state subcontracting decision, as though we were reducing the value by a fixed amount.

Even this is an approximation, since we make no allowance for decisions after time T.

Dangers can arise in accepting historical costs, calculated in a given manner, when these are to be used for changing methods of operation. We need to be clear on which things change and which remain fixed.

(3B) In a refuse collection study, it was feasible to do the existing work with 3 vehicles instead of 4. The problem arose as to how we were to define the cost of the vehicle. The department calculated an hourly cost by some form of depreciation plus maintenance, and these costs were used. However, it was soon realized that the total load collected was the same, and hence 3 vehicles were doing the work of 4. This would mean changes in maintenance cost per unit time; it may also mean an earlier replacement period. Thus the historical costs were suspect.

In a similar decision vein, Churchman[24] mentions 'opportunity costs' and stresses that these assume optimality of policies in areas where these opportunities arise, and that therefore any definition makes assumptions about certain consequences.

Sometimes, when building a model, costs can be inadvertently duplicated by an attempt to define a special entity. It must be remembered that any such definition may be implicit in the model.

(3C) In a problem concerned with the production of greetings cards, the possibility of obsolescence of a particular design arose. If x is the production quantity and z is the demand, a cost $k(x - z)$ was included as the definition of obsolescence 'cost'. However, this was erroneous, since once the production decision was made at a cost $\alpha + \beta x$, no further actual costs arose even if an excess of cards were produced. The total cost model already included this production cost.

(3D) In a study of economic batch quantities the question of the definition of set-up costs arose. Only if the decision influenced this should it be included. If the total set-up time plus production time was no greater than that available then it should be costed only if excess capacity was sold at an appropriate price per unit of capacity. If the total time was greater than capacity allowed it should be costed only if the company were to purchase extra capacity at an appropriate price.

(3E) The traditional economic batch quantity model is, perhaps, the most well known of our beloved standard procedures in Decision Analysis. However, there appears to be insufficient attention given to the costing of inventory levels. If Q is the order quantity (and here we restrict ourselves to the simplest deterministic model), v is the value of one unit of inventory and r is the interest rate appropriate in a particular case, the inventory holding cost is given as

$$rvQ/2$$

which represents the net interest lost through holding inventory.

The question which does not seem to have been tackled, in this context, is 'what is v?' If the stock is final inventory, is v the sales value, or the production cost, per unit? The answer is that it may be neither.

In order to answer this question it is important that we go back to first principles and take the accountant's approach of identifying the precise cash flows. Let us assume that the situation is the very simple one in which a material is purchased, is processed quickly to form a final stock and then sold. Let the demand rate be uniform, at a rate D per year. Let the income be uniform at a rate iD per year. Let purchase and production (and other direct) costs be p per unit. Let a be the fixed cost incurred in each cycle. Let us suppose we make m

106

production runs in a year and let us examine the cash fluctuations arising from this specific item. These are given in Figure 50.

The average net cash position throughout the year is not the same as that which would be given by using average inventory. The precise effect on 'interest' charges would depend on whether the overall cash position, when the above is superimposed on other cash flows, is always positive, always negative or a mixture of both. In the last case the interest rates appropriate may differ in the positive and negative regions. Let us consider the situation when it is always positive or always negative. The net interest loss is then $r \times$ the average net cash position as

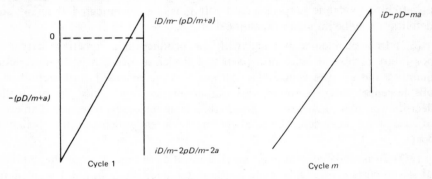

Figure 50. Economic batch quantity problem

determined from the above figure, taking 0 as a zero datum position. Thus we have

$$\text{NIL} = \frac{r}{m}\{iD/2 + (m + 1)(p - i) D/2 + m(m + 1) a/2\}$$

$$= rvQ/2$$

where

$$v = \{i + (m + 1)(p - i) + (m + 1) a/Q\}$$

We see that v is not independent of Q and that the fixed costs also contribute to lost interest.

Roy[109] discusses some difficulties in cost definition.

Chambers[21] discusses the limited uses of some modern accounting methods of measurement of system performance.

(4) In a study of a Central Sterile Supply Unit, in a hospital, the problem of 'dirt' arose. What was it? How was it to be defined in such a way that its influence on sterility could be determined? This particular study led to difficulties because 'everyone knew what dirt was—so why all the fuss?' Again the answer to this depends on a cause–effect study relating the 'content' of dirt to its effects, and this requires a determination of the agents in dirt conducive to influencing changes in levels of sterility.

(5) In a study of building design, 'view' and 'noise' were important variables. To be able to define 'view' there is the question of ascertaining the effects it produces, such as impressions of distance, impressions of space. To be able to define 'noise', there is again the problem of ascertaining the effects to be considered and then the problem of ascertaining the features of noise which influence these, such as frequency, amplitude.

(6) In some situations the notion of 'life of a bus' or of a 'building' arises. This can be important when considering capital investment. However, it becomes increasingly difficult to determine when a life comes to an end. In the case of a house it certainly does not arise when the house 'falls down'. In the case of a 'bus' it can happen that the form of the original bus is not maintained, since it is progressively altered.

(7) In a transport department there is the problem of defining 'major' and 'minor' repairs. This raises the question of why this dichotomous taxonomy was needed. The dichotomy arises because of the two locations (garage or workshops) in which a repair will be carried out, and hence this effectively defines 'major' and 'minor'. Thus we know what will happen to a repair classed as 'major' or 'minor' as far as its repair location is concerned.

(8) Hanssmann[54] mentions the problem of 'cost/flexibility' of air transport fleets. Flexibility is a multidimensional concept involving the 'ease of conversion for various uses'. However, it really has no meaning without determination of these uses and conversions. Concepts of 'more' or 'less' flexibility are vital in arriving at the final decision.

(9) Definition of 'ship complexity' is needed when estimating the work content in a ship for tendering purposes. Before we can do this we need to understand the nature of such a concept as it influences work content and hence the various features of the ship which contribute to this complexity. After this we may be able to provide a single measure so that ships with the same complexity contribute the same factor to work content.

(10) Baylis[7] discusses the flexibility of manpower and says:

'We must certainly define, as exactly as possible, what is meant by flexibility, if only because we want the man to be flexible in the right sort of way.'

(11) An interesting example of definition arises in considering 'accessibility' in a supermarket. One way of defining this was suggested, *viz.*, the 'amount of pilfering' which goes on. Clearly 'pilfering' seems conceptually correlated to accessibility but why should the correspondence be one–one? Is it not possible that supermarkets with the same level of pilfering may have different levels of accessibility? The answer to this must depend on how the definition of 'accessibility' is to be used. Its use lies in being able to predict some other variable, which may then be controlled. If we are trying to control 'pilfering' then the above definition is valueless. What is probably in mind is a set of special variables, which can be measured and used as layout and design features of the supermarket.

(12) In the problem of Figure 46, we again meet the problem of definition of such things as quality and service. We have discussed the problem of a satisfactory definition of quality of a single item. Let us now turn to the problem of defining overall quality.

Let us suppose that we have, however, to our satisfaction, established a satisfactory definition of individual quality in terms of scale of defects. Let us suppose that, on some scale of defects, we have a distribution of defects given by Figure 51, representing 'overall quality' of the total product.

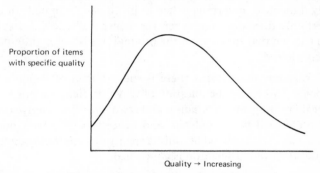

Quality → Increasing

Figure 51. Distribution of quality

How are we then to define 'overall quality'? The following are possibilities:

A_q: Average defect level;
$(AW)_q$: Average weighted defect level;
P_q: Proportion with defect level $\geqslant c$.

A_q is a simple average; $(AW)_q$ tries to incorporate the fact that the effects of different defect levels are different; P_q reflects the wish to keep defect levels above a critical level. Which is right? Different answers may result in different decisions.

Similarly if we examine service, for an individual, this might be in terms of delay in delivery. If we have Figure 52, similar to Figure 51, how do we measure 'overall service'?

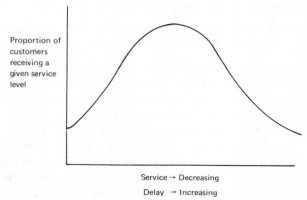

Service → Decreasing

Delay → Increasing

Figure 52. Distribution of service

As with quality, we have several possibilities, the choice of which may influence our bonus decision:

A_s: Average delay;

$(AW)_s$: Average weighted delay;

P_s: Proportion with delay $\leqslant c$.

(13) Much discussion has taken place on the definition of 'pleasure' and 'pain' in the context of hedonism, to no real avail. Nonetheless we spend considerable money in the health services on drugs whose only effect, in some cases, will be to reduce pain. The rationalization of this aspect within the other aspects of the health services requires that some definition be eventually found.

(14) In the thermal insulation contracting industry contract estimates involve consideration of 'site accessibility' and of 'intricacy' of work. It is tackled subjectively and a standardized estimating system would require that these concepts be defined.

Further examples of the questionable nature of definitions may be found in the general area of productivity measurement where ratios of expressions are suggested, the meaningfulness of which is not defined.

There are some circumstances in which conceptually accepted, but inadequately defined, variables arise, and where there is some choice as to whether or not one should define them in a given context.

Consider, for example, the variables q, g, o of Figure 42 where we have:

$$q \to g \to o$$

If we are really only interested in the $g \to o$ relationship, then why should we bother to define g, particularly when this presents difficulties?

If several variables influence customer goodwill then knowledge of the $g \to o$ relationship would be helpful.

Thus, instead of having to determine (see Figure 42)

$$l \to o, \quad q \to o,$$

we could determine

$$\begin{array}{c} l \searrow \\ \quad g \to o \\ q \nearrow \end{array}$$

We see that if it were possible to agree on a universal definition of goodwill, g, and if we could find objective ways of relating goodwill, g, to orders, o, this could be an objective part of the model. It may be that the relationships between service, l, and g, and between quality, q, and g, could be estimated subjectively, and combined with the objective method relating g to o, to provide the total relationships required.

If there exists a general theory of customer goodwill then this could be used to provide a submodel of the main model. If this theory were accepted as having more substance than a subjective assessment might give, then this may add to the acceptance of the model. If the whole exercise is done subjectively then one might readily question the need to use the variable g at all.

In considering the definition of variables, we do have a choice as to what we do. It may be thought that no definition exists for a given variable, but this then leads to ambiguities in meaning and hence inhibits logical analysis. It may be thought that it is not worthwhile to define the variable, in the light of economic resources needed and benefits from such definition. This provides one of the methodological issues of Decision Analysis which is unexplored. Reference to Figure 37 should be made, where the representation problem is portrayed.

The reader should see Cooper, Leavitt and Shelly[28] who discuss problems of definition of behavioural factors, which provide our greatest difficulty in constructing models.

C   SUBJECTIVE MEASUREMENTS

When it comes to measuring variables the subjective method must not be underestimated. The argument so far is that measurements exist in principle but may be difficult to determine. Initial subjective methods often provide a motive for more refined methods when the value of the study can be demonstrated in principle on this basis.

Example

Dick[35] discusses research, its measurement and the factors influencing this.

In measuring the success of a project, the following variables were used:

(a) potential benefit;
(b) the probability that the research would be successful in attaining the perceived research results;
(c) the probability that the results would be used.

Subjective levels of success were used, on a subjective scale, *viz.*:

1 very good; 2 above average; 3 average; 4 below average; 5 poor.

In identifying the variables influencing success the following were chosen:

(a) adequacy of definition of project;
(b) origin of project (e.g. project leader);
(c) difficulty;
(d) ability of research worker;
(e) research skills;
(f) subject knowledge (relative to project).

All of these were subjectively measured and a points scale was used.

It must be realized that there are dangers in doing this sort of thing. If the subjective measures are taken to be surrogates for more realistic measures, it is quite possible that they might not match these well. On the other hand, to pursue the problem of measurement further could be very expensive and difficult. There is again a clear choice facing the analyst. It is to be noted that we could argue that the decisions ensuing will at least be compatible with the subjective judgements or that, without some subjective assessment, we have no means of ascertaining the magnitude of potential system performance, and that such a procedure might at least give us some idea of this which might then lead to further more objective studies. We return to this point when we study the determination of relationships.

2.2.3.2   IDENTIFICATION OF RELATIONS

We will now deal with a variety of aspects of the identification of relationships between subsets of variables which we have provisionally identified. It must be borne in mind that there is an interrelationship between the two identification processes, as is indicated in Figure 49, and, in particular, that a failure to identify particular sorts of relationship may be because the variables identified are inappropriate or inappropriately defined. Once again this aspect will become easier the more we are able to identify and successfully describe and resolve particular types of decision situation.

The aspects we will now cover are:

A. Causality;
B. Ultimate certainty;
C. Principle of simplicity, Occam's razor;
D. Explanatory *vs.* statistical models;
E. Synthesis, comparison and experimentation;
F. Input effort, output value and data;
G. Subjective content of model building;
H. Reversibility of relationships.

A   CAUSALITY

(i) *Forms of Causality*

The sorts of relations which arise in Decision Analysis are referred to as:

(α) deterministic causal;
(β) partial deterministic causal;
(γ) probabilistic causal;
(δ) correlation non-causal.

Let us confine ourselves to functional relations.

(α) *Deterministic Causal.* Given x, then y is predetermined; e.g. x might be a production programme, y might be manpower requirement.

(β) *Partial Deterministic Causal.* Given x, then $y \in R(x)$; e.g. $l(x) \leqslant y \leqslant u(x)$.

(γ) *Probabilistic Causal.* Given x, then y has a known probability; e.g. $p(y = Y/x) = p(Y, x)$.

(δ) *Correlation Non-causal.* Given x, y there is a variable z such that z is causally related to x, z is causally related to y; thus we might have Figure 53.

Figure 53. A non-causal correlation

(ii) Case when x is a Possible Control Variable

The difference between $((\alpha), (\beta), (\gamma))$ and (δ) is that in (α), (β), (γ) we can, to some extent, control y by controlling x, whereas in (δ) we cannot control y by controlling x.

Example

If y is run-out frequency, and x is re-order quantity, then controlling x will control y.

(iii) Case when x is not a Possible Control Variable

Examples

(1) We have the present controversy centring around smoking, x, being related to lung cancer, y; it has been suggested that there may be a personal characteristic causing both x and y. Thus we might have Figure 54.

Figure 54. Smoking and lung cancer

In the absence of evidence to the contrary, controlling x may not control y.

(2) It might be observed that maintenance frequency, x, is associated with breakdown rate, y. However, it may be that job interest, z, influences both x and y and hence we may have Figure 55.

Figure 55. Maintenance and breakdowns

(3) It was observed that undernourishment, y, was associated with amount of soot, x, in the atmosphere; however, it was found that the income group, z, influenced the amount of food, f, a person could afford, and also the area, a, in which he could afford to live. Thus we have Figure 56.

Figure 56. Soot and undernourishment

We could not control undernourishment by controlling soot fall (see Ackoff[1]).

(4) It was observed that candy consumption, x, was associated with marriage rate, y; however, age group, z, was related to marriage rate, y, and was also related to candy consumption, x. Thus we have Figure 57.

Figure 57. Candy consumption and marriage rate

Quite obviously we cannot control the marriage rate by controlling the candy consumption.

(5) It has been stated that 'the better relations are between Operational Researcher and Management, then the more likely implementation will result'. However, this does not mean that 'better relations will increase the chance of implementation in a given situation'. It may be that Management are initially sympathetic to Operational Research, z, and this in itself results in good relations, y, and in implementation, x. We might have Figure 58.

Figure 58. Implementation and good relations

(6) Chernoff and Moses[23] give an example of the monotonic increasing relationship between the speed, x, of a runner and their ability, y, to spell. However, both of these attributes tend to increase with age, z, up to a point, and hence age may be a linking variable, as given in Figure 59.

Figure 59. Running speed and spelling ability

Needless to say, as also is the case with Example 4, age is not a causal variable itself.

Blalock[13] and Simon[118] have very good discussions of causality.

(iv) Predictive Use of a Correlation Analysis

In this case a correlation may be admissible within the context of the analysis.

Examples

(1) In Example 3, if we wanted to find out exactly how much malnutrition there was in a given area we could take soot fall and the correlation relation known to exist.

(2) In Example 1, if we needed to know how much lung cancer there would be in a given area we could just look at the average smoking level.

(3) In order to estimate distances in a location problem, a correlation between 'as crow flies' and 'actual' may be useful.

Figures of between 1·1 and 1·2 were used for the ratio of 'actual distance' to 'crow distance'.

(4) In a recent study of refuse collection, the basic model was of the form:

$$T = \frac{\alpha\beta}{n} + \gamma b$$

where: $T \equiv$ trip collection time; $n \equiv$ number of men on vehicle; $b \equiv$ number of bins in trip.

However, it was difficult to determine b. It was easy to determine $h \equiv$ number of houses, and since this was reasonably correlated with b, h was used as a predictor for T.

(5) In a study of orthotic services, it was required to estimate the demand for orthotic appliances. The absence of records, or the inappropriate form of the records, made direct estimation of demand difficult. It was not just a case of taking a sample of hospitals and multiplying up, because it was suspected that the demand would not just depend on hospital size. Demand was considered to be more related to the incidence of ailments in an area, and this was expected to vary from area to area. The study then reduced to determining such correlate ailments, to sampling a few hospitals to find the correlation between such ailments and demand, and then to measuring total demand by measuring total ailments and using the correlation analysis.

(6) Weiss[142] states that if the cities of a country are ranked in terms of size, then an empirically approximate formula for population size is given by:

$$\text{Population} \sim P_1/j^a$$

where j is the rank of a specific city.

(7) In a recent study of ambulance services, it was required to determine the geographical distribution of patients. It was found that the location and size of schools could be used as an indicator of this distribution.

(v) Decision Context of Relationships

In all cases, care must be taken in the interpretation of a relation between variables, which often leads to the misuse of statistics. Consider the following example.

Example

It was on record that males (M) caused $x\%$ of all road accidents, (A), whereas they constituted $y\%$ of all road drivers, with $x > y$. Inference: females (F) safer than males (M).

However, what we really want is a relation of the form:

$$M \xrightarrow{\text{Condition } C} A \text{ with probability } P_M(C)$$
$$F \xrightarrow{\text{Condition } C} A \text{ with probability } P_F(C)$$

A further investigation may show that the conditions, C, under which females drive are the most favourable (short distances at restricted low speeds on straight roads). Hence it would be incorrect to infer that females are safer under any conditions. This stresses the need to be able to recognize pertinent factors not evident in the original data. These factors will usually arise in the light of the decisions to be taken on the basis of the analysis. Thus are we considering that all lorry drivers should be female?

(vi) Causality and Forecasting

Although it is dangerous to incorporate too many variables in an effort to forecast, the search for causal factors which are more predictable, together with their effects, may be more reliable, if more costly, than trying to use mathematical forecasting procedures of the extrapolation kind.

Examples

(1) Horwath[61] suggests that, in trying to forecast the needs for hospital buildings, we may look at road accidents. These are a function of population growth (predictable, within reason) and accident prevention measures (the trends of which are known). Using these two causal factors a better forecast of road accidents may be made than use of exponential smoothing, say. Naturally it is only really useful when the trends referred to are relatively new.

(2) Wold[154] mentions the introduction of antibiotics in the mid-1940s which was a new factor in the mortality trends. Such changes introduce discontinuities in trends.

(3) In the nuclear power station industry, the problem of forecasting the operational availability of newly installed operating power stations is a difficult one. One might look at the history of past designs of power stations and try to use any trend to forecast the availability of the new design. On the other hand, as operational experience is gained then this information may also be used. Some Bayesian approach may be possible involving also a learning mechanism. Alternatively, one might make use of the knowledge of the physics of the new design to forecast availability. This may contain considerable work, however, even if possible and, in addition, the uncertainties may even be larger than using a non-explanatory statistical approach.

(4) Forecasts might be made dependent on knowledge of decisions which influence the actual outcome. Smith[123] draws our attention to the need for good judgement, in forecasting, as to the nature of policy changes which might take place and influence, for example, the demand for manpower.

(5) Flagle[45] points out the changing criteria in the Health Services arising from an ongoing concern with the rights of men to medical care. Since the change in

such rights will influence the demand for services, consideration of the evolution of such rights will be relevant to forecasting such demand.

The problems of causality, identification of variables and forecasting are inextricably intertwined. We can formally present a general aspect of this inter-relationship as follows. It will be seen that some of the previous examples give good illustrations of this, e.g. the diagnostic example in which considerable choice of variables exists and in which probabilistic predictability is a function of such choice.

Any object can be described in many ways. If we subject such an object to an environment, e, then it will exhibit a behaviour, $b(e)$, which may, or may not, be deterministic.

Suppose, for a certain behaviour variable b, there exist functions $e_1(b)$, $e_2(b)$, . . ., $e_n(b)$ such that $e_1(b)$, $e_2(b)$, . . ., $e_n(b) \equiv e(b)$ implies b, i.e. a deterministic causal system.

Then $b = f(e_1, e_2, ..., e_n)$.

However, in general, we do not know e_1, . . ., e_n. We choose surrogates z_1, . . ., z_m which we feel are 'good' predictors of b.

However, z_i will itself be a function of $(e_1, ..., e_n)$. The $\{z_i\}$ may be a subset of e_1, . . ., e_n.

Now, for a specific $(z_1, ..., z_m) = z$ there will be a region of $(e_1, ..., e_n)$ which will give z in general.

Thus if e_1, . . ., e_n have a probability distribution function $F(e_1, ..., e_n)$ we can determine probability $(b/z_1, ..., z_m)$, viz.,

$$\sum_{e_1, ..., e_n} \text{probability } (b/e_1, ..., e_n) \text{ probability } (e_1, ..., e_n/z)$$

Thus the measurement process involving z_1, . . ., z_m is a probabilistic causal process. In general we would like $z \equiv (e_1, ..., e_n)$ but do not know this.

Note that any set z_1, . . ., z_m are permissible. They are arbitrary, but their predictive power has to be examined.

It is interesting to note that the poorer the prediction, the longer we need to observe to determine the precise predictive power. The more deterministic, then the quicker we can substantiate relationships. Thus an attempt to 'explain' is predictive in validation effort.

Also we face the problem of invariance of relationships with time which is related to the problem of 'sufficiency' of conditions. Poorly predictive results may arise because of lack of invariance with time but, also, because of insufficiency of identification of the appropriate $\{z_i\}$ variables.

In considering causality and forecasting it must be remembered that a forecast,

Figure 60. Influence of forecast on behaviour

being the provision of information in a given context, can influence the outcome itself via a feedback mechanism, and, indeed, may itself be a major factor influencing the final outcome. Figure 60 illustrates this.

Examples

(1) Simon[118] discusses the bandwaggon effect of forecasting in the political sphere. In this case we have outcome $x = g(f)$, f is forecast. If we wish to find the forecast f which fulfils itself, we solve the equation $f = g(f)$.

(2) In forecasting the performance of a production system, since the operators know what is expected, they can work harder or less hard to meet the forecast performance, within limits. Clearly again the effect of the forecast on the actual outcome is important.

B ULTIMATE CERTAINTY

One problem we meet arises from the belief in the ultimate certainty of relations if enough variables are introduced. All our relations are based on past evidence, or experiment, and are, therefore, finitely based. With the variety of variables available at any one time we can determine a 'perfect fit' relation by bringing in enough variables (see Gruenberger[48]).

Examples

(1) In inventory control we could assume a relation of the form:

$$d_n = f(d_{n-1})$$

where f is a polynomial of degree equal to one less than the number of observations; of course, we might find that the next demand violated this. We can then simply do the same thing again with one further observation to fit. This is not 'scientific explanation' in any sense. The choice of functional form has to come from some knowledge of the nature of the system concerned, i.e. we must try to understand the demand mechanism.

The above approach becomes even more suspect if we try to relate, say, demand to a wide variety of environmental factors, such as likelihoods of elections, balance of payments, and so on, for, providing we introduce enough of them, we can get a certainty relation, which may, however, be violated at the next observation.

(2) In a recent transport study, a relationship between vehicle costs and age of vehicle was sought. It has been postulated that the incidence of repair operations was Poisson, and that there was a linear relationship between age t, and cumulative costs, $C(t)$ of the form

$$C(t) = \alpha e^{kt} + \varepsilon$$

However, there was no explanation of such cost behaviour, and an attempt to fit regression curves must be carefully considered. It might equally well be true that if $c(t)$ is the cost in period t, then

$$c(t) = \beta e^{\gamma t} + \varepsilon$$

and these two models are not compatible.

Similar remarks apply to the Poisson assumption, although the existence of random damages, etc., gives some plausibility to it in the past. Nevertheless, without some supporting argument, such an approach must be considered carefully.

In the above example there is also the question of explaining the ε term. It may be just a residual term of an unexplained nature. On the other hand it may be a genuine random input to the system arising from accidents. In this latter sense the model could be precise. In the former sense it is imprecise. The approach to handling the statistical element may well differ in either case and a choice of procedure must therefore depend on a deeper understanding of the problem.

One of the dangers in the above problem is that an attempt might be made to remove the error term by adding further parts to the model, even though the error is a natural random term. This danger is pointed out by Bross[19] when referring to the complex epicyclic framework which the Ptolemaics build up to explain the differences between predicted and actual planetary behaviour.

Blalock[13] says

'But empirically minded quantitative sociologists sometimes in effect endorse an anti theoretical position by throwing numerous variables into a regression equation with the idea of selecting out a subset which explains the most variance. To be sure, this kind of dragnet approach is often useful as an exploratory device, or as an insurance in case most of the variables thought to be important turn out to be only weakly related to the dependent variables. But beyond this it can hardly be judged an efficient procedure given the limitless number of variables that can usually be brought into the picture.'†

However, despite this supportable point of view, we have no methodology which helps alleviate this problem in any way.

See Strauss[29] in which the attempt to find 'exactness' by including an 'infinite' number of points (by going back far enough) is frowned upon. We look for representations with few variables, which leads us to the following principle.

C   PRINCIPLE OF SIMPLICITY, OCCAM'S RAZOR

It is an established principle of such scientific investigations to look for a few governing factors and to invoke the 'principle of simplicity'. The error terms will not be zero but they may be acceptable.

To be able to determine simple relationships we need to understand the workings of the system with which we are dealing.

Examples

(1) In building a model of demand for whisky in a given year, we understand the seasonal variations because we know the occasions, and their occurrences, which will influence such demand, and hence our model will simply relate demand to time of the year, and not look for complicated interrelationships between series of demands.

† Hubert M. Blalock, Jr., *Theory Construction: From Verbal to Mathematical Formulations*, 1969. Reprinted by permission of Prentice-Hall, Inc., Englewood Cliffs, New Jersey.

(2) In Example 1 of Section B, the choice of variables to use is part of the problem of variable identification and depends largely on an awareness of rough characteristics of the variations of, say d_n, in relation to d_{n-1} and d_{n-2}, say. It may be that enough is understood about the system to accept such a simple description, even though the consequential error may be larger than if we worked in terms of larger series.

The reason for such relationships to be valid may arise directly from knowledge of the ways in which customers plan their own production. Thus if the customers plan ahead, then d_{n-1} and d_{n-2} might give a measure of stock on order, and this might be corrected for anticipated usage, u, present stock levels, s, which might be random variables, and we might find $d_n = A - d_{n-1} - d_{n-2} + u - s$, where s, u may vary according to the circumstances of the customer at the time of placing his order d_n, and be largely independent of this particular supplier.

D EXPLANATORY vs. STATISTICAL MODELS

In the above section we have touched upon the problem of statistical description vs. understanding, which is a central problem in any scientific study. In attempting to understand relationships, we try to explain the relationship in terms of simpler postulates. Of course these postulates themselves have to be validated and may have to be subjected to statistical validation themselves. If they are already accepted, then it adds more confidence to the acceptance of a hypothesis based upon them than would a straight statistical study (see Figure 49).

The method by which we begin with postulates and build up a model, test it and estimate parameters is referred to by Blackett[12] as an 'a priori method', which is the same as an 'explanatory method'.

Examples

(1) Blackett[12] mentions that a statistical model indicated that large convoys were safer than small ones. However, because of possible large statistical errors, they were hesitant to recommend the introduction of larger convoys on this basis. An explanation of why large convoys should be safer was sought, and found, and the appropriate action recommended (see Figures 61, 62).

The following postulates seemed to be acceptable:

(a) the probability of a U-boat seeing a convoy is independent of the convoy size;
(b) the probability of a U-boat penetrating the escorts is dependent on the linear escort density;
(c) the expected number of ships in the convoy sunk is independent of the convoy size once the escort is penetrated.

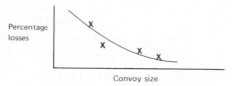

Figure 61. Statistical study

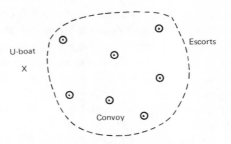

Figure 62. Explanatory study

Thus, for a fixed linear density, the expected number of ships sunk is independent of the convoy size. Hence the proportion sunk is inversely proportional to the convoy size.

(2) Blackett mentions Lanchester's laws as being of the *a priori* kind. Thus if $x(t)$, $y(t)$ represent the levels of enemy forces at any point in time, the following equations form the basis of a potential explanation of dynamic behaviour:

$$\dot{x} = ax - by$$
$$\dot{y} = cy - dx$$

(3) In a certain inventory ordering situation, the previous orders $x_1, x_2, \ldots, x_n$ placed were known, the previous supplies $s_1, s_2, \ldots, s_n$ were known, and the previous requirements $r_1, r_2, \ldots, r_n$ were known.

An attempt was made to produce a regression model of s_n on $x_n, x_{n-1}, x_{n-2}, \ldots, x_1, s_{n-1}, s_{n-2}, \ldots, s_1$. However, this was arbitrary and some attempt to understand the situation was needed.

In reality we have:

$$x_n = \pi(x_{n-1}, x_{n-2}, \ldots, x_1; s_{n-1}, s_{n-2}, \ldots, s_1; r_n, r_{n-1}, \ldots, r_1),$$
$$s_n = \phi(x_n, x_{n-1}, \ldots, x_1).$$

ϕ is the supply function; π is the decision function. We can reduce these to:

$$x_n = \alpha(r_n, r_{n-1}, \ldots, r_1),$$
$$s_n = \beta(r_n, r_{n-1}, \ldots, r_1).$$

A relationship between s_n and $x_n, x_{n-1}, \ldots, x_1, s_{n-1}, s_{n-2}, \ldots, s_1$ exists but it is confounded with π which we may wish to change. We need the relationship ϕ, in some form, and we may be able to estimate parameters from knowledge of observations on the variables concerned.

(4) In manpower planning one can try to forecast availability of manpower by extrapolation techniques. However, an effort to understand the dynamics of the system might give more predictive models. Thus if $\mathbf{x}(t)$ represents the state of the system at any point in time, with $x_i(t)$ being the category i level of manpower, we may have a dynamic equation of the form:

$$\dot{\mathbf{x}}(t) = T\mathbf{x}(t) + \mathbf{z}(t)$$

where $\mathbf{z}(t)$ is input at time t and, together with T, will be a function of policy.

(5) In a study of the demand for tyres (see Kendrick[69]) an extrapolative

technique was not adopted. The demand for tyres was seen to be dependent on the distribution of sales of cars over a period of time and details of these sales were made dependent variables in the model.

(6) In a hospital study the problem arose as to the availability of beds at a given point a few days ahead. This was necessary for an admissions procedure. Again extrapolation techniques have limited use. Given the present mix of patients and the durations of stay to date, it is possible to produce a probability distribution of the bed state a few days ahead, using the probability distributions of durations of stay.

Thus, if $P_i(s)$ is the probability that an ith category patient will have a total duration of stay equal to s, and he has already been in hospital t days, then the probability that he will leave $(s - t)$ days from now is:

$$P_i(s/t) = \frac{P_i(s)}{\sum_{w > t} P_i(w)}$$

(7) In a recent study in the shipbuilding industry a student had to find a simpler means of estimating the work content of specific units of a ship. His first attempt was at a purely statistical model with no explanatory content, other than that one variable seemed important, $viz.$, area. He began with the model:

$$T = kA^n + \varepsilon, \qquad\qquad \textbf{A}$$

and found the minimum variance solution.

The thought then struck him that if perhaps he took logs, it might help and he reduced it to

$$\log T = nk \log A + \log \varepsilon \qquad\qquad \textbf{B}$$

This was incorrect, if the first equation was right, since then the second would be

$$\log T = nk \log A + \log\left(1 + \frac{\varepsilon}{kA^n}\right)$$

$$\simeq nk \log A + \varepsilon/kA^n \qquad\qquad \textbf{C}$$

But then, why should we not have started with **B** in any case, since we had no less reason for **B** than for **A**?

This then led to a search for an explanatory model in idealized cases, and this gave

$$T = \alpha\sqrt{(AP)} + \beta\sqrt{A}, \qquad\qquad \textbf{D}$$

where P was a second parameter.

This was then generalized to cover less idealized cases by fitting the model

$$T = \alpha\sqrt{(AP)} + \beta\sqrt{A} + \varepsilon. \qquad\qquad \textbf{E}$$

Even this was not perfect, since the error involved actually came into the A, P expression in a complex way and $\varepsilon = \varepsilon(A, P, k, c)$ where k, c were other parameters. Nonetheless, it was much more satisfactory than the first arbitrary attempts and one had much more confidence in **E** than in **A**.

Wold[154] distinguishes between 'descriptive' and 'explanatory' models. He states that the model 'more fertilizer → higher yield' is an explanatory one. The model could be a straight statistical description, or it could be explanatory if it could be deduced from other models. Thus if it is known that ingredient x produces a higher yield and that the fertilizer contains x, and no other influencing ingredients, then 'more fertilizer → higher yield' can be explained.

The fact that laws may be unexplained may in no way reduce their value, but may reduce our confidence in their invariance.

Examples

The Pareto law that 'wealth will be distributed in a certain way' is not yet explained. Neither is Newton's law of gravitation explained. But they are accepted and used.

Ehrenberg[40] discusses modelling in marketing. He sees two situations:

(a) that in which the scientist knows something and wants to model it;
(b) that in which the scientist knows nothing about a system and wishes to model that, which he describes as scientification of non-knowledge, i.e. SONKING.

In the latter context he indicates his reservations against significance testing for null hypotheses:

'. . . statistical significance merely means that there is a good chance of a number being different from zero. One should not exaggerate the worthwhileness of a coefficient simply because it differs from zero.'

Presumably what he is saying is that there are many other models, and even many with this form and non-zero parameter, and we are simply excluding one model with one level of this coefficient (equal to zero).

He then goes on to state three possible approaches to getting a model of television viewing:

(a) hypothesize comprehensive stochastic model in the absence of knowledge of viewing patterns (*a priori* method);
(b) multivariate statistical analysis, using a selection of all complex factors which are thought to influence viewing;
(c) search for generalized law-like relationships (simple laws describing specific aspects).

For example: $d_{st} = k r_s r_t$ where d_{st} is audience who view at time s on day 1 and at time t on day 2; r_s, r_t are ratings.

In the marketing area (brand switching) he gives illustrations of (a), (b), (c):

(a) attempt to use Markov theory, brand switching, repeat buying, with no real evidence initially;
(b) explain things by multiple regression;
(c) 'look and see' approach for patterns (laws), such as 'average number of units bought by new buyers is constant', or 'proportion of repeat buyers is a function of average units purchased'.

In some cases it is believed that certain patterns of behaviour are probabilistic but changing. This gives rise to difficulties in validation and in estimation. One approach is to specify explanatory models specifying the probabilities at any point in time in terms of functions of system states at that time, and to estimate the parameters from the observed behaviour. This approach has been taken in a marketing study in which consumers can change their probabilities of choice of products as a function of certain state variables.

The difficulty with this approach is that since many 'explanatory' models may describe the same pattern of behaviour, to within specified error limits, we may have no real basis for choosing any one such model. Some further substantiation of the explanatory model is needed outside its comparison with behaviour.

In some situations it is felt that there is no explanatory derivation of hypotheses on which other observed data is superimposed to seek out a single hypothesis, or is used for statistical decision theory analyses, and that all we can do is to re-generate the actual events as they happened, in a simulation process, and base our decisions on performance as it would have been under the alternative policies. While accepting the central difficulty with the 'hypothesis' method, if an underlying hypothesis did exist, the data might not adequately reflect this and poor policy decisions could be made. As a stronger point, one might argue that there is no reason to believe that any invariant hypothesis exists.

Example

In the fishing industry, data was available on catch rates by various skippers in various areas at various times. No theory was available to formulate a hypothesis about the statistical nature of catch rates, and the original data, with a sampling mechanism, was used as input to a simulation.

Although, in relatively new situations, one is always faced with the problem of hypothesis generation, it is possible that the cumulative evidence from a wide variety of similar problem areas might indicate very strongly a common hypothesis. This is another reason why an attempt to characterize decision situations is very useful.

Example

In hospital emergency problems it is often taken as likely that the patterns of emergencies are Poisson at any time of day. It is possible that the combined evidence from many different areas would very strongly support this and it might not be possible to think of any other hypothesis which would lead to higher support.

We must therefore be aware of the dangers inherent in routine statistical analyses whose analysis presupposes hypotheses the origin of which is unsubstantiated. Ideally, statistical analysis should lead to a search for other support for any such selected hypotheses. Naturally, as has been indicated, this support itself will have been statistically verified, and we simply push the problem back one stage. Nonetheless the added confidence arising from such support is greater than would be achieved by further, limited, collection of data to be used with the original statistical analyses. This is related to the process of synthesis discussed in the next section. It is also related to the hierarchical theory of theory construction as discussed by Margeneau,[78] in which he demonstrates that certain theories can explain subtheories. In doing so, these give more confidence to the lower-level theories.

Having raised these cautionary remarks we realize that if we are to develop a theory we need some hypotheses and somewhere along the line of continuous thought they must be stated. In some areas, notably physics, the ability to conjure up theores, to be subsequently tested against observations, has been highly successful. Coleman[27] quotes Maxwell, *viz.*,

'. . . investigations of molecular science have proceeded for the most part by postulating hypotheses and comparing deductions from these hypotheses with fact'.

This is the reverse of the process arising in Blackett's convoy size example. Tocher[136] gives three sources of inadequacy in models:

(a) The mechanism of real world is not understood and the empirical relations are only valid in a given range of experience; extrapolation is dangerous.

Example

In forecasting the demand for a service, the time series extrapolation analysis makes no attempt to study the underlying principles governing this trend. The forecast could be wildly out within a few years, but if the real mechanics and their trends had been studied better estimates may have arisen, e.g. in marketing models, dynamic explanatory models may be necessary instead of statistical extrapolation.

(b) The mechanism is understood, but the parameters are uncertain.

Examples

(1) Opportunity costs are understood but no measures exist.

(2) The effect of a bonus scheme on company and foremen can be modelled and understood, but the precise parameters are unknown.

(3) The mechanism giving rise to smaller populations of ships lost as convoy size increases are understood, but the precise parameter is not known (Blackett[12]).

(c) Random future events (presumably a question of identifying and catering for these) are part of the uncertainty problem.

E   SYNTHESIS, COMPARISON AND EXPERIMENTATION

In some problems there is an element of choice as to whether the effect of certain alternatives should be obtained by explanatory synthesis or obtained using a historical, or experimental, comparative approach; the answer depends on availability, or cost of, data and analysis.

Examples

(1) In determining the effect of ship design on profitability of operations, the comparative method would require the history of several different ships covering

the designs to be considered (or designs from which the effects of the proposed designs can be extrapolated). However, it may turn out that not enough different designs have been used to provide any reasonable basis of comparison. The problem is then tackled by getting data on catch rates, weather conditions, and building up a synthetic simulation which will enable the effects of different designs to be determined.

(2) In determining the effect of various maintenance policies on company performance, it may be that either few different policies have been used, and/or the conditions of operation are so different that no reliable basis of comparison is possible. The problem is then treated by getting data on component performance, work loads, etc., and synthesizing the total behaviour in terms of the maintenance policy components.

(3) Thomson[137] discusses the problem of determining the effects of certain factors on traffic flow rates. A very simple synthetic model gives

$$\mathbf{q} = \mathbf{f}(\mathbf{c}, t), \quad \mathbf{c} = \mathbf{g}(v), \quad v = h(\mathbf{q})$$

where $\mathbf{q}$, $\mathbf{c}$, t, v are, respectively, traffic flow rates, costs, tax and average speed. These relationships are the steady-state ones. To determine the required effect, of changing t, on $\mathbf{q}$, $\mathbf{c}$, v is not possible without experimentation and/or synthesis, since no experience exists for the changes being considered. If the first relationship can be obtained, say by survey, then the whole model can be synthesized, since the latter two relationships can be determined by logical analysis using appropriate assumptions.

(4) If we are concerned with changing the number of taxi licences, it may be that these have been fairly constant for some years. It may be that the demand for taxis depends on the expected waiting time, and hence we would need to estimate the effect of this on demand. In this case we can only experiment.

We then have three parts of the model to synthesize, *viz.*,

Waiting time = f (number of taxis, demand);
Demand = g (waiting time);
Profit = h (number of taxis, demand).

(5) Suppose we were concerned with determining the optimum training period for certain operators. Among other things we would need to know the influence of training period T on production wastage W. If we only had data on one training period we would have to decide how the relationship $W(T)$ was to be obtained. The ways open are:

(a) try to get data from other companies and make due allowance for the differences in circumstance; this is quick but subject to error;
(b) make a small change in T, get the differential dW/dT, and find the optimum in the region of T using this approximation; this might be slow and we would make changes on an evolutionary basis, but economic gains may be lost; this method is referred to by Blackett[12] as the 'variational method'; in such cases

we have no *a priori* understanding other than an assumption that a specific set of variables form the causal set; the general expression is given by:

$$dy = \left(\frac{dy}{dx_1}\right)dx_1 + \left(\frac{dy}{dx_2}\right)dx_2 + \cdots + \left(\frac{dy}{dx_n}\right)dx_n$$

where y is the variable to be controlled and x_1, x_2, . . ., x_n are the control variables; such approaches are used in the evolutionary control of chemical processes (Lowe[76]);

(c) find an explanatory form for W, and then experiment just enough to determine the parameters.

(6) In a paper by Dukes, Buckman and Dixson[39] the measurement of work carried out is raised and several measures are presented, *viz.*: (a) expenditure in work done; (b) times for a given job; (c) cost of materials used; (d) number of orders completed.

Difficulties arose because:

(i) in (a) there was a variation between authorities in costing methods and distributions of tradesmen;
(ii) in (b) variations arise from different travelling allowances, and accuracy of time sheets.

Things like this made comparisons of 'effectiveness' difficult, and hence the comparison of incentive schemes difficult.

It must not be overlooked that experimentation in a real life situation has costs associated with it because of its influence on the organization.

Example

In a study of the maintenance of buildings it was thought that a certain amount of directly employed labour would be beneficial in conjunction with contractual arrangements. However, because this is a real physical change, any experimentation may result in difficulties in reverting to the old system if it proves disadvantageous.

As Blackett[12] pointed out in the context of the convoy problem, and has been indicated in the refuse collection problem, one must ensure that a proper comparison is made during experimentation by ensuring that allowance is made for possible changes in various conditions. In order to be able to do this we need a model of the situation to account for the effect of the old and proposed alternatives with and without these changed conditions, otherwise the new one may appear to be better but may not be so.

Example

In the suggested change in building maintenance, by including directly employed labour, experimentation would need to be tested over a period of time. During this period other things can change, such as maintenance standards. The experimental system may appear better costwise but the standards may drop. One may not know what the effect of the old system might have been had these same standards been allowed. It might have been more valid to use a synthetic model to determine the cost performance of the new and old system under the various maintenance standards possible, than to experiment.

An extensive coverage of similar points can be found in Wall, Orcutt, Robinson, Suits, de Wolff.[139]

In the preceding discussion some difficulties arising in the context of experimentation in Decision Analysis have been raised. In addition, the discussion on testing of models will indicate that experimentation, at least via the implementation of the model, is not always appropriate. Morse,[93] however, states that 'Operations Research is an experimental science'. This is very idealistic, although some experimentation with parts of a model may be quite practicable.

F   INPUT EFFORT, OUTPUT VALUE AND DATA

It must be borne in mind that the effort put into deriving parametric values or relations must be geared to the value of the study and needs for fine examination. We shall return to this point in a later chapter.

Blackett[12] states that when data is scarce it may still be useful enough to draw conclusions. Thus it may well be that rough estimates of mean and variance indicate, with a considerable margin, which of two alternatives is best, without needing a mass of information to verify precise values. Where data is scarce and expensive, a tentative look at the dependence of the solution on this may be advisable.

The following quotation from Charles Babbage is relevant:

'Errors using inadequate data are much less than those using no data at all.'

One would find this difficult to justify formally, but the general meaning is clear.

Examples

(1) Certain costs may be very difficult to determine, e.g. storage or interest costs. The dependence of the solution on these must be examined prior to entering into such costly investigations.

(2) An interesting problem arose in the estimation of the manner in which annual costs of operation of buses vary with time, allowing for overhauls. One could make the assumption that

$$c(t) = a + bt + \varepsilon$$

irrespective of overhauls, if one had no further information. Only the total fleet costs for a year are known, and a, b can be estimated. The dependence of the solution on these estimates may then be examined prior to making a decision on the need for more detailed information.

G   SUBJECTIVE CONTENT OF DERIVATION OF RELATIONS

We have already mentioned the subjective element in problem formulation and in choosing variables, and the following examples will serve to stress the

128

subjective element in selection of hypotheses about relations. The real understanding of a situation may be helped or hindered by the subjective element.

In the introductory section we also mentioned the problem of representing, at
all, certain aspects in the model, and it is important to realize that non-formalized
judgements may be subjectively used alongside those aspects which we can more
easily formalize.

Examples

(1) Consider the bus overhaul example in Section F. After an overhaul, the
engineer knows that there is a drop-off in work done on a bus, which it is not

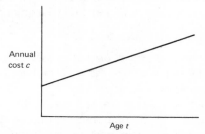

Figure 63. Original annual cost/age
function

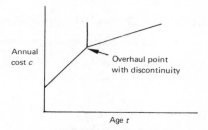

Figure 64. Subjectively adjusted annual cost/age function

possible to pick up in the routine data which deals with total fleet costs. An
estimate of this drop-off can be made, and the model adjusted.

The point is that the form chosen must depend on some other information than
that available in the records. Instead of having Figure 63 we have Figure 64.

In this instance the subjective element gives rise to a better understanding.

(2) In a problem concerned with setting aside an emergency unit, one advantage
stated was that the separation of waiting-list patients from emergency patients
would improve the efficiency of waiting-list scheduling by removing some of the
random input. It was clearly a difficult thing to measure the change in efficiency,
and hence the improved consequential waiting-list throughput. The approach
adopted was to estimate the throughput efficiency needed to break even with the
new system. The present throughput efficiency was known and the ability to

achieve the increase required was subjectively derived. It seemed clear that it was unlikely that the required throughput efficiency could be achieved.

(3) Another example arises in trying to estimate the deterrent effect on non-payment of bus fares by having specific numbers of inspectors on a bus route.

(4) In a recent study of intensive care units in a hospital, no data was available on the distribution or durations of stay to be expected in the new units. The physicians were asked to give subjective estimates of the average duration of stay for each diagnosis, and the total distribution was built up using actual data on the arrival patterns of each diagnosis.

(5) In a recent study of freighter terminals, the future pattern of traffic was unknown. Although the influence of solutions under various possible patterns is possible, the likely region must be obtained subjectively if extensive simulation is to be avoided.

(6) An organization had a mixed vehicle fleet. The question was raised as to how much more economic to operate was one type than another. Certain economic data was available. However, the reduction in variety could lead to an improvement in maintenance, but also to the risk of putting the organization in the hands of one supplier. Both of these factors were difficult to incorporate directly into the model.

(7) In the same problem, attempts to improve the utilization of vehicles raised the possibility of having different drivers on the same vehicle. It was strongly felt that 'one vehicle—one driver' resulted in a much better treatment of the vehicles, but it was difficult to justify.

In some problems lack of objective data can prevent a project being done since no motive may exist to press on to collect the data. However, if subjective judgements are incorporated, the results can then be used to provide a more objective estimate of the potential gains for the study which may then motivate the collection of objective statistics.

Examples

(1) In the building maintenance area there exists the problem of when to inspect various items. The objective of such an exercise is to detect deterioration before it reaches a costly critical phase. The data needed includes knowledge of the distribution of deterioration cycles of various items so that the effect of an inspection scheme may be seen. However, this data does not exist. The procedure adopted was to take various maintenance requests and to ask for subjective estimates of when the engineer felt that the defect would have first been noticeable, and what he felt the costs would be if it were left a further six months, for example. This data would be used in determining whether, in the light of these subjective estimates, processed in an objective manner, enough potential gain would exist to motivate objective collection of facts.

(2) Forrester[46] uses the subjective opinion of experts to derive relationships between variables in his world dynamics model. The lack of data and the urgency

of the matter make this, initially, necessary. The outputs of the model might then reflect the magnitude of anticipated behaviour and lead to the selection of parts which might then be treated more objectively. The model is therefore only a mechanism to provide evidence for selecting further work.

(3) In medical and engineering diagnostics, objective data might not exist for the probabilities of causes of specific symptoms. However, the experience of the surgeon or the engineer might be useful in establishing the probabilities on the basis of which the outputs of the model might be used to decide what objective studies should be carried out.

It must be stressed that the use of experts does have its dangers, as was pinpointed by Engel, Caywood, Berger, Magee, Miser and Thrall.[43] This was based on evidence submitted for the Anti-Ballistic-Missile programme, to which a large number of experts contributed. The paper notes that there was failure to agree even that differences could be pinpointed, and that the logic itself was inadequate. Nevertheless what real alternatives do we have in such situations? The same may well prove to be the case with Forrester's problem.

Northrop, Davis, Swanton and Merlin[97] discuss the use of experts in a detailed study, and stress the benefit of communication, leading to better understandings of data aspects, which the use of such judgements can bring.

H REVERSIBILITY OF RELATIONSHIPS

Wold[154] raises the question of whether relationships between variables are reversible.

Examples

(1) He uses as an example the income incentive relationship. In Figure 65, if we increase incentive, income will increase and we move from A to B. If we now reduce income target to the same level as at H we may need more incentive than before and arrive at point H'.

This is rather like the hysteresis loop in electromagnetics; it means that the relationship between variables may depend on the way in which we arrive at the various positions.

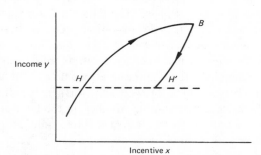

Figure 65.   Irreversible income/incentive
function

(2) The same question could be raised in Decision Theory when we consider the value of money.

Thus we might have Figure 66.

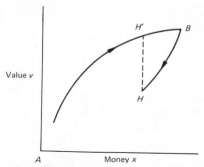

Figure 66. Irreversible value function

As we move from *A* to *B*, the value (using, say, von Neumann and Morgenstern's theory[138]) may increase. However, if we reduce the money to *H* we might find the value reduced below that of *H'*.

(3) Michael[85] mentions the Hawthorn experiment in which certain environmental factors were changed and productivity improved. On reverting to the original environmental factors the productivity was maintained. Thus the process was irreversible.

In essence this really means that the hypotheses are incomplete and that the basic needs are for a dynamic, rather than static, theory. Thus in the incentive/income example of Wold we might have the equation:

$$dy = f(\text{sign}(dx), x, y) \, dx$$

In the case of the money/value example it may mean that the value theory should reflect previous conditions in a dynamic manner and that reducing one's income from a position previously held has an undesirable effect.

2.2.4   Estimating and Testing for Models

Having identified and defined our variables, having identified the relations between the variables, we can now synthesize the overall model from its various components, unless we resort to the comparative or experimental methods in terms of the basic alternatives being examined.

Interwoven with these steps is the necessity to test the validity of the relations and of the particular values given to parameters in the model.

This is known as the 'Principle of Ontological Relativism' which states that all constructs should, if they are meaningful, be testable in principle.

It is necessary to point out that there are several sorts of testing, *viz.*:

(A) testing while the model is being built—*a priori* testing;
(B) testing on the basis of the outputs of the analysis;
(C) testing by implementation.

A SIMULTANEOUS BUILDING AND TESTING

In this case the model is synthesized from its components. The components may contain already validated variables and relationships, or they may be tested on the basis of existing data, or on the basis of setting up short-term experiments to be completed before the acceptance of any recommendations arising from the model.

Examples

(1) It may have already been established that new product time/demand profiles lie in a certain class, and data may exist to establish the particular parameters of a specific product. Testing is then replaced by estimating parameters, a point to which we shall return later.

(2) It may have been already established for other purposes that scrap rate bears a certain functional relationship to throughput rate, which will be used in the model. Testing has already been carried out.

(3) Extensive data may exist on past demand for a product, and it may remain to establish the time relationships to be used in the model. Testing is then equivalent to statistical validation of certain hypotheses.

(4) Forrester[46] builds a synthetic model relating the behaviour of several world variables such as population, investment and pollution. The knowledge of the components is subjectively derived and the 'testing' is inherent in the mutual acceptability of these relationships by experts in the field.

At this stage of testing we are not actually making primary decisions and observing the outcomes. This is additional testing to be discussed later on.

We see that such testing is intimately entwined with statistics, hypothesis testing and estimation and, although this subject matter is no less relevant to testing by implementation, it is worthwhile saying a little now about the philosophical nature of such subject matter at this stage. This will have a bearing on previously dealt with topics of variable and relationship identification. At the same time it will serve to emphasize the secondary decisions we implicitly take in our studies.

Examples

(1) Consider the following problem:

p: number of passengers;
t: calendar time;
f: fare;
Postulate $H: p = \alpha - \beta t - \gamma f + \varepsilon$;
$\varepsilon = N(0, \sigma^2)$

(a) In testing H, we may test: $H_0: \beta = 0$; $H_0': \gamma = 0$. Then:

   (i) H is only one of a given set of possibilities and the settling on H may be subjective;

(ii) the principle of testing is that we construct a statistic F (observations) and find probability $(F > N/\text{null hypotheses}) = p(F, N)$. This is making use of direct inference;

(iii) we set $p(F, N)$ at some level, say 0·05, and reject H if $F > N$;

(iv) this means that if H is true we have only a 5% chance of rejecting it. The philosophy is similar to that of errors of type I in sampling, dealt with in many books on Statistics (e.g. Davies[31]).

(b) In estimating β, we carry out the following steps:

(i) we may construct a statistic t, where

$$t = \frac{\beta - \hat{\beta}}{S}$$

where $\hat{\beta}$, S depend on observations;

(ii) for a given β, we can find $\varDelta$, ε, such that

$$\text{probability}\left\{-\varDelta \leqslant \frac{\beta - \hat{\beta}}{S} \leqslant \varDelta\right\} = \varepsilon$$

i.e. probability $\{\beta - \varDelta S \leqslant \hat{\beta} \leqslant \beta + \varDelta S\} = \varepsilon = 0\cdot95$, say;

(iii) if we then 'decide' that $\hat{\beta} - \varDelta S \leqslant \beta \leqslant \hat{\beta} + \varDelta S$, we will be correct 95% of the time, whatever the value of β.

We then need to determine the economic consequences of deciding that β lies in the range stipulated, when in fact it does not. In general, of course, the economic consequences depend on choosing a specific value of β when another value of β is true. We could use the rule of deciding that $\beta = \hat{\beta}$ and would then need to determine the probability of distribution of $\hat{\beta}$ given β. This would, however, require knowledge of the probability distribution of S and this depends on the unknown variance σ^2.

The important point is that statistical testing involves the use of an *a priori* statistical function in which we:

(i) choose the statements we wish to accept or reject;

(ii) choose the size of the risks we are prepared to accept in making incorrect statements;

(iii) choose the decision parameters accordingly.

We cannot talk in terms of the probability of a general hypothesis being true or false unless we have some *a priori* probabilities for the competing alternatives in the first place, and unless we make use of some large sample theory for approximation purposes (see de Groot[33]). Thus we cannot say 'probability $(\hat{\beta} - \varDelta S \leqslant \beta \leqslant \hat{\beta} + \varDelta S) = 0\cdot95$' unless we have some *a priori* probability distribution for β, and then we can use conditional probabilities as follows:

$$p(\beta/\text{observations}) = \frac{p(\text{observations}/\beta)\,p(\beta)}{\sum\limits_{\beta} p(\beta)\,p(\text{observations}/\beta)}$$

(2) In a problem involving very slowly moving inventory items, the use of

134

moving averages was considered. However, this was very unlikely to provide useful information. The problem could be treated from a Statistical Decision Theory point of view by considering the risks involved under various hypotheses and decision rules, based on data of demands and inventory levels.

As has been pointed out, and is relevant to the above two examples, we may have no reason to use any particular hypotheses. This may well be very serious for the passenger problem. In the case of the inventory control problem the possibility of using a Poisson approximation, with unknown mean, may be acceptable, but may, in principle, be equally unsupported as might be the linearity assumption in the first example.

Thus hypothesis testing and estimating are decision oriented and objective methods in no way reduce this feature. In principle we should evaluate the consequences, in relationship to the primary decision, of accepting specific hypotheses and estimates when other hypotheses and parametric values are, in fact, true.

Chernoff and Moses[23] give a useful discussion on the relationship between statistics and decision.

Bowen[15] discusses some of the problems of statistical methodology he has encountered, emphasizing the interdependence of the decision and the adequacy of data and hypothesis acceptance, stressing the need to try to establish prior reasons for considering specific types of distribution, and stressing the limited value of traditional significance testing.

In testing relationships there are certain barriers which we cannot transgress, *viz.*:

 (i) we can never prove general infinite deterministic empirical relations;
 (ii) we can only disprove general infinite deterministic empirical relations;
(iii) we can never prove nor disprove probabilistic relations.

As a result of this we recognize the Principle of Epistemological Relativism, which denies the existence of apodictic truth in empirical investigations, and the Principle of Perspective Relativism, which states that all empirical theories are relative to input hypotheses. These hypotheses themselves are not absolute. We can continue to regress in an attempt to explain hypotheses at one level by others at a higher level, but we always remain in a relative position, although we may gain more confidence by doing so.

Examples

(1) In example (2) of Section B we may begin with a general theory that d_n is related to d_{n-1} and d_{n-2} and try to fit the parameters. As has been suggested, the derivation of this theory may come from another theory such as one explaining an individual company's ordering procedure and developing a total model to cover all customers. The individual theory might postulate certain decision rules, but we cannot prove this theory, if only for the fact that we cannot examine all potential purchasers. We thus have:

Theory 1 $\rightarrow$ Theory 2 $\rightarrow \cdots$ process of explanation.

(2) In the explanation of the convoy size/loss relationship, the input postulates, or theories, are no less dependent on this principle. They may be intuitive, but nonetheless they have to be tested and are not absolute.

B TESTING ON THE BASIS OF THE OUTPUTS OF THE ANALYSIS

So far we have talked about testing the component relations and variables. However, there is another useful test which can be carried out, and that is the testability of consequences of a compounding of the relations. In the extreme case we may present the prescribed action to the decisionmaker and he may reject it automatically because it does not satisfy certain requirements (we discussed the determination of admissible actions in the problem formulation stage) in that the implied consequences were not acceptable.

This may arise because a consequence variable was omitted in the model building, which failed to be detected by the finiteness of the model building activity.

Examples

(1) The analyst did not realize that deterioration was a possible variable governing inventory control, and since he did not bring it up neither did the decisionmaker; it became evident when the average stock he recommended seemed very large.

(2) During a recent discussion on economic batch quantity the problem appeared to be trivial and an obvious solution was suggested. This did not satisfy the foreman because it conflicted with one aspect that neither he nor we had thought of mentioning; this was 'shortage of space' (items had two parts and it was necessary to run off one and hold in storage until the other had been run off).

It may arise because the relations used were dependent on conditions now about to be changed, but not discussed in the original model.

Examples

(1) The assumption of certain processing factors, or constraints, which were now about to be changed.

(2) The decisionmaker may know of certain radical changes in his order book not consistent with previous statistical history, such as in a workshops problem in which changes in work load were imminent. Thus the solution may become obviously not valid because the decisionmaker can see, quite readily, a better solution in the light of these changes.

The failure of the analyst to identify the correct variables and relations to use can easily produce solutions not acceptable for obvious reasons and hence this form of testing is useful, *viz.*, acceptability of solution or consequences.

It can, of course, be an expensive way of testing a model, since building the model can be expensive. Negative results at this end can only be avoided by a more rigorous investigation in the first place, although this may entail covering areas not, ultimately, relevant.

It is interesting to note that, if there is a conflict between intuition and the conclusion of the analysis, this should be testable as required by the Principle of Ontological Relativism. The reasons for the conflict should be sought out and these should result in the demonstration that certain assumptions in the model are wrong or that the decisionmaker was wrong. Intuition may be used as an instrument of control.

Example

In an inventory control problem, in which many thousands of items were kept, it seemed difficult to convince the executive principally concerned that ordering costs were very relevant. Intuitively he felt there was great scope for reducing stock without considering the order costs seriously. Eventually it was realized by the Decision Analyst that the real point was that the ordering procedure was a block procedure on which a list of orders was placed at the end of a period and that it was highly likely that, whatever the frequency of ordering for individual items, a block order covering several items would be placed in any case at the end of a period. The executive was thinking, quite correctly, in terms of the marginal ordering costs per item, whereas the Decision Analyst was thinking in terms of an individual item ordering cost. The ordering costs were still relevant in principle, but not very important in practice, since it was clear that considerable stock reductions could be made before such costs became influential.

C TESTING BY IMPLEMENTATION

Ideally the ultimate test arises from comparing actual with predicted results. However, this falls down for several reasons.

(α) *Optimality*

Testing for 'optimality', by implementation, falls down when:

(i) only one solution is actually implemented, hence allowing no comparison of all alternatives;

(ii) the subjective criterion approach is used, such as the 'best' combination of 'delays and costs', where 'best' is a subjective valuation.

There are two aspects of testing in case (ii):

(a) testing that the measurements made represent the preferences;

(b) testing that the preferences stated reflect the appropriate outcomes.

Case (a) simply falls within the ambit of the previous discussions in which the subject system becomes no different from the object system on an input–output behavioural descriptive basis.

Case (b) poses some difficulties. If the value judgements reflect uncertainties, we have the difficulty mentioned in case (δ) of this section. If this is not the case and, in principle, one can determine the eventual outcomes related to a value judgement, then some form of testing may exist, perhaps parallel to the method of testing probability estimation as suggested by Helmer[56] who considers the possibility of measuring a probability estimator's 'accuracy' and 'reliability' in a class of problems which may physically be quite distinct. Thus, in the value case, one might determine in a sample of situations how actual outcomes are ranked relative to the initial judgements.

Example

In inventory control the decisionmaker may make judgements on the relative ranking of combinations, (c, r), of cost and run out probability. His judgements may be describable by a function $v(c, r) = v_0 - \lambda c - \mu r$. The '$\mu$' factor then reflects some real monetary consequences of running out of stock. An examination of the system might establish some actual monetary consequences arising from run-outs (such as premium purchasing, lost production time). On this basis it may be seen that μ is a good or a bad estimate.

A similar approach in other situations may give some idea as to whether the judgement ability of the decisionmaker is good or bad.

(β) *Faithfulness of Implementation*

There is the possibility that implementation will not be carried out faithfully.

Examples

(1) In a hospital study of a new intensive care unit, it was stated that certain patients would use it and would stay in it a certain time. If this policy is changed on implementation, the results may be invalid.

(2) In a study of a new berth for container loading and unloading it was stated that certain procedures for loading and unloading would be used. If this policy is changed, the solution may not be valid.

Naturally one can argue that the test was fair and that the model was invalid since it did not represent the true situation. However, the changes which take place may not be necessary, may occur by accident, and might revert to the original specification of the model if brought to the attention of the decisionmakers. The model may, in any case, be quite valid at the time it was constructed.

(γ) *Changes in Other Factors*

Blackett[12] mentions the difficulties of inferring that military decisions were successful, when so many other changes also took place over the same period.

Examples

(1) He gives the example of painting Whitley aircraft and the estimated effect of a 30% increase in U-boats sunk. He points out that this was not assessable in implementation since so many other measures were introduced at the same time.

(2) Similarly with the effects of changes in convoy size.

(δ) *Decisionmaking Under Uncertainty*

It is to be noted that if an action is prescribed within an uncertain or probabilistic context it cannot be validated in terms of actual outcome.

Example

A recommendation in a capital investment situation may be based on the assessment of risks involved without knowing the actual outcomes. Clearly the decision may turn out to be a bad one in retrospect, but it may still have been a wise one from a prior point of view. Testing by implementation in this case can no more than test propositions of the kind 'if you take action "a" and the conditions turn out to be "c", then your profit will be $p(a,c)$'.

2.2.5 Controlling the Model

In order of application this should come after 'Obtaining Solution', but it is more intimately tied up, in principle, with the model building phases. The main point we can make is that neither models nor solutions are invariant with time.

Sometimes the criterion may change.

Examples

(1) In a seller's market we may maximize profit; in a buyer's market we may minimize cost.

(2) Flagle[45] points out the changing criteria in the Health Services arising from an ongoing concern with the rights of men to medical care.

Changes in the environment which can arise, can be with respect to characteristics such as: demand rate; variability (over time); predictability (organizational changes); costs such as the introduction of a discount system; prices; legislation; technological constraints.

Sometimes a person acquires knowledge about changes in environment which are only picked up by statistical analysis after a costly delay.

Sometimes, if the environment changes and computational costs change, an entirely different model must operate.

Examples

(1) If we increase the variety of items of inventory, we have a much more space competitive position than we had before, and solution procedure may have to change.

(2) We may get changes in production characteristics, necessitating an entirely new view on the inventory control problem; thus an improvement in the reliability of equipment may make 'in process' inventory undesirable.

(3) A priority scheduling procedure in the simple negative exponential case may become more complex if, through the introduction of additional new machines, the negative exponential distribution fails to be valid.

(4) A routine time-tabling linear programming procedure may be efficient under one set of curricula and constraints, but not if these change.

Methods of automatic control of solution have been developed. Thus the 'exponential smoothing technique' does this to some extent. Unfortunately it is not possible to produce a mechanism which can:

(a) identify all characteristic changes;

(b) modify the decision rule accordingly when such changes take place.

The answer to the problem of design of such control mechanisms is to be found in the area of Statistical Decision Theory, in principle, as has already been mentioned. There are many hypotheses in general consistent to some degree or other with a given sequence of events, and any control mechanism has to weigh up the risks involved in drawing one inference when another is true. Every such mechanism will behave in a given manner under specific environmental conditions and it is the relative behaviour which leads to a choice of a particular mechanism.

Example

A moving-average control mechanism for slowly moving parts might, unnecessarily, result in a fluctuating reorder level, whereas the environment might be statistically stable enough to merit a fixed reorder level. We need to examine the effect of any such procedure on specific environmental conditions, allowing for the possibility of trends in demand rate if this seems to be a serious risk under the circumstances.

We have to bear in mind that a model may be simple under one set of environmental conditions (e.g. uniform demand) and complex under other conditions (non-uniform demand). In the latter case, even if models were developed, the solution cost may be prohibitive except under severe suboptimization. Thus, such a mechanistic approach to environmental change may involve rather complex studies of problem simplification under different environmental conditions.

We also need to monitor the effects of a solution as a safeguard against inadequate derivation of the solution. Thus the original data could have been inaccurate or biased, the logic of the model could have been inaccurate, and even the calculation process could have been in error.

2.3 The Solution Phase

2.3.1 Forms of Solution

We have already stated that there are three forms of 'solution', *viz.*:

(a) if action a is taken then consequence θ follows, where a is one of a group of alternatives;

(b) action a ought to be taken, where a is one of a group of alternatives;

(c) the consequences of action a will be θ.

(c) is included to cater for such things as critical path analysis, which simply derives some property of a given network of activities. If, of course, we wish to vary these activities in some way, then this becomes part of (a). Thus, in principle, we only have forms (a) and (b).

2.3.2 Problem Solution Procedure Characteristics

Let us now look at some of the methods of getting solutions to problems once they have been modelled. We shall see, once again, that the relationship between the model and the solution method is a strong one.

These can be divided into categories according to:

(A) how the optimality condition is expressed;

(B) how the alternatives are analysed;

(C) the extent of coverage of the set of alternatives.

(A), (B) and (C) are not exclusive, but they are distinct features of the solution phase.

A   EXPRESSION OF OPTIMALITY CONDITION

(α) *Enumeration*

In this case, although a value function may exist, the problem is so complex that no practicable condition of optimality exists in terms of the decision variables, other than the explicit demonstration that one solution is at least as good as all others by exhaustive enumeration.

In essence this means that, until we have exhausted all the possibilities, we do not know whether any solution is the best. No properties of an optimal solution are brought to bear on the analysis.

Examples

(1) In many sequencing problems there is no practicable optimality expression and we may proceed by enumerating possible sequences and evaluating them one by one.

(2) In many priority scheduling problems, there is no practicable expression of optimality and we may proceed by enumerating certain policies and evaluating them one by one.

(β) *Calculus*

In some cases the most general expression of optimality lies in the calculus optimality expression.

In its simplest form it is given by $v'(x) = 0$, if $v(x)$ is the value function. When constraints arise this can be modified. Even if x is an integer, we can put this in the form: $x(x - 1)(x - 2) \ldots = 0$, but solving this may be difficult.

Whatever the situation, the calculus approach works by imposing restrictions on the derivatives involved, when they exist.

The advantages of the calculus method, when it is practicable, are that:

(i) it allows the feasible region to be covered fully whilst only directly considering a relatively restricted set of alternatives;

(ii) it is general, providing derivatives exist.

See Courant[29] for an exposition of calculus.

(γ) *Dynamic Programming*

A more restricted optimality expression is the dynamic programming one when it is applicable. The simplest form is:

$$v(x) = \min_{y} [c(x, y) + v(y)]$$

The essential point about the dynamic programming principle of optimality is that it expresses the optimality in terms of a problem–subproblem structure. This is expressed by demonstrating, in certain circumstances, that the solution to a problem is optimal if that part of the solution pertinent to subproblems is optimal for the subproblems. This is expressed formally in White.[145] It contrasts with the calculus principle of optimality, which expresses the fact that if a solution is optimal, it is optimal in its own neighbourhood and the criterion function cannot increase in this neighbourhood.

(δ) Branch and Bound

This optimality principle is similar to that of dynamic programming in that it utilizes a problem–subproblem structure in a different form.

Let $a_1, a_2, \ldots, a_k$, be various attributes of a solution. Thus if $(x_1, x_2, \ldots, x_n)$ is a feasible solution, a_1 might be equivalent to $x_1 = 1$; then $\tilde{a}_1$ is equivalent to $x_1 = 0$, if we have a zero–one programming problem. Let $A_{ijk\ldots}$ be the class of solutions having attributes a_i, a_j, a_k. Then $A_{ijk\ldots} = A_i \cap A_j \cap A_k \ldots$.

Let $F(S)$ be the optimum value of $g(\mathbf{x})$ subject to $\mathbf{x} \in S$, and suppose we are maximizing.

Then:

$$F(S) = \max [F(S \cap A_1); F(S \cap \tilde{A}_1)]$$

In the simple allocation problem of maximizing $\sum_i g_i(x_i)$ subject to $\sum_i a_i x_i \leqslant c$, $x_i = 0$ or 1, we then have, if S is the set of all feasible solutions and a_i is equivalent to $x_i = 1$,

$$F(S) = \max \left[\max_{\substack{x_2, \ldots, x_n \\ \Sigma x_i = c - a_1}} \left[g_1(1) + \sum_{i=2}^{n} g_i(x_i) \right] ; \right.$$

$$\left. \max_{\substack{x_2, \ldots, x_n \\ \Sigma x_i - c}} \left[g_1(0) + \sum_{i=2}^{n} g_i(x_i) \right] \right]$$

$$= \max [F(S_1); F(\tilde{S}_1)]$$

$S_1 \equiv$ all feasible $\mathbf{x}$ with $x_1 = 1$; $\tilde{S}_1 \equiv$ all feasible $\mathbf{x}$ with $x_1 = 0$.

The process is repeated, eliminating $S_n(\tilde{S}_n)$ at stage n if $F(S_n) < F(\tilde{S}_n)$ $(F(\tilde{S}_n) < F(S_n))$, providing we define $F(S) = -\infty$ if S is infeasible.

See Lawler[74] for an exposition of branch and bound methods.

(ε) Algorithmic

The calculus and (to a lesser extent) the dynamic programming optimality expressions may not be very useful in themselves. In order to get solutions we need algorithms, and optimality conditions will be needed at each stage of the solution routine to tell us whether to stop or carry out further calculations.

Although the calculus optimality expression is, in many cases, necessary and sufficient, the direct determination of such algorithms from this may not be obvious. Many algorithms for solving problems are derived from *a priori* considerations. Many do not require differentiability.

Examples

(1) The simplex algorithm of linear programming is derived independently of the calculus optimality expression. A solution is optimal at some stage of the calculations if certain elements have certain signs.

(2) Similarly with Howard's[62] algorithm in dynamic programming, where we try to solve the equation:

$$g + v(i) = \max_k [q_i^k + \sum_j p_{ij}^k v(j)], \quad i = 1, 2, \ldots, m$$

Howard's algorithm enables these equations to be solved.

(3) In some sequencing problems, algorithms exist for determining an optimum solution, which are not necessarily derived from the previous principles of optimality.

Thus in Bellman's[8] 2-machine problem of sequencing n jobs through the machines, the following algorithm can be derived from *a priori* considerations, *viz.*: let a_i be the time of item i on machine 1, b_i be the time of item i on machine 2; suppose we wish to minimize total time to complete the n jobs; then find the smallest of the set $\{a_1, a_2, \ldots, a_n, b_1, b_2, \ldots, b_n\}$; if it is an a, put this item first and apply the same reasoning to the remaining items; if it is a b, put it as the last item and apply the same reasoning to the remaining items; continue until all items are exhausted; the sequence obtained will be optimal.

(ζ) Heuristic

There appears to be no agreed definition of what constitutes 'heuristic programming'.

Reitman[107] states:

'One of the more annoying problems facing those who have been concerned with heuristic programming has been the task of making clear just what the term covers.'

The essential distinctions he tries to draw out are those between 'algorithmic' and 'heuristic' programming. He gives several points, but we quote only three:

'We would suggest that the existence of an algorithm presumes:

(a) an explicitly specifiable class of problems all of which may be solved by
(b) the program for the algorithm
     to
(c) some well defined criterion of solution.'

In this context an algorithm has an inbuilt optimality testing procedure, which an heuristic programme does not. The heuristic programme is one that, empirically, has been found to be useful in a class of problems, without considerations of mathematical optimality.

Example

Various 'algorithms' for the travelling-salesman problem have been designed 'intuitively' and have had empirical success, although they may not guarantee optimality of solution within the conceived class of alternatives.

Some heuristic procedures are, however, more concerned with the time taken to get a solution (perhaps the best solution) and the feature of the procedure is not the degree of optimality, but rather the time taken to get the required solution. Some forms of branch and bound are heuristic in this sense, although they use the branch and bound principle, which can guarantee an optimum solution. The same may be said of, for example, the linear programming simplex algorithm. Clearly, further consideration of the definition of 'heuristic' is needed.

Whichever view we take on the nature of heuristic procedures, they are concerned with the choice of steps, in the process of getting the solution, on the basis of rules which are not derived wholly from a mathematical analysis of the model, but are intuitive and partly validated on the basis of experimental testing. Thus, in the travelling-salesman problem we need a procedure to change routes at each step in the analysis, and, of the many procedures which are available, some are chosen on intuitive grounds without knowing in advance the full properties of such procedures for the problem on hand.

(μ) Physical Analogue

Sometimes it is possible to construct a physical analogue, the steady-state solution of which corresponds to the optimal solution to the original problem.

Examples

(1) Consider the problem illustrated by Figure 67.

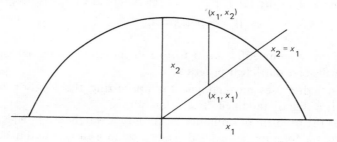

Figure 67. A simple optimizing analogue

In this problem two heavy weights are constrained to run smoothly along one of two curves, one on each, and to lie in the same vertical plane. This, of course, presupposes that this can be done without interfering with the potential energy principle to be used. However, this is simply to illustrate the ideas behind analogues. The equation of the curve is $x_2 = f(x_1)$; the total potential energy is $(x_2 + x_1)k$. Hence this analogue minimizes $x_2 + x_1$ subject to $x_2 = f(x_1)$, $x_i \geq 0$ (we restrict movement to satisfy this).

(2) Haley and Stringer[50] discuss an analogue for the standard transportation problem, as illustrated by Figure 68.

In this analogue we have a series of strings and pulleys with weights attached to the strings running over the pulleys. Figure 68 represents one constraint of a transportation problem with $2n$ constraints. We will have n strings, and pulley sets, running parallel to this one, and n strings, and pulley sets, running perpendicular to this one. The ith string of the first set is joined to the jth string of the second set by a weight proportional to $W - c_{ij}$ through which both strings can move freely. String i has fixed length $2b_i$ and string j has fixed length $2a_j$.

144

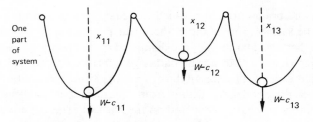

Figure 68. Transport optimizing analogue

Assuming the pulleys are close enough and the strings long enough, we have, approximately:

$$x_{i1} + x_{i2} + \cdots + x_{im} \simeq b_i \quad \text{for all } i$$
$$x_{1j} + x_{2j} + \cdots + x_{nj} \simeq a_j \quad \text{for all } j$$

Suppose we have a linear programme to minimize $\sum_i \sum_j c_{ij} x_{ij}$ subject to

$$\sum_j x_{ij} = b_i, \qquad \sum_i x_{ij} = a_j, \qquad x_{ij} \geqslant 0.$$

The string lengths are $\{2b_i\}$, $\{2a_j\}$ and the potential energy is proportional to

$$K - \sum_i \sum_j x_{ij}(W - c_{ij}) = K - W \sum_i b_i + \sum_i \sum_j c_{ij} x_{ij},$$

and, since the system settles down to one of minimum potential energy, this analogue will solve our linear programme.

(3) Haley[49] discusses an analogue for optimizing the location of depots. Figure 69 is a slightly modified illustration of this.

Consider the problem of optimum location of a warehouse in which we wish to minimize the total miles travelled. Take a smooth surface and make holes at all points corresponding to destinations to be supplied. Consider a string system through the holes joined at a central point X, with weights at each point, i, on the strings, proportional to the number of journeys, n_i, to be made to that point.

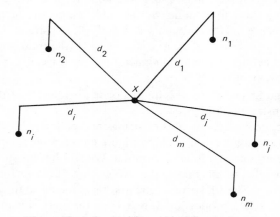

Figure 69. A depot siting optimizing analogue

Let the lengths of the strings be L. Let d_i be the distance from X to point i. Then the system settles down to minimize the potential energy, which is:

$$K - \alpha \sum_i n_i(L - d_i) = K - \alpha \sum_i n_i L + \alpha \sum_i n_i d_i.$$

Hence the solution minimizes $\sum_i n_i d_i$ as required.

(4) Example 2 caters for the transport problem only. It is possible to construct mechanisms to solve the general linear programming problem:

minimize $[\mathbf{c}'\mathbf{x}]$ subject to: $A\mathbf{x} = \mathbf{b}$; $\mathbf{x} \geqslant 0$; $a_{ij} \geqslant 0$ all i, j; $a_{ij} \neq 0$ for some j for each i.

The following analogue can easily be modified when $a_{ij} < 0$.

The basic model consists of a matrix of cylinders.

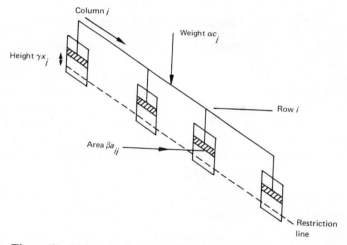

Figure 70. Linear programming fluid analogue (jth column)

The jth column of the matrix is represented by cylinders with rigidly connected pistons, constrained to move the same distance. The volume below each piston is filled with fluid. We assume no vacuums can develop. A restriction is placed in each cylinder, at the same height, preventing the piston from sitting on the bottom of the cylinder. A weight proportional to c_j is supported, in total, by all m rigidly connected pistons. The weight is assumed to be very heavy with respect to the fluid weight. The piston in the ith position of column j will have an area proportional to a_{ij}. The height of a piston above its restriction is proportional to x_j.

Figure 70 indicates what the jth column would look like.

The ith row of the matrix is a series of cylinders interconnected to allow free flow of fluid between chambers. The connections are below the restriction line to ensure that full fluid pressure (positive or negative) is brought to bear on the piston faces. The total volume of fluid shared between cylinders in the ith row is a constant. Since the pistons are not allowed to have $x_j < 0$, the total volume above the restriction line will also be a constant. Let this be V_i (see Figure 71).

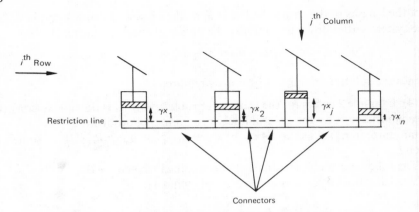

Figure 71. Linear programming fluid analogue (ith row)

Clearly the cylinders must be large enough to ensure maximum x_j values are permissible.

If the system assumes some initial state and is left to move freely, it will eventually settle down to a position of minimum potential energy. Because of the convexity of the functions involved this minimum will be a global minimum.

For such a settling down to be possible there will have to be damping forces at work.

Since we assume the liquid relatively weightless, this potential energy is given by

$$PE = k + \alpha \mathbf{c}' \mathbf{x}$$

Since the volumes between the restrictions and the pistons in each cylinder are constrained so that the total in each row is constant, we have:

$$\beta \gamma A \mathbf{x} = \mathbf{V}$$

The restrictions ensure that

$$\alpha x_j \geqslant 0, \quad j = 1, 2, \ldots, n$$

We therefore see that the minimum potential energy position solves the original linear programme.

(5) It is possible to extend the above approach to non-linear programming. Consider the problem:

minimize $\sum_{j=1}^{n} g_j(x_j)$ subject to: $A\mathbf{x} = \mathbf{b}; \mathbf{x} \geqslant 0$.

We will make the following additional assumptions at this stage to ensure that no difficulties arise in conceiving of the effective operation of the analogue, although it is possible that some of these may be relaxed:

A_1: $g_j(x_j)$ is differentiable over the range of anticipated operation;
A_2: $g_j'(x_j) > 0$ over the range of anticipated operation;
A_3: $g_j(x_j) > x_j$ over the range of anticipated operation;
A_4: $g_j(0) > 0$;
A_5: the objective function has a finite minimum within the feasible region.

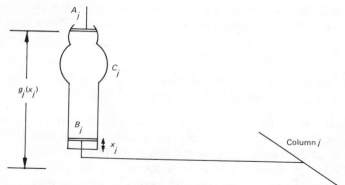

Figure 72. Non-linear programming fluid analogue (jth column)

We achieve our new analogue by adding, for each column j in Figure 70, a further cylinder with piston rigidly connected to the column j bar. Figure 72 shows the new cylinder and connections.

Piston B_j is connected to column bar j. Piston A_j has a unit weight placed upon it. Cylinder C_j has a variable cross-section. Piston heads A_j, B_j are expanding to take up the full cross-section at each position achieved.

The total potential energy is then given by:

$$\text{PE} = k + \alpha \sum_{j=1}^{n} g_j(x_j)$$

Other equations remain as for the linear model.

In discussing the above examples the possible use of analogues for solving problems directly has been mentioned. It must be mentioned that it is possible to use these to demonstrate duality principles and to derive computational methods (see White[151]).

Sinden[121] discusses mechanical analogues.

In each of these cases the principle of optimality is equivalent to the principle of minimal potential energy.

B   ANALYSIS OF ALTERNATIVES

Here we distinguish between:
(a) analytic evaluation;
(b) numerical evaluation;
(c) simulation.

(a) *Analytic Evaluation*

In rare circumstances we can give an analytic expression for the optimal solution in terms of the parameters of the problem.

Example

Economic batch quantity: $Q = \sqrt{(\alpha D/\beta)}$.

148

More often than not, not only can we not get the optimal solution in terms of the parameters, but we cannot even express the outcome θ as a function of the alternative a.

Example

In many production scheduling problems it is not possible to express the total production time as a function of the parameters of the policy.

The advantage of the analytic forms are that routine sensitivity analysis with respect to parameters is facilitated, and computations are at their minimal level.

It is to be noted that an analogue is a very special form of simulation in which there may be an inbuilt optimality characteristic. In addition an analogue operates according to natural laws, whereas a simulation may have a forced pattern of behaviour.

(b) *Numerical Evaluation*

If we cannot produce analytic explicit expressions we can sometimes produce practicable computational routines.

Examples

(1) In linear programming, although we cannot express the optimal outcome θ as a function of the constraints, we can compute the value of an alternative, and the optimal alternative, for specific parameters.

(2) In a production scheduling problem, the theory of Markov processes may provide a routine numerical computation for each set of parameters.

(c) *Simulation*

There are situations in which we cannot, practicably, carry out any calculations as above. We may then resort to the technique of representing the physical behaviour of a system in such a manner that this behaviour can be condensed into a much shorter space than the real time of the system. The 'actual' behaviour is then observed, for each alternative being considered, and the choice made on the basis of this behaviour.

Although such systems still have a Markov representation, the corresponding calculations may be impracticable.

Simulation is relatively simple and requires virtually no mathematical knowledge, but may be tedious, time consuming, and limited in its coverage of alternatives, particularly if the simulation is digital.

C   COVERAGE OF SET OF ALTERNATIVES

We first of all point out that we always begin with a nominal set of alternatives, C, which are themselves subsets of a wider range of alternatives.

Example

With linear programming problems, the set of admissible alternatives is not absolute. We can always pursue the consequences of violating a constraint.

We also note that alternatives can be defined explicitly or implicitly, a point made in Section 2.1.

Example

Explicit: Do we replace now or take a decision next year?

Implicit: $X \equiv \{x : Ax \leqslant b\}$.

Having said this, then the distinction we now wish to draw is between (relative) complete coverage of X and restricted coverage of X.

(α) Complete Coverage of X

The analytic, algorithmic, and complete enumerative processes will give complete coverage of alternatives.

(β) Restricted Coverage of X

Some heuristic procedures will give limited coverage, since they may not guarantee optimality in X. Simulation procedures are notoriously restricted in X (X is much larger than effective coverage). Las Vegas (discussed later on) procedures are sampling procedures over X, in an effort to compromise between computational costs and risks of 'short-fall'.

The coverage of alternatives is a recurring problem in Decision Analysis projects. We face the secondary decision problem of choosing the method of solution, bearing in mind the costs of doing it, the extra coverage obtained and the extra increase in the value of the solution obtained. We shall, later on, indicate some of the ways in which we try to compromise between computational effort and solution coverage, but, at this stage, we can only stress that this is a realistic decision to be taken which can seriously affect the value of a solution, net of the costs of getting it. We should at least consider the more powerful methods. If we fail, then we have lost a limited amount of effort. If we succeed, we avoid a great deal of effort in other methods. The more general a method is, such as simulation, the more expensive it is relative to more specific methods if the latter can be determined. In some ways the problem we have is similar to problems we face in Statistical Decision Theory where we have to evaluate the risks of adopting one approach when another might be better.

In the above discussion we have referred to optimality principles and to the analysis procedures by which these principles might be applied. There are, however, other principles involved in solving problems, and associated specific procedures for applying them. White[145] covers such principles and Figure 73 illustrates the overall picture. Reference to that paper should be made for more details. Later on we will discuss, in detail, some principles for handling constraints in particular. The problems arising in handling uncertainties also arise from time to time throughout the book.

Mulligan[94] discusses various characteristics of optimization problems and gives a flow chart showing how calculations might proceed.

When considering the choice of techniques the previous considerations should be taken into account. The following example illustrates, qualitatively, the attributes of dynamic programming as a technique, taken from White.[147]

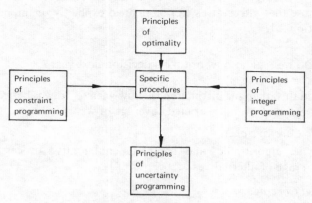

Figure 73. Principles of solution procedures

We will concentrate on several typical types of equation, *viz.*,

$$f_n(i) = \min_k [q_n(i,k) + f_{n-1}(T_k(i))] \qquad \textbf{FD}$$

$$b_n(i) = \min_k [b_{n-1}(T_k^{-1}(i)) + q(T_k^{-1}(i),k)] \qquad \textbf{BD}$$

$$\tilde{f}_n(i) = \min_k \left[\tilde{q}_n(i,k) + \sum_j p_{ij}^k \tilde{f}_{n-1}(j) \right] \qquad \textbf{ST}$$

$$\tilde{f}(i) + g = \min_k \left[\tilde{q}(i,k) + \sum_j p_{ij}^k \tilde{f}(j) \right] \qquad \textbf{SS}$$

k: decision
i: state of system
n: stage
$T_k(i)$: transformed state at stage $n - 1$, given state i at stage n and decision k;
$T_k^{-1}(i)$: inverse transform, assumed one–one;
$q_n(i,k)$: cost in period n if we begin in state i and take decision k;
$\tilde{q}_n(i,k)$: expected cost in period n if we begin in state i and take decision k;
$\tilde{q}(i,k)$: as for $\tilde{q}_n(i,k)$ but independent of n;
$f_n(i)$: minimal cost over n periods of time beginning in state i; **FD** ≡ forward deterministic equation;
$b_n(i)$: minimal cost over n periods of time ending in state i; **BD** ≡ backward deterministic equation;
$\tilde{f}_n(i)$: minimal expected cost over n periods of time beginning in state i; **ST**: stochastic transient;
$\tilde{f}(i)$: transient value of state i in a long-term steady-state process; **SS**: stochastic steady state.

Examples of these are:

FD: problem of installing equipment over n years, when we know the present state of capacity, i; known demand;

BD: above problem where we can choose the initial capacity and specify the final capacity; known demand;

ST: an inventory control problem beginning with inventory i and operating over n weeks; stochastic demand;

SS: the above problem, when n is assumed very large; stochastic demand.

We will use these equations and examples on which to hinge the following comments.

We will assume that the problem has been correctly formulated and that the functional equations portray equally well the real problem as do the competing techniques. The functional equation may therefore be complex, with a large number of states, but we must begin with a common basis. In particular, an explicit statement of criteria is needed.

1. *Optimality Attribute.* Providing the formulation is possible, it will produce the optimum solution relative to the stated problem.

In many circumstances alternative techniques do not produce this relative optimum and a judgement has to be made as to whether the technique is acceptable or not.

Let us consider a simple inventory problem for which formulation **ST** or **SS** applies, e.g. $f_n(i) = \min_k [\bar{q}(i,k) + \sum_j p_{ij}^k f_{n-1}(j)]$.

Suppose we never have to consider more than m stock levels at each decision epoch and that we have N possible inventory reorder quantities at each such epoch.

The number of possible policies is then:

$$N^m \qquad \qquad \textbf{E.1}$$

With $N = m = 10$, we have 10,000,000,000 policies.

Admittedly many can be ruled out by various means. Admittedly many simpler techniques also exist for this simple problem. However, this example is used to demonstrate the magnitude of the number of policies in a simple case.

Now let us proceed to a more complex case for which, for example, one can think of no alternative but our good old safeguard, simulation.

The above example then gives us some idea of the enormous number of possible policies. Clearly one must be selective in handling this problem.

We can either use the 'intuition' approach, or some 'logical-reduction' approach, or the 'local policy' approach in which one does not deviate from the present policy (if one can find it, that is) too much. In the end analysis the actual number of policies simulated is very small with respect to the total number of possible policies, and one therefore risks suboptimization relative to the problem formulated and one then has to judge the adequacy of the solution in terms of expenditure of effort.

Attempts to allow for a variety of policies by using parametric forms still severely reduce the coverage of alternatives. For example, if, in our simple problem, we used as a decision rule:

$$k = \alpha - \beta i$$

rounded to the nearest order quantity, one can calculate the number of policies which do not allow more than an N order quantity as being approximately given by

$$N^2 \, 2^{m-2} \qquad\qquad\qquad \textbf{E.2}$$

The ratio **E.2/E.1** is then:

$$(2/N)^{m-2} \qquad\qquad\qquad \textbf{E.3}$$

With $N = m = 10$, **E.3** $= 5^{-8}$.

This is, of course, all very well if we could handle the computational problems of dynamic programming. However, if we can conceive of a complexity measure (say number of states), C, it is clear that, for the same type of output, there will be a critical number $\bar{C}$, such that:

if $C \leqslant \bar{C}$, dynamic programming is better than simulation
if $C \geqslant \bar{C}$, dynamic programming is worse than simulation

It is not, therefore, a question of saying yes or no to one technique rather than another, but rather one of trying to determine regions in which one is better than another.

This presentation is, of course, purely conceptual, but reflects the nature of the problem.

Perhaps we may end with a conjecture that $\bar{C}$ may be larger than we might presuppose. The state problem in dynamic programming is still the same state problem in simulation which, in the latter case, may dictate the need for longer runs as the number of states increase. In addition, the simulation approach is a simulated Markov model. Some attention to numerical methods for Markov models, with particular structures, might be useful therefore.

In some instances the use of dynamic programming for repetitive applications can clearly be too costly and *ad hoc* methods of solution may have to be developed. However, there is still the question of the degree of optimality of such methods, and dynamic programming, which will give the optimal answer, may be used as a 'verification technique'.

An example in which this was applied was in the area of purchasing of parts, which were needed in various quantities at various times, and in which maximal quantity discounts made large batching ideal, but with the consequential penalties of high inventory. The equation derived is a variant of **FD**, *viz.*,

$$f(i) = \min_{k} \, [c(i,k) + f(k)], \quad f(T) = 0$$

$f(i)$: minimal cost from period i (to which present purchases will last) to the time horizon T;

$c(i,k)$: purchase plus inventory holding costs covering period i to k, to which the next purchase order will last.

2. *Model Component Structures.* If we conceive of dynamic programming as a numerical, rather than analytic, technique, it has the advantage that its application does not depend on the various input components having special structures.

Thus

(i) variables can be integers;

(ii) functions can be discontinuous, non-differentiable, non-linear.

Thus in the case of a problem of installing equipment, with equation **FD**, our decisions may be in terms of an integer number of units of equipment, and installation costs may be of the form:

$$q(i,k) = a + bk, \quad k > 0$$
$$= 0, \qquad k = 0$$
$$a, b > 0$$

3. *Sensitivity Analysis with Respect to Duration*. In applying any technique to long-term planning problems, the inevitable problem of the duration of the planning period arises, and this then raises the question of the degree of dependence of the solution on the duration. Dynamic programming provides a natural sensitivity analysis for this situation.

A particular planning problem gave rise to a derivative form of equation **BD**, *viz.*,

$$f_n = \min_{0 \leqslant m < n} [f_m + \alpha^m q(m,n)], \quad f_0 = 0$$

α: discount factor;

n: epoch in time when demand equals capacity;

m: last installation point;

$q(m,n)$: discounted cost of capacity needed to meet extra demand in periods m to n.

From this analysis, the decision epoch function, $m(n)$ was derived as in Figure 74.

As we vary n, we can easily see how m_1 varies and hence establish the dependence of the first decision on the horizon period n.

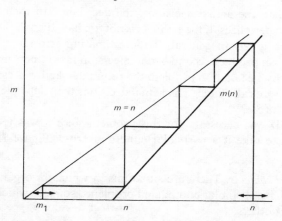

Figure 74. Capacity installation policy (deterministic)

In a similar problem in which a manufacturer had the problem of determining how many, and what, sizes of raw material to purchase, an equation of type **FD** was used to determine the relationship between the optimum solution and the number of sizes allowed. The reduction of the number of sizes reduced work flow and was of a help to the supplier and had to be set off against the reduction of actual operational effectiveness.

4. *Dynamic Response and Static Estimates.* In some dynamic problems an estimate of such things as demand is made over the duration of operation and an optimal sequence of decisions is made. Because the demand is then treated as deterministic, the decisions are treated as fixed, whereas in actual realization, estimates will differ from actualities.

Now dynamic programming produces decision rules and hence responds to the situation as it materializes. If the estimates are used to derive the decision

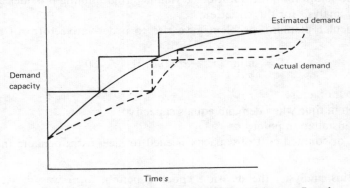

Figure 75. Capacity installation policy (uncertain). ——— Installations relative to estimate. ———— Applying decision rule in face of actual demand

rules, rather than the actual decisions, the decisions can then respond to the situation as it materializes. If the estimate is not too bad, then the loss in optimality will not be too great. In general, if the estimating errors are first order, the decision rules will produce second-order effects on loss of performance.

In the capacity installation problem the future demand was estimated and the decision rules were calculated. The actual decisions then depended upon how the actual demand arose.

The form **FD** was necessary for this problem since it was required to know what decision to take if a particular condition arose. Figure 75 illustrates the situation.

5. *Multiple Problems.* There are situations in which an organization is faced with a multiplicity of similar and related problems, some of which can be seen as subproblems of others.

Thus, in a problem concerned with adding or modifying existing transformer configurations in the national grid, there was a multiplicity of related problems.

If 'i' was the state of the system in a given area, then this might be a state into which another area might subsequently move. In addition, the state into which i is eventually transformed might be the state of another area at this point in time.

In a problem concerned with rolling steel strip, the state of any job might be its gauge at any stage, and other jobs at other times might eventually pass through this state or be reached from this state.

In such circumstances the dynamic programming calculations are no longer as redundant as they were, since the computational process results in many similar and related problems being solved.

The common equations for this group are both of the **FD** and **BD** type or modifications as follows:

$$f(i) = \min_j [q(i,j) + f(j)], \qquad f(N) = 0$$
$$b(i) = \min_j [b(j) + q(j,i)], \qquad b(1) = 0$$

6. *Related Long- and Short-term Criteria.* A feature of any approach to a sequential decision problem is its ability to determine decisions at any stage as a result of stated long-term criteria. In essence, therefore, it produces a short-term criterion for solving the decision problem at any stage.

Thus, for example, in the type **SS** equation, the criterion for determining k, given i, is

$$\bar{q}(i,k) + \sum_j p_{ij}^k \, \bar{f}(j)$$

This is a short-term criterion derivative from the long-term criterion of minimum expected cost, for example.

In some situations attempts are made to determine short-term criteria without deriving them logically from long-term criteria, and this leads to an inability to defend properly the short-term criteria.

A typical example exists in the area of investment analysis, where, given a time series of net cash flows, $t_1, t_2, \ldots, t_n, \ldots$, stemming from an investment opportunity, the criterion suggested is the present worth criterion, *viz.*,

$$v(t_1, t_2, \ldots, t_n) = \sum_n \alpha^n t_n$$

If this is done for all considered alternatives, including the null alternative, then it is suggested that one should choose the one with the highest v value.

However, this need not reflect the long-term objectives. If the long-term objective were to maximize expected net income, after T periods, and the probability distributions of cash flow and future opportunities were given, then only in special circumstances will this long-term criterion produce this short-term criterion, and, in this case, dynamic programming (see White[144, 146]) can not only establish this but also help determine α as a result of the dynamic long-term behaviour, and not on some qualitative study of 'present circumstances'.

Naturally there will be computational considerations. However, when conceptual issues arise, it is always useful to be able to demonstrate whether a line of argument is sensible and rigorous enough. By using dynamic programming on simple problems which fall within the area being studied, it may be possible to refute or to support the general contentions, which may then be used as an inductive basis for the more complex situation.

Thus, conceptually, the capacity to relate long- and short-term requirements is a useful attribute of dynamic programming.

2.3.3 Comparing Solutions

At this stage, before proceeding to solution procedures, a cautionary point is made. Sometimes it is the practice of selecting a solution on the basis of comparison of the output of a model with recorded behaviour under an existing set of circumstances, and this can be dangerous.

Using statistical methods we may derive a relationship between an alternative and its consequences in the form $\theta = E(a)$, E being the estimate, ignoring variability. It may happen that the actual $\theta = A(a)$ for a given a is known. It is not necessarily correct to compare $A(a)$ with $E(b)$ when comparing a and b. We should compare $E(a)$ with $E(b)$, since we must compare the behaviours of alternatives under the same assumptions.

It will almost certainly be the case that the model used for estimating purposes will not be perfect and it would be dangerous therefore to compare $A(a)$ with $E(b)$ since actual behaviour may be somewhat removed from estimated behaviour, i.e. $A(a)$ may not be identical with $E(a)$. We have already pointed out the ultimate unreality of models and this must be taken into account when accepting solutions on any basis. It may be better to know that 'b' is better than 'a' relative to E, in which the assumptions are the same for both 'b' and 'a', than to know that 'b' relative to E is better than 'a' relative to A. This belief rests on the premise that if 'b' is better than 'a' relative to one set of assumptions, it will be better than 'a' for assumptions near to these which will include the real assumptions if we are reasonably careful in our modelling.

Example

In a recent study it was required to estimate the time to collect a given load of refuse using different team sizes. 'a' was the actual team size in one instance. $E(\cdot)$ was estimated and, for a new policy, 'b', $E(b)$ was compared with $A(a)$. This was dangerous, since if $E(\cdot)$ is subject to error, the absolute effect may not be validly represented, but the sign of the difference, $E(a) - E(b)$, and even its absolute magnitude, may well still be valid if the errors are not too large.

In the above example, it was demonstrated that, under certain assumptions, time $= \theta = \lambda/a + \mu$.

Even if λ, μ were estimated and were in error, one would obtain the right order of magnitude for $E(a) - E(b)$, or at least invariance in sign, if the errors were not too large.

The above model is, in itself, only an approximation in form, thus introducing another error and reinforcing the argument of comparison.

Hausmann[54] reinforces this viewpoint when he states:

'We can frequently predict the relative value of alternatives much more precisely than their absolute performance'.

2.3.4 Verifying the Method

If we use a specific solution method for some aspects of the study, we must not assume, automatically, that the results are right, even if the basic model is. It is useful to test the method by comparing the output with results in known cases. This is known as verification.

Examples

(1) In a recent study of spare engines for buses, the analytic approach was not feasible, and a simulation programme was developed. Restrictions on the programme to make it behave as a standard queueing problem were made and the results compared with analytic predictions.

(2) In a recent study of purchasing parts, the problem was to determine batch sizes when requirements for a sequence of weeks were given. An *ad hoc* method was developed. Its degree of approximation to the optimal solution, relative to the model used, was tested by using a dynamic programming approach which obtained the optimal answer, again relative to the model used.

2.3.5 Quick Methods of Solution

Clearly, once a model has been built, there are always ways of solving it if we are prepared to invest enough time and effort in doing this. However, as has already been stated, the cost of a study must be reflected in the value of study. We already have quick statistical methods (see Duckworth and Wyatt[38]) and it is useful to consider quick Decision Analysis solution methods as well when problems have specific features. We shall now deal with a few possibilities. Inevitably we shall involve suboptimization, but, then, we always suboptimize in a sense. We shall return to the concept of 'suboptimizing' later on.

In what follows, we will see that certain changes in the 'real' model (i.e. the one which we accept as representing reality from our point of view) will be made. Such changes can be thought of as producing approximate models, in some sense. In making such approximations it is useful to be able to conceive of 'real' situations which the new model might describe. Bellman[10] says:

'Try to make the approximation reflect some physical operation which is meaningful in the actual process under study.'

Thus, for example, we shall consider substituting one distribution for another, and we need to be able to conceive of the new situation being possible.

Before proceeding it is important to stress once again that there is an interdependence between model and solution method and that to ease the solution we may need to reduce the model.

Hollander[60] states:

'Without over-simplification, the factors that must be taken into account may

158

number in the millions. Techniques that are quite tractable for a hundred or even a thousand variables, run into limitations when confronted with millions. Often, computation resources and time increase exponentially with size, so that entirely new approaches must be found.'

However, even in smaller problems we must match the approach to resources, and simple methods, accompanied by some form of check, may need to be considered.

We shall, inevitably, have to consider the justification of the approaches discussed. Later on, in the chapter on suboptimization, we will formally recognize the secondary decisions facing us in getting solutions. In this section these will not be stressed as a central theme, but it will be necessary from time to time to discuss them as a means of demonstrating that real choices exist and can be discussed in some framework. To some extent, therefore, this section must overlap with the chapter on suboptimization, but, we would hope, to some benefit.

2.3.5.1 THE EXCLUSION PRINCIPLE

In many instances the problems are too complex to consider all aspects in the initial study. Sometimes it is useful to exclude certain factors initially and to consider these in the light of the initial results found. If the results conflict with these other considerations, modifications are needed. If little conflict arises then a lot of effort is saved.

It is perhaps worth stressing at this stage the nature of the secondary decision we face, which is a sequential decision. We can either go for a comprehensive model and/or solution method, with reasonable confidence that we will get the optimal, relative, solution, at a reasonably well estimated cost, not knowing, in general, the achievable optimum; or we can go for a reduced model and/or solution method, with no guarantee that a near optimal, relative, solution will be obtained, but with some chance of doing this, at a reasonably well estimated cost. If, in the second case, a check is made to determine whether the solution is in some sense acceptable, and it is, no further work is needed; if it is not acceptable we may have to go back to the comprehensive model. The right secondary decision to take depends on the estimated chances of success and the estimated costs of the second alternative, and the problem resembles a problem in Statistical Decision Theory. Figure 76 illustrates this.

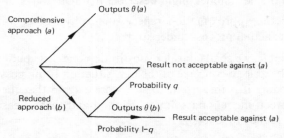

Figure 76. Secondary comprehensive or reduced model decisions

It must be stressed that this model of the secondary decisions of concern is by no means precise and is merely meant to be indicative of the situation.

We will discuss the exclusion principle under two headings, *viz.*:

(A) excluding consequences and constraints;
(B) excluding primary decision interactions.

A   EXCLUDING CONSEQUENCES AND CONSTRAINTS

In some instances the relationship between control variables and certain consequences is not known or is difficult to calculate. Such consequences may also be difficult to measure. If we neglect these consequences, which include violation of constraints, when analysing the problem in the first instance, it may be that the final, conditional, solution, is judged not to make much difference in the given area of consequences, in which case we have no problem. If, however, the final conditional solution could significantly change these consequences, then we have to experiment, or carry out the relevant calculations.

Examples

(1) In a problem in bus routing (Lampkin and Saalmans[72]) 'service' and 'cost' were the final consequences. However, service will influence 'usage' in an unknown way. If the final choice between service and cost produces a service level which is not significantly removed from the present one, then we have no problem of estimating usage, providing we are simply comparing with the present situation. If, however, it is envisaged that radically different usages might be desirable, they have to be estimated somehow.

(2) When one is concerned with the economic replacement of a fleet of vehicles, two factors complicate the classical solution, *viz.*:

(i) availability of capital funds for purchase (constraint);
(ii) discount allowances for bulk purchase (cost consequence).

If one ignores (i), (ii) initially and obtains the suboptimal solution in the form 'replace every T^* years', one can estimate the effect of this on the ability to carry it out relative to (i) and losses through too infrequent replacement influencing (ii).

It may be that deviations from T^* will allow (i) and (ii) to be acceptable with small effect on the other economic aspects.

In Figure 77 T^* is the classical optimal replacement period; T_c is the replacement period equivalent to the budget allowance for capital replacement; T_d is the replacement period which ensures the annual frequency of replacement results in enough vehicles being replaced to get maximum quantity discounts.

If $T_c \leqslant T^* \leqslant T_d$, we have a true optimal solution. If not, then one of the desirable consequences is at a level which is not the best one, and we must then evaluate the effect of T^*, or deviations from T^*, on these factors.

In the case of T_c this is not an inviolable consequence in any case, and the argument for T^* may be used to obtain a change in T_c. However, the essential point is that to try to incorporate T_d, T_c initially into the study can, sometimes unnecessarily, complicate matters.

160

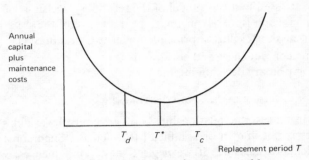

Figure 77. A constrained replacement problem

(3) In planning forestry cutting and replanting programmes, one needs to consider the economic and aesthetic variables. However, the latter variables are extremely difficult to define and to incorporate. Also, some framework is needed within which intelligent development of such values can be derived. Clearly the economic aspects are important and a starting point may be taken by optimizing with respect to the economic factors, and then presenting the forest configurations arising from these to the decisionmakers. It is possible that they may be acceptable, thus saving a lot of time. Even if not, this can be used as a starting point to determine ultimate aesthetic values by getting the decisionmakers to say why the solution is not acceptable, modifying the economic programme accordingly, regenerating a new solution, testing its aesthetic implications, and so on.

(4) It is difficult to get the compromise between input costs and effect on health. In some cases such problems may exist which one can resolve. Thus if the cost of a medical programme of a 'preventive' kind is c, and the cost of treatment to attain a specific level of health is t_w without the preventive programme and t_p with the preventive programme, providing

$$c < t_w - t_p$$

and other things are equal, this solution must be better. This is, of course, relative to the level of health, and corresponding medical policy, in use at the time. As a cautionary point, since the effects of this level of health and policy are not known, even if $c < t_w - t_p$ the use of the preventive programme may turn out to be worse if this higher-level problem is tackled.

(5) In Example (3) with many trees of different ages at any time, a programme taking into account market constraints, plus distribution costs, etc., might be prohibitive. One could consider the optimal life cycle of each type of tree and see how these could be fitted together in the best way to meet constraints in the most economic manner. Deviations from the individual optimum may be handled easily, and even if it does not work, the initial cost is small as compared with an initial comprehensive method.

(6) In a study of optimal packing case sizes for a cigarette manufacturer, constraints arose as to which sizes could be stocked and handled. However, this radically complicates the analysis and one can suppress these initially to see if

the economically desirable set seriously conflicts with these. If it does, and cannot be easily modified to fit these, not much time has been lost, since the initial study is simple.

(7) In a study of economic batch quantities, the constraints arising from consideration of capacity limitations were initially ignored. When the economic batch quantities were obtained, a check was then made to see whether, in the light of the quantities of each commodity needed in a specific time period, it was feasible to produce the quantities required. It was. If this had not been the case then the solution would have been invalid. It might have been possible to use this solution as a starting point to consider the feasibility of a schedule in the light of the constraints.

B EXCLUDING PRIMARY DECISION INTERACTIONS

As has been often stated, Decision Analysis tries to take a comprehensive view of a problem area and its interactions with other problem areas. However,

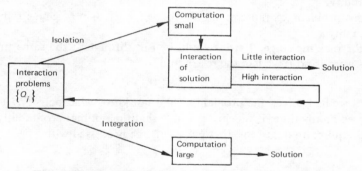

Figure 78. Secondary integration or isolation decisions

although an overview of the total problem is useful in guiding the starting point, it is sometimes computationally burdensome to approach such interactions with a comprehensive model at the outset. If we attempt to isolate parts of the problem, as with the exclusion of consequences, we can check the degree of interaction of the solution with other primary problem areas. If we are lucky the interaction may not be great. If we are unlucky we will have lost relatively little time and effort with respect to the time and effort required to resolve the totally interactive problem. Figure 78 depicts the secondary problem situation for this problem.

Examples

(1) It happens that production scheduling involves the use of common facilities and storage space for a variety of items. To build in the interaction initially may prevent a reasonable solution procedure from being determined. It is sometimes useful to be able to consider them separately and then to check the interaction aspects, in the hope of getting a simpler solution.

When scheduling the production of spares, a certain company uses a batching procedure for each item and evaluates separate production programmes. It is just possible that at some time the total storage requirement may be in excess of actual because of the tendency of quantity discounts to result in large batches. However, once the separable programmes have been produced, it is an easy matter to see the extent to which capacity limitations will be violated.

(2) A multi-equipment, sequential, profitability study involved the possibilities of doing some jobs together on certain processes, e.g. pickling and annealing. The combinatorial aspects were made unmanageable unless some assumptions were made about 'average' utilization of such equipment independent of the mix of jobs.

It remained to be established that the final mix produced did not seriously violate the assumptions, for the purposes of the study.

The end result was a profitability index per ton, which was found to be highly correlated with gauge, independently of width, which supported the initial contention that the processes would be fairly highly utilized, since we could choose the widths to achieve this without significantly reducing maximal profitability.

In this problem x_{ij}^k represented the tons of steel strip of gauge i and width j with quality k.

At the pickling stage, 2 strips could be run through at the same time. If the widths were j and j' we had the restriction

$$j + j' \leqslant 18''$$

Until we had solved the problem we did not know what pairs (j,j') would be processed at any time. It was just possible that the optimal profitability solution would require, on occasions, that pairs (j,j') be processed with

$$j + j' < 18''$$

However, it was assumed that nearly all the time $j + j' = 18''$, and the optimal solution did, as it happened, allow this to be achieved.

Similarly for the annealing process, where coils of different widths and gauges could be mixed together in furnaces which could only take limited total heights and weights.

(3) When trying to determine production facilities for a set of jobs, the jobs may be grouped into urgent and not so urgent. When trying to determine the facilities required it is probably useful to look at the urgent ones separately to estimate the facilities needed. The time available for other jobs is likely to be high, leaving problems of catering for these a minor one. If the time left over is not so large, then an increase in facilities may be needed for the others. However, the simplified 'separability' approach may save time, and effort. It all depends on the 'importance' factor for the urgent jobs, requiring much more facilities than would be needed simply from a balance point of view. Figure 79 illustrates the problem.

In the above approach, let L_2 be the level of capacity needed to leave capacity free for non-urgent jobs equal to the demand. Let L_1 be the level of capacity required to produce the maximal allowable waiting time for urgent jobs if they were always given priority.

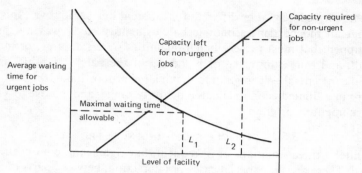

Figure 79. Separation of urgent and non-urgent jobs

Then clearly if $L_2 \gg L_1$, even if, in practice, the urgent jobs have to wait a period for non-urgent jobs, the average waiting time will not be much reduced. If $L_2 \not\gg L_1$ then there will be a problem of interaction between the two classes of jobs. Ultimately this can be tested by simulation. In any case, if the approach fails, not much time and effort is lost.

(4) A recent study was concerned with containerization and loading and unloading of ships. There was the possibility of interference between containers coming to, and going from, the berth, depending on the patterns of activity. One way of getting a solution was to neglect the space problem and the interference aspect and to concentrate on the loading and unloading of ships, assuming fixed facilities, and that loads were available for the ship as soon as required and could be loaded as soon as the ship was unloaded. Once an acceptable solution was obtained this way, the interference factor could be assessed. If no reasonable way out could be found, then the interaction would have to be modelled into the situation properly.

(5) In a trawler study, the problem was to determine the size of a mother ship servicing a group of trawlers. The total economic solution depended on operating and capital costs, cycle time and catch rates. The cycle time depended on distance from port, fishing time, ship speeds, etc. Part of the cycle time depended on queueing problems which might arise from trawlers having to wait to unload. However, to consider the dynamic queueing aspects directly within the total model would complicate matters. In the first instance it is not unreasonable to suppress this factor and assume no queueing. The optimal solution, including optimal cycle times and trawler numbers, can then be found. The extent of possible interference in queueing can then be calculated. If this is not too large then the original method is validated. If it is largish then the cost of reducing this, by choosing the correct unloading equipment and quantity, can be calculated. If this cost has any significant influence on the validity of the initial solution, then one must return to the original model and incorporate the queueing problem directly.

(6) In a certain study, different items were produced together on the same production facility. It was required to find an economic batch quantity, but

164

clearly these were likely to be different for different items. However, this did not
mean that an independent economic batch quantity study was not useful. It
might happen that most present batch quantities were too large, or most were
too small, and thus a lowering or highering of the batch quantities might be
worthwhile in general. We might find that a large proportion of the commodities
come within a limited economic batch quantity range, and a move to a point in
this range might be profitable.

2.3.5.2 INFREQUENT CONTINGENCIES PRINCIPLE

In White[149] three situations of infrequent, but significant, contingencies were
discussed. These are very special cases of interaction, between parts of a model,
but not between primary decisions. Under certain circumstances it is possible to
use anticipated properties of the solution to simplify the problem, and yet to
cover the interactions.

There are many problems encountered in Decision Analysis in which it is
required to find a decision, or decision rule, which results in the best compromise
between the incidence of penalties paid when certain situations arise and the costs
of the preventive measures taken to control the incidence level of such situations.
Thus, for example:
(a) in inventory problems we search for decision rules which constrain the
    incidence of stock run-out situations, while paying attention to the costs of
    providing the stock levels which influence this incidence level;
(b) in maintenance problems we concern ourselves with inspection procedures
    which constrain the incidence of major failures, while paying attention to the
    costs of such inspection procedures which influence this incidence level;
(c) in queueing situations we search for priority decision rules, or size of service
    facility, which constrain the incidence of queueing situations, while paying
    attention to production costs and capital costs which influence this incidence
    level.

Now, in each of the above, and similar instances, once the criteria, alternatives,
consequences and the relevant relationships between these elements have been
identified, it is the easiest thing in the world to provide a model for the purpose of
either evaluating each alternative, or even prescribing the best alternative. Thus,
in particular, if we are interested in long-term behaviour (and by 'long-term' we
mean a large number of transitions through which the system will move), we
may, in theory, be able to represent these as discrete Markov processes and use
the dynamic programming approach to reduce them to Howard's steady-state,
completely ergodic equation:

$$g + v(i) = \min_k [q_i^k + \sum_j p_{ij}^k v(j)] \qquad \textbf{1}$$

where:

i = one of the possible discrete states;

k = an alternative action;

q_i^k = expected gain in the next period (positive cost or negative return)
associated with being in state i and taking action k;

p_{ij}^k = probability of moving from i to j in next period when alternative k is chosen;

$v(j)$ = a value function;

g = optimum long-term gain per unit time.

In the case when we are only examining a major decision, such as how many service facilities to have, then we drop the minimization sign in equation **1** if the operational decision rule concerned is given, and simply solve equation **1** for the various q_i^k, p_{ij}^k, now determined by level of service facilities.

Equation **1** is a general approach, but not the only one of course. Thus, for a given decision rule, we can always set up the appropriate recurrence relationships for any queueing or inventory control situation, although they may be very complex.

We have no wish to expound on the sorts of models which can be constructed, but simply to point out that they do exist. However, as is well known, there is a vast gap between ability to construct models and ability to solve them in such a way that there is an appropriate gain of value of solution over time, effort and costs, put into obtaining the solution. It is well known in queueing theory that, once we depart from standard distributions, obtaining a solution in an analytic form is sometimes not possible; in such cases, neither may a computational algorithm exist which is economically appropriate in its use. Thus in equation **1** (which may be used for a queueing problem) if the number of states is very large, its solution is clearly out of the question.

In view of the above, it is natural to look for ways of building a model which still retain the magnitude of the essential conflicts in the problem and are economically manageable. This is possible in the sort of problem mentioned initially, providing we accept as an initial posit, θ:

'The primary motive of the system being investigated is to try to avoid certain contingencies.'

Thus the purpose of providing enough facilities is primarily to reduce the queue; the purpose of providing stock is to ensure that certain activities needing it will not be held up; the purpose of providing inspection procedures is to avoid serious failures.

These observations are naturally qualified. Clearly the answer in each case would be to provide enormous service resources if the incidence level is actually reduced to zero, and, since there is clearly not an infinite negative value on such contingencies, such solutions are not appropriate. Nonetheless, the prime purpose is to avoid these contingencies and it is to be expected that, in many instances, there will indeed be a high negative value on such contingencies. If this is the case then the optimal solution (if we are after an optimum—in the restricted sense that is) is likely to involve a low incidence of such contingencies.

In the following three skeleton studies the ways in which the previous observations can be used to provide an economic solution procedure are illustrated. The technique reduces to putting the incidence equal to zero, for certain purposes, which facilitates an otherwise difficult computational problem. Naturally we

166

need to test our premises at the end of the investigation and the way this is done is considered. Without some form of control we would run the risk of being out in our solution. If the initial premise is refuted we need to think again, or fall back on the handyman's general purpose tool—simulation. However, if the primary analysis is quite small, not much is lost and much can be gained.

What follows will be well known, in principle, to all experienced Decision Analysts, although the specific studies are new. However, such 'techniques' can play a vital role in the structuring of our methodology, and give rise to a search for other 'techniques' equally useful to relative newcomers to Decision Analysis. By this process we believe that Decision Analysis can itself become more clearly defined.

Finally, the studies covered are only skeletons of actual studies, sufficient for the purpose of demonstrating the technique.

Examples

(1) The system with which we shall concern ourselves consists of N open-hearth furnaces ($N = 5$ in this instance) and B chargers ($B = 3$ at the moment).

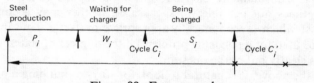

Figure 80. Furnace cycle

The production cycle times of each furnace are independently and identically distributed; the charging times of each charger are independently and identically distributed.

From time to time open-hearth furnaces will be held up because of bunching, i.e. more than B furnaces may be requiring charging at the same time.

The problem is to determine, in particular, whether a further charger is economically justifiable, and, in general, what the optimal number of chargers is. Priority is given to steel-making which is recognized as the bottleneck.

The complete cycle, C_i, of a specific furnace, i, can be broken into three phases, as shown in Figure 80.

If we take a random point in time, then a necessary and sufficient condition that at least one furnace will be waiting is that at least $B + 1$ furnaces require charging.

Let us refer to the combined waiting and charging period as π_i. Then the above condition is equivalent to the overlapping of at least $B + 1$ periods π_i at that point in time; if at least $B + 1$ periods overlap, then we have at least $B + 1$ furnaces either waiting or being charged, but we cannot have more than B being charged, and hence at least one is waiting; conversely if less than $B + 1$ periods overlap, then they must all overlap in a charging period, since otherwise we would have a furnace waiting unnecessarily. Figure 81 illustrates this.

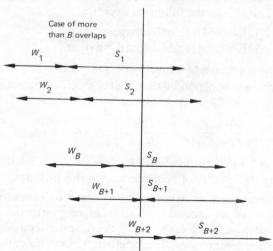

Figure 81. Furnace operational states

Now the proportion of time spent by an individual furnace in its π phase is:

$$(\hat{W} + \hat{S})/(\hat{P} + \hat{S} + \hat{W}) = \rho \qquad 2$$

where $\sim$ is used to denote the average value of each variable.

Referring to our posit θ, in this instance this becomes the posit that the economics of the situation will require that the average waiting time, $\hat{W}$, will be much smaller than $\hat{S}$ and $\hat{P}$.

Thus we then have an approximation for ρ:

$$\rho \sim \hat{S}/(\hat{P} + \hat{S}) \qquad 3$$

In the limit when $\hat{W} = 0$, there will be no interdependence between cycle lengths of each furnace; if $\hat{W}$ is small there will be only a small interdependence between the cycle lengths of each furnace. Therefore, as a first approximation, the proportion of time, λ_K, in which we have K overlapping phases, of the type π, being equal to the long-run probability that K such phases will overlap, is given by:

$$\lambda_K = \binom{N}{K} \rho^K (1 - \rho)^{N-K}. \qquad 4$$

The total annual time spent waiting, in years, by the group of furnaces is then given by:

$$W(B) = \sum_{K > B} (K - B) \lambda_K \qquad 5$$

If A is the annual total cost of a charger, and if f is the annual net output value of a single furnace, with no time spent waiting or being charged, then B should be chosen to minimize:

$$C(B) = f \sum_{K > B} (K - B) \lambda_K + AB \qquad 6$$

168

The specific problem of whether or not to add an extra charger reduced, in the case when $N = 5$, $B = 3$, to the following decision:

if $A < f(\lambda_4 + \lambda_5)$ then add a fourth charger;
if $A > f(\lambda_4 + \lambda_5)$ then do not add a fourth charger.

The decision was not to add a fourth charger.

The approximate proportion of time that a specific furnace will be waiting is given by:

$$\frac{\hat{W}(B)}{\hat{W}(B) + \hat{S} + \hat{P}} = \frac{W(B)}{N} = \left[\sum_{K>B} (K - B)\lambda_K \right] / N \qquad 7$$

From equation 7 we can estimate $\hat{W}(B)$. It was found that $\hat{W}(3)$, $\hat{W}(4) \ll \hat{S}, \hat{P}$, thus establishing the validity of proposition θ in this instance.

(2) The problem posed was whether it was useful to have a special unit which received and retained all general surgical emergency arrivals, rather than have the present situation in which each unit in the hospital set aside spare beds each day to receive such emergencies. The brief study now presented is only a small part of this total problem, in which we initially examined the influence of the size of such a special unit on the effectiveness with which it could cope with the emergency arrivals.

The distribution functions for arrival patterns and service patterns (duration of stay) were examined and it was established that the arrival pattern was reasonably compatible with a negative exponential distribution.

The situation is therefore a queueing-type situation in which, however, the queue is never allowed to form. The actions taken when emergencies exceed spare beds are numerous, resulting, however, in undesirable interference with the system. In order to avoid dependence on outside resources, one way of handling such excesses is to give an early discharge to suitable patients. This, therefore, indirectly influences the service distribution (duration of stay). It is useful, therefore, to examine the influence of unit size on this factor, assuming the unit copes in this way for excess emergencies.

If we allow the queues to form in the conventional queueing system, if we have C beds and if ρ is the traffic intensity, the steady-state probability that there will be n patients (waiting and being served) in the system at any time is given by:

$$P(n) = \frac{\rho^n}{n!} P(0) \quad (n \leqslant C) \qquad 8$$

$$P(n) = \left(\frac{\rho}{C}\right)^n \frac{C^C}{C!} P(0) \quad (n \geqslant C) \qquad 9$$

where:

$$P(0)^{-1} = \sum_{n \leqslant C} \left(\frac{\rho^n}{n!}\right) + \frac{C^C}{C!} \sum_{n>C} \left(\frac{\rho}{C}\right)^n \qquad 10$$

$\rho = \lambda/\mu$, λ = mean arrival rate, μ = mean service rate.

Now let us look at a possible time history of such a system, as given in Figure 82.

The shaded areas indicate those conditions in which an emergency would have to wait unless (as we assume in this study) some of those already being served were given an early discharge. The effect of early discharges would be to produce a history as shown in Figure 83.

Now let us assume that any solution acceptable to the medical authorities is such as to require that the average excess be small in the sense that the proportional reduction in duration of stay is small. This is our posit θ.

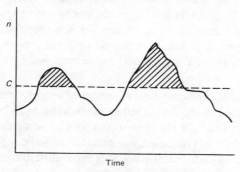

Figure 82. Potential queueing behaviour

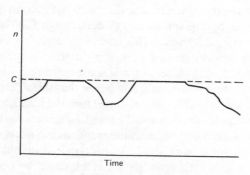

Figure 83. Elimination of queue by early discharge

In this case we can still use the original traffic intensity, ρ, as an approximation to the final traffic intensity, and therefore use equations 8–10 to estimate the potential queues which would have to be absorbed instantaneously.

We can then calculate the average lost patient days/day through early discharge, necessitated in dissipating the queue, as follows:

$$L(C) = \sum_{n>C} (n-C)P(n) = \rho^{C+1}P(0)/(C-\rho)^2(C-1)! \qquad \textbf{11}$$

The average required patient days/day is given as follows:

$$R = \text{arrival rate} \times \text{average duration of stay (required)}$$
$$= \rho \qquad \textbf{12}$$

170

Hence the average reduction in duration of stay, required to accommodate excess emergencies via early discharges, is approximately given by:

$$\Delta(\mu^{-1}(C)) = L(C)/\rho\mu = \rho^C P(0)/(C-\rho)^2(C-1)!\,\mu \qquad \textbf{13}$$

Even if we turn to outside resources to help in the case of excess emergencies, equations **8–10** will still give an estimate of the potential queue build-up since, in this case, the effect is to reduce the demand on the special unit. Provided the average excess potential queue is small with respect to average arrival rate, then the potential queue build-up is still dictated by equations **8–10**.

In this case the objective of this past exercise was specifically to find the proportional reduction in duration of stay, and thus the testing of θ is implicit in equation **13**. The values of C considered are determined by setting upper limits on $\Delta(\mu^{-1}(C))$.

(3) This problem concerns the determination of a re-order policy for a specific type of steel sheet used in the manufacture of such things as boilers.

The pattern of demand for the sheet was taken to be determined by the production pattern and, in this instance, was established to be reasonably consistent with an independently distributed weekly demand distribution, although this is not necessary in what follows.

The nature of supply was such that an order for steel sheets might be satisfied in varying portions at varying times. The distribution function for the proportion of an order delivered by a given time was determined for the historical order pattern, which had existed hitherto. This tended to centre on a fixed size of order quantity, and there was the danger that, if a different order size were chosen, this distribution would not suffice, but it was expected that the order quantities would still be large, rather than small, and hence that this distribution would not be unreasonable to use. It was further assumed that the likelihood of a significant overlap between orders placed was small enough to ignore, so that we could treat the arrival quantities from one order as independent of another order.

The prime purpose of having stock is, of course, to avoid run-outs. In this case if a run-out occurred, then the deficit stock could be obtained at a small stockholders on payment of a 10% premium, with a virtually instant delivery.

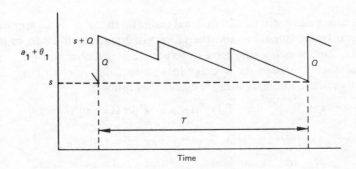

Figure 84. Stock level pattern

The problem was to determine an optimal economic re-order rule over a long time period, bearing in mind interest, discount and penalty costs.

Since the re-order decision depended not only on stock on hand, but also on stock on order, but not yet delivered, a re-order decision rule of the following kind was investigated:

'Re-order a quantity Q when the sum of the stock on hand (a) and the stock on order (θ) equals a critical level (s).'

Consider two successive re-order epochs, and let t be any week between the two, measured from the first one as the datum point, indicated in Figure 84.

Let b_t = the stock level (allowing negative stock) at the end of time t if no emergency replenishments were allowed and production was simply delayed.

Let:

a_t = actual stock on hand at the end of time period t allowing emergency replenishments;

d_t = total demand up to the end of period t;

δ_t = individual demand in period t;

e_t = total emergency supplies up to end of period t;

ε_t = individual emergency supplies in period t;

T = realized cycle length;

θ_t = stock on order at end of time period t;

ϕ_t = stock delivered in time period t;

α = premium payment per unit of emergency purchase;

β = stock holding cost per unit of stock per period.

Then we obtain:

$$b_t = s + Q - \theta_t - d_t \qquad \textbf{14}$$

$$a_t = s + Q - \theta_t - d_t + e_t \qquad \textbf{15}$$

In the special case when $t = 0$, we have to interpret a_0 as the stock on hand at the beginning of the cycle, and obtain:

$$a_0 = s + Q - \theta_0 \qquad \textbf{16}$$

At the end of the cycle we have:

$$a_T = s + Q - \theta_T - d_T + e_T \qquad \textbf{17}$$

Now the cycle terminates when $a_T + \theta_T = s$. Hence, from equation **17**, the cycle terminates when:

$$d_T = Q + e_T \qquad \textbf{18}$$

Now our posit θ is, in this instance, the posit that, in the optimal solution, e_T will be small. In this case the cycle time T is primarily determined by the value of T at which we get:

$$d_T = Q \qquad \textbf{19}$$

From equation **14**:

$$b_t = b_{t-1} - (\theta_t - \theta_{t-1}) - (d_t - d_{t-1})$$
$$= b_{t-1} + \phi_t - \delta_t \qquad \textbf{20}$$

We now have, using equation **20**:

$$-\varepsilon_t = \min\,[a_{t-1} + \phi_t - \delta_t, 0]$$
$$= \min\,[b_{t-1} + e_{t-1} + \phi_t - \delta_t, 0]$$
$$= \min\,[b_t + e_{t-1}, 0] \qquad\qquad \textbf{21}$$

Now, although e_{t-1} is correlated with b_t, if, as we posit, e_{t-1} is small, then the distribution of ε_t is determined by the distribution of b_t, to a large extent; thus the mean and variance of b_t are much larger than the mean and variance of e_{t-1} (if our posit is true). In Figure 85, which illustrates this, we are saying that ε_t is much more dependent on primary demand and primary replenishment characteristics than on the possibilities of run-outs at earlier stages, although it is correlated with them.

Invoking our posit we can now determine the average emergency cost/cycle as:

$$\text{Expected emergency cost (EEC)/cycle} = -\alpha \exp_T \sum_{t=1}^{T} \exp_t (\min\,[b_t + e_{t-1}, 0]) \qquad \textbf{22}$$

$$\simeq -\alpha \exp_T \sum_{t=1}^{T} \exp_t (\min\,[b_t, 0]) \qquad \textbf{22}'$$

where the distribution of T is taken from equation **19**.

Using similar reasoning and the fact that $a_t = b_t + e_t$, we have:

$$\text{The expected stockholding cost (ESH)/cycle} = \beta \exp_T \sum_{t=1}^{T} \exp_t (b_t + e_t) \qquad \textbf{23}$$

$$\simeq \beta \exp_T \sum_{t=1}^{T} \exp_t (b_t) \qquad \textbf{23}'$$

The purchase cost of order quantity Q is $P(Q)$.
The problem then reduces to finding s, Q to minimize:

$$\frac{\text{EEC}(s,\,Q) + \text{ESH}(s,\,Q) + P(Q)}{\exp_T (T)} \qquad \textbf{24}$$

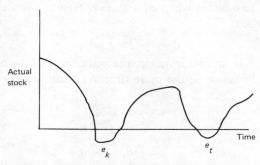

Figure 85. Emergency requirements pattern

It will be seen that the essential contribution, by ignoring e_t, is that we can calculate, relatively easily, all the quantities required, without having to consider the complicated interaction between e_t and the other variables.

The only difficult part was the determination of the distribution of θ_t. This had a contribution from several previous cycles and its distribution was obtained by assuming that there was no interference, from the point of view of satisfying orders at the beginning of each cycle, between cycles. Then the distribution of cycle length and distribution of proportion of an order delivered by a given time, were all that was needed to find the distribution of θ_t.

The solution was obtained by considering various values of (s, Q) and choosing the optimum from among these. A check was made on the distribution of $-\min[b_t, 0]$ and this had a very small variance and mean. Thus $e_T = (\sum_1^T \varepsilon_t)$ had a small mean and variance. After operation for some time, even after reducing the stocks by 50%, no run-outs had been experienced. The mean of e_T was much smaller than Q, thus validating equation 18. Finally, the relative independence between the delivery cycles of two successive orders was established by showing that it was very likely that most of one order would be delivered before another was ordered.

The checks were made for all T within the likely range of T given by (s, Q).

The principles would not be complete without some attempt to structure the general situation with which we are dealing. The following is a rather heuristic approach to this, which may lead to a more precise and rigorous analysis at a later date, although this is expected to be rather complicated.

Perhaps one point ought to be stressed, *viz.*, the 'assumption' of infrequent occurrence followed by a 'demonstration' of infrequent occurrence is not a circular argument.

The 'assumption' is essentially the starting point of an iterative process (in principle) for handling equations 26 and 27 given below. The 'demonstration' is essentially the next stage in the iteration. In the studies mentioned it was felt that there was no need to go further, although, in general, this need not be the case.

Let the general control vector be **x**.

Let the behavioural characteristics be: **z**, ε, where ε relates to the infrequent undesirable occurrences referred to in the main part of the text.

The general problem can then be stated as one of

$$\underset{\mathbf{x}}{\text{minimizing}} [X(\mathbf{x}, \mathbf{z}, \varepsilon)] \qquad 25$$

subject to:

$$\mathbf{z} = f(\mathbf{x}, \varepsilon) \qquad 26$$

$$\varepsilon = g(\mathbf{x}, \varepsilon) \qquad 27$$

In example A:

x = B;

z: is not applicable;

ε = **w** (waiting time vector);

X: is given by equation 6, substituting equations 4 and 2;

g: is obtained from equation 7.

In example B:

$\mathbf{x} = C$;

$\mathbf{z}$: is not applicable;

$\varepsilon = P(n), n \geqslant C$;

X: has not been examined;

g: is obtained from equations **8–10** using $\rho = \lambda\{\mu^{-1} + \Delta(\mu^{-1}(C))\}$ in equation **13**.

In example C:

$\mathbf{x} = (s, Q)$;

$\mathbf{z} = (\mathbf{a}, d_T)$;

$\varepsilon = \varepsilon$;

X is given by equation **24** substituting equations **18, 22, 23**;
f is given by equation **15** (for each t) and equation **18**, using

$$e_T = \sum_{t=1}^{T} \varepsilon_t$$

g is given by equation **21**, using

$$e_{t-1} = \sum_{s=1}^{t-1} \varepsilon_s$$

In terms of the general formulation, the approach is equivalent to the following:

(i) put: $\varepsilon^0 = 0$;

(ii) put: $\mathbf{z} = f(\mathbf{x}, \mathbf{0})$, $\varepsilon = g(\mathbf{x}, \mathbf{0})$;

(iii) maximize$_\mathbf{x}$ $[X(\mathbf{x}, \mathbf{z}, \varepsilon)]$ to give $\mathbf{x}^0$;

(iv) check that: $\varepsilon^1 = g(\mathbf{x}^0, \mathbf{0})$ is small enough to make the approximation in (ii) valid within the region of $\mathbf{x}^0$, i.e.: in region of $\mathbf{x}^0$

$$1 \simeq f(\mathbf{x}, \mathbf{0})/f(\mathbf{x}, \varepsilon^1)$$
$$1 \simeq g(\mathbf{x}, \mathbf{0})/g(\mathbf{x}, \varepsilon^1)$$

Strictly speaking one should use the iterative process of defining a sequence $\{\varepsilon^n\}$ and $\{\mathbf{x}^n\}$ as follows:

$$\varepsilon^n = g(\mathbf{x}^{n-1}, \varepsilon^{n-1})$$
$$\mathbf{x}^{n-1} \underset{\mathbf{x}}{\text{minimizing}} \, [X(\mathbf{x}, f(\mathbf{x}, \varepsilon^{n-1}), g(\mathbf{x}, \varepsilon^{n-1}))]$$

However, this may not be necessary and we may be lucky in that, at the first stage, the smallness of ε^1 is sufficient to indicate the initial solution $\mathbf{x}^0$ as a good approximation. In the three cases studied, ε^1 was, indeed, very small (in case B this was within an anticipated region of $C = 50$).

The following examples use similar principles. Thus Example 4 uses a postulate that 'the probability of no queue is small', as distinct from the assumption that 'the probability that a queue exists is small'. They are briefly covered, but strengthen the approach developed in the more detailed studies.

(4) In a certain production problem, the total workload varied from week to week, but with reasonable spare capacity on average. Sometimes there arose the

question of whether weekend working to complete the load was desirable. If it was done, it very often involved some plant being very uneconomically used, and it was possible to delay the work until the next week, with possible economies in production. Now the work in any week depends on the normal input demands plus any work held over until that week. On the assumption that this would, in the optimal solution, seldom be much, we can use the dynamic programming approach to solve this problem.

Let:

s be the set of jobs to be done in a week;

x denote the set actually done in that week;

z be the new arrivals in the next week;

$p(z)$ be the probability of z, and let it be independently distributed from week to week;

$c(s, x)$ be the production cost of decision x for the given set s;

$v(s)$ be the transient value of s in the optimal steady-state solution;

g be the average cost per unit time using the optimal policy.

Then:

$$v(s) + g = \min_{x} [c(s, x) + \sum_{z} p(z) v(z + s - x)] \qquad 1$$

If we assume $s - x \ll z$ most of the time, we have a new equation:

$$V(s) + G = \min_{x} [c(s, x) + \sum_{z} p(z) V(z)] \qquad 2$$

Let $V = \sum_{z} p(z) V(z)$.

This gives:

$$V + G = \sum_{s} p(s) \min_{x} [c(s, x) + V]$$

i.e.

$$G = \sum_{s} p(s) \min_{x} [c(s, x)]$$

Thus:

$$V(s) = \min_{x} [c(s, x) + V - G] \qquad 3$$

Using $V(s)$ as an approximation to $v(s)$, equation 1 becomes

$$v(s) + g = \min_{x} [c(s, x) + \sum_{z} p(z) \min_{y} [c(z + s - x, y)] + (V - G)] \qquad 4$$

Thus the problem can be solved essentially as a 2-stage process.

We need, of course, to check that the extent to which work is delayed, in the optimal solution, is not too large.

In White[153] a fuller account of the problem may be found. In particular it is necessary to place certain constraints on the range of x.

(5) In a problem concerning the scheduling of ambulances, it was an empirical fact that most of the patients were very late for appointments. It was therefore

reasonable to assume that whenever an ambulance returned to base it was important to despatch it as soon as possible since there would frequently be a queue of patients to be picked up who would, in any event, be late for appointment. This enabled the total schedule time to be determined without having to decide when to send out an ambulance.

In this case we assume the probability of no queue is small.

In other circumstances it could arise that the capacity was such as to keep in advance of appointments' needs, in which case ambulances would not necessarily be despatched on return to base.

(6) Consider a queueing problem with N channels, and constant service time, s, for each. Let a cycle commence at the beginning of a service.

Consider the beginning of a cycle for channel 1 as given in Figure 86.

Figure 86. Individual channel cycle

Let t be the cycle time.

If there are n people in the system at the beginning of the cycle, we have two possibilities:

(a) $n > N$;
(b) $n \leqslant N$.

If we assume that the probability that $n > N$ is very small, then we need only consider case (b).

In case (b), since channels 2, 3, ..., N will become empty and must commence service again before channel 1, channel 1 will commence service again at a time $t = \max(s, \tau)$ where τ is the time taken for N further arrivals.

Figure 86 gives the case when $t > s$.

t is therefore substantially independent of n, and the state of the other channels.

Hence we can assume the channels almost independent and have an average cycle time of aN, if 'a' is the average interarrival time. This could be obtained from the distribution of t but the difference will be small if 'a' is infrequent.

Then the probability of having r channels occupied at any point in time is

$$\simeq \binom{N}{r}\left(\frac{s}{aN}\right)^r$$

This depends only on mean interarrival time a and mean service time s.

We can now calculate the probability of a facility not being available when an item arrives, when the arrival pattern is negative exponential, since then the arrival is independent of system condition. This is:

$$\left(\frac{s}{aN}\right)^N$$

We have seen that we can have infrequent but significant contingencies to cater for in some problems, and we can facilitate the solution in a certain way. There are other instances when small, but persistent, contingencies also arise, the effect on profitability of which may be significant, but in which the effects on other factors needed to be considered to solve the problem are small. We may, for the latter purpose, ignore them.

(7) In the overage problem, in which an allowance for defective production has to be made in advance of production, the effect of excess production, for example, will depend on the level of opportunities for using this. The level of opportunities will depend on the general mix and level of production, which will only be marginally influenced by the overage policy, providing the overage is not more than, say, α %. Thus, in calculating the effect of excess production one may, as a first approximation, assume that the present pattern of handling excesses prevails. If the optimal solution then indicates a need for large overages, the model needs reconstructing.

Formally the model is as follows:

$E = f(P, \theta, D)$;
$EE = g(\theta, 0)$;
$O = h(\theta, D)$;
E: excess production;
EE: economic effects of excess production;
θ: overage policy;
P: production policy;
D: production demand;
O: opportunities for using excess.

The method suggested reduces to assuming O is relatively independent of θ, providing it is not too large.

(8) In a study of the operations of depots, responsible for carrying out work of various kinds, it was required to determine the size of depot labour force. It was possible that labour could be idle, because there was no job in the queue which could be completed in the day, and hence they would not start it. It seemed reasonable to suppress this factor when determining queue behaviour and to check this when the final solution was obtained. If the frequency of this event was small, it was justified. To include it directly would have resulted in a complicated analysis.

2.3.5.3 DOMINANT VARIABLE PRINCIPLE

In some cases there can be several variables in terms of which decisions are evaluated, but some of them may be in conflict with others at a first glance, and possibly inhibit further study. However, further thought may prove that no conflict arises. Thus, treating one of them as a dominating variable may reduce calculations.

In the end analysis we still have to find ways of checking that such procedures will result in an overall improvement in performance. This might be achievable by experimentation, simulation or analysis, depending on the problem concerned.

Examples

(1) In a furnace loading problem, attempts to be selective, in order to improve furnace utilization, may give rise to apparent increase in waiting time for some. However, improved utilization gives an increased service rate and, in the long run, not only the average waiting time, but also the 'spread', may improve. Thus a procedure which, with certain safeguards (such as no job to be left longer than one week), concentrates on instantaneous utilization as a dominating variable, may give a good long-run service also.

We can easily calculate the maximum achievable service rate by assuming that the capacity of furnaces is utilized to maximum. This rate can be used to get estimates of the waiting time. If this is significantly better than at present, an effort to obtain maximal utilization could be made.

(2) In a maintenance scheduling exercise, jobs are geographically dispersed. If we wait until enough jobs have been collected in one area, this may seem to reduce the service. However, the transport time between jobs is reduced and the

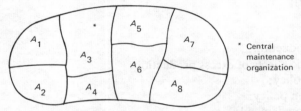

Figure 87. Area maintenance scheduling

net service may be better in the long run since the service rate is effectively improved. Thus concentrating on interjob travelling time as a dominant variable may save computational time (see Figure 87).

If one treated jobs in sequence, assuming they arrive geographically randomly in total area A, one can calculate average lost man hours travelling, and hence some average service rate. If one served areas $A_1, A_2, \ldots, A_8$ in sequence, one can determine average travelling man hours, and get a new effective service rate. In each case an estimate of waiting time may be derivable, allowing a comparison.

(3) In vehicle routing problems, given the pattern of loads to be picked up or delivered, there are many constraints which could arise, e.g. vehicle may be unsuitable for a given customer, crews may be given differing work contents, etc. However, one important variable is operating cost. Many routing procedures operate on a basis of cutting down 'distance' travelled. This is a dominant variable. Solutions obtained this way are then examined for their other implications. If they violate these too greatly, then a new approach is needed. However, if they do not violate them too much, minor adjustments can be made, and we avoid having to build in all the complexities.

2.3.5.4 INDEPENDENT MARGINAL IMPROVEMENT PRINCIPLE

Sometimes a decision situation is made up of two types of decision. One method of solving this is to fix one, optimize the other, then fix this and optimize the first, and so on.

Thus we have:

$$\max_{x \in R(y)} \max_{y \in S(x)} [v(x, y)]$$

Fix $y = y_1$

Find x_1 to $\max\limits_{x \in R(y_1)} [v(x, y_1)]$

Find y_2 to $\max\limits_{y_2 \in S(x_1)} [v(x_1, y)]$

and so on.

However, although this will always improve v, it may result in a local optimum if care is not taken.

Examples

(1) Consider the problem of locating two warehouses and allocating customers to them so as to minimize total costs.

In this case x is the location decision; y is the allocation decision.

The following method has been suggested:

 (i) choose initial locations;
 (ii) allocate customers to nearest location;
(iii) using this allocation, relocate the warehouses;
(iv) go back to (ii) and repeat until the solution converges.

Consider the following situation of four customers and two warehouses, with demand from A, B, C, D equal to 1, 2, 3, 4 respectively (not necessary of course), as illustrated by Figure 88.

Let $AB > BD$.

Let us take initial solutions $((A, B \rightarrow X), (C, D \rightarrow Y))$, or $((A, C \rightarrow Z), (B, D \rightarrow W))$, or $((A, D \rightarrow h), (B, C \rightarrow h))$.

Then consider the first initial solution and consider step (iii). This will result in X remaining on the line AB but moving to B, and Y remaining on the line CD but moving to D. Repeating step (ii) we will still allocate AB to X and CD to Y. Hence we converge at the solution $((A, B \rightarrow B), (C, D \rightarrow D))$.

Suppose we now consider the second initial solution, then we end up at $((A, C \rightarrow C), (B, D \rightarrow D))$.

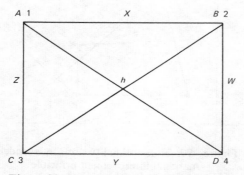

Figure 88. Warehouse allocation problem

For the third initial solution, we end up with the previous solution, *viz.*, $((A, C \to C), (B, D \to D))$.

Thus three different initial points give us two final solutions which do not, in general, have the same cost.

(2) When producing various combinations of things from a specific piece of raw material, two problems arise, *viz.*,

(a) what should the raw material mix be?
(b) how should we use this to produce requirements?

The combined problem can be complex. One way to solve this may be to:

(i) determine the raw materials to minimize (material + production) costs on the basis of a specific production policy for using it;
(ii) determine the best production policy for the mix determined in (i), to optimize (production + material) costs;
(iii) repeat cycle at (i) (see Figure 89).

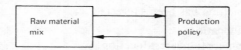

Figure 89. Raw material purchase and
production problem

This will result in improved policies but we may have a suboptimal result in the end.

In situations in which a local optimum is also a global optimum then the above procedure will suffice. This happens, for example, when $v(x,y)$ is concave (convex) in its arguments, if we are maximizing (minimizing), providing the global optimum is strictly interior to the constraints placed upon x, y. Otherwise this may not be the case, as is easily demonstrated by the linear programming problem illustrated by Figure 90.

In Figure 90, if we begin with A we end up with C, which is a local optimum (for independent variations only of x, y) but is not a global optimum, which is at D.

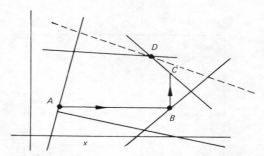

Figure 90. Non-optimality of independent
marginal improvement principle

Damon and Schramm[30] study the differences between simultaneous optimization and sequential optimization, in which sequential optimization is carried out by each area estimating the behaviour of the other areas at each point in time for the purposes of making their own decisions at such points. This is similar to the above approach, but is dynamic in the sense that decisions are made at each point in time on the basis of past behaviour, whereas in the above example the production policy is evaluated on a simultaneous basis, for a given time horizon, for a given raw material mix.

2.3.5.5 PRESENT DECISIONS AND FUTURE TIME PATTERNS ROBUSTNESS PRINCIPLE

Sometimes decisions are made at one point in time, the outcome of which depends on future patterns of events and decisions. At this point in time such perceived time patterns may take a specific form, but as time goes on they may change. To cater for these changes, say on a probabilistic basis, may be difficult, whereas the optimal decision, now, may not be very sensitive to such changes. If this turns out to be the case it saves a lot of work.

Examples

(1) In a company producing boilers, the demand for plate is seen to take a specific form at one point in time, spreading over many weeks ahead. This 'picture' will change as time goes on, and new orders arrive and some rescheduling also takes place. However, the optimal decision on ordering, now, may not be very sensitive to changes in this pattern.

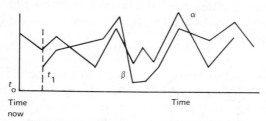

Figure 91. Changing demand patterns

In Figure 91 curve α is the estimated requirements as at time t_0 now. At time t_1 we have a new estimate curve, β, looking ahead one time period further than at t_1.

In order to validate a decision procedure based only on the picture as it is at a given point in time, we need to know the manner in which such pictures change over time.

(2) In a company purchasing items for its production programme, the demand in a sequence of time periods was known, but the demand after these time periods was not known. The economic conflicts were that a batching process would provide a high discount rate, but would order items before needed. The real solution depends on the orders after the time span covered. It may be that the decision to be made now does not depend, in some circumstances, on the orders to come after the end of the period covered, e.g. if we cover weeks 1–20, it may be

that weeks 1–10 will be batched together whatever the orders in weeks 21, 22, . . ., etc.

One technique which plays a role in such situations is dynamic programming in which the concern with immediate decisions can be reflected in the way the equations are handled.

Example

Refer to Figures 74 and 75 of Section 2.3.2 where backward and forward dynamic programming formulations are shown to have some value in this sort of situation.

2.3.5.6 COMBINED METHODS PRINCIPLE

We will discuss three methods, *viz.*:

(A) combined use of analytic and simulation approaches;
(B) combined use of enumerative and algorithmic approaches;
(C) combined use of approximate and exact approaches.

A COMBINED USE OF ANALYTIC AND SIMULATION APPROACHES

In some cases it is only necessary to establish an order of magnitude of results and some compromise between analytic and simulation approaches may be useful. Analytic solutions may not be available under the true conditions of the model. However, analytic solutions may be possible for 'distortions' of the model. The simulation is then used as a control mechanism to see if the magnitudes of conclusions of the analytic model are supported by the simulation in the region of the optimal solution.

Examples

(1) In a problem of determining whether a new emergency unit should be set up in a hospital, the probability distributions were assumed to be continuous, in time, whereas the departure pattern was restricted to certain times of the day. The optimal solution, under continuity conditions, indicated a clear reduction in throughput with any reasonably sized unit. A simulation run was used to test whether, in the region of acceptable solutions, the behaviour in terms of expected shortages, throughputs, etc., was in reasonable agreement with the analytic solution.

In this connection, it is worth going back to the statement in Section 2.3.3 by Hanssmann[54] who states:

'We can frequently predict the relative value of alternatives much more precisely than absolute performance.'

Thus, in the above example, it is easy to discriminate between the two alternatives, with and without the unit, but not to get absolute performance of each.

(2) In a study of provision of spares for a Transport Department the analytics of the 'real' situation was difficult and simulation seemed to be the only prospect. This was all right as a 'research project approach', but the multiple application

to other Transport Departments was envisaged and repeated simulation was undesirable. One way out of this was to compare simulation and simplified analysis for parametric values (e.g. fleet size, costs, etc.), which would span the Departments envisaged. Some idea of the usefulness of the approximation over a given range could be used to decide whether the approximation was valid (see Figure 92).

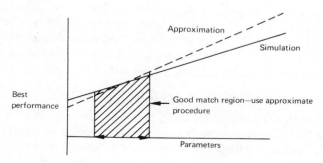

Figure 92. Simulation *vs.* simplified analysis for spare engines

One would, of course, only do the calculations and testing for a few suitably chosen values, interpolating for the rest.

B   COMBINED USE OF ENUMERATIVE AND ALGORITHMIC APPROACHES

We have already referred to situations in which combined hierarchical decisions arise. Sometimes it is the policy to enumerate the higher-level decisions, and to use an algorithm to solve the lower-level operational decision problem.

Examples

(1) Hanssmann[54] gives an example of a combined enumerative and algorithm process. The 'strategic' decision (facilities location) was analysed by enumeration; the 'tactical' decision (supply and distribution) was analysed by linear programming.

(2) In a study of shipbuilding schedules and facilities, the higher-level facilities decision was made enumerative, and the optimal labour forces and sequences for the schedules were obtained using a mathematical algorithm.

In each of these cases the justification arose from the essentially limited feasible and profitable areas for the higher-level decisions, whereas the other decisions were very numerous in their alternatives.

C   COMBINED USE OF APPROXIMATE AND EXACT APPROACHES

When a problem is repetitive, either over time or for a class of problems, it can be expensive to calculate the precise optimum in each case. It is sometimes useful to develop an approximate technique and to test its efficiency on a sample of situations.

Example

A company had the repetitive (over time and for different items) problem of batching production to get the best compromise between stockholding costs and quantity discounts. They developed an approximate method and tested its efficiency using dynamic programming, which gave the true answer to the problems as they were formulated.

In the above example, the problem as formulated was not the true problem, since dynamic changes in the order position were not taken into account in the individual calculations. The approximate method could conceivably have been better. However, given the formulation used for the approximate method, the dynamic programming approach was a valid test of the method.

2.3.5.7 GROUPING PRINCIPLE

Throughout the domain of Decision Analysis we meet, from time to time, problems in which certain variables assume many values in different ways. For example, we may be dealing with a variety of products; or we may be dealing with a variety of machines; or we may be dealing with a variety of locations; or we may be dealing with a variety of product states. And so on.

This variety very often creates considerable computational problems and leads to a search for ways of grouping them without severely infringing the validity of the problem formulation and model.

As with the other quick methods of solution, then so do we face the same problem, *viz.*, we can elect to use the comprehensive expensive method, or we can elect to go for the less comprehensive, less expensive method. Naturally, checks have to be made to ascertain that the latter approach is reasonable.

The following will illustrate some of the possible situations, *viz.*:

(A) state or event grouping;
(B) grouping of parametrized sets of problems;
(C) grouping of interacting items;
(D) grouping of decisions;
(E) grouping via the Pareto law.

A   GROUPING OF STATES OR EVENTS

Example

In dynamic programming the dimensionality of the states can give rise to mammoth computational and storage difficulties.

Since the solution mechanism is essentially a discrete process, we can group states (and events) and solve the reduced model, which becomes computationally feasible, e.g. the problem

$$f_n(i) = \min_j \, [c(i,j) + f_{n-1}(j)], \quad i = 1, 2, \ldots, m$$

becomes

$$f_n^*(I) = \min_j \, [c^*(I,J) + f_{n-1}^*(J)], \quad I = 1, 2, \ldots, M$$

where we only allow moves within the set $\{I\}$ (see Figure 93).

Figure 93. State grouping

If we only want to go from $i = 1$ to $i = m$, then we fix datum points in group I_r, to be used in getting from 1 to m. Suppose i_r is a representative point in I_r. Then we solve the problems of getting between each pair in each closed set I_r, and assume that to get from i, in I_r, to j in I_s, we move from i to i_r in an optimal manner, then from i_r to i_s via the representative points in an optimal manner, and then from i_s to j in an optimal manner.

If we need to cover all i, we travel within groups and then between groups. Thus we find sequences in each group which cover all points in a group, and then find sequences of groups.

We might be able to say something about the errors involved, and indeed, in considering this methodology, the errors involved must, of course, receive consideration. Thus the justification might derive to some extent from a demonstration that if i, j are in a group I_1, there exists a better route between i and j within I_1 than any route containing points not in I_1.

As an illustration, Table 7 considers a case with: $m = 5$, $M = 3$, $I_1 = 1 \equiv (1)$, $I_2 = 2 \equiv (2,3)$, $I_3 = 3 \equiv (4,5)$; representatives of I_1, I_2, I_3 are $i = 1$, 3, 5, respectively. The grouping sequence over n stages might be: $2 \to 3 \to \to \to 3 \to 3 \to 2$. Then to get from $i = 3$ to $i = 3$, over n stages, we would go $3 \to 5 \to \to \cdots 5 \to 5 \to 3$.

Table 7: State grouping

Grouping model $i\ (I)$				
5 (3)	5 (3)	5 (3)	5 (3)	5 (3)
4	4	4	4	4
3 (2)	3 (2)	3 (2)	3 (2)	3 (2)
2	2	2	2	2
1 (1)	1 (1)	1 (1)	1 (1)	1 (1)
n	$n - 1$	2	1	0

B   GROUPING OF PARAMETRIZED SETS OF PROBLEMS

Example

There are cases in which a company is concerned with the independent control of a variety of stock items, running into many thousands sometimes.

In such cases it is usual to get a crude grouping of the items according to certain characteristics, such as:

lead time characteristics (long, medium, short);
penalty cost characteristics (high, medium, low);
deterioration characteristics (high, medium, low).

186

This way, we may reduce the number of groups to a few, and use mean parameters for each group.

The degree of suboptimality should be checked by a sample testing procedure. Thus if $p_1, p_2, \ldots, p_k$ are the various characteristic variables, we need to carry out a statistical analysis to determine the distribution of such parameters in a subjectively chosen group. For any such distribution the average error in using mean values can be calculated. If this is too large, the group needs to be broken down further. In addition, since we only have a sample of values of $p_1, p_2, \ldots, p_k$, we must determine our confidence in the estimation of the distribution. The acceptance of any grouping must be seen in the light of extra work needed for refinement against gains in confidence and degree of optimality.

C GROUPING OF INTERACTING ITEMS

Example

In production scheduling we may be faced, in any one week, with a very large number of jobs and operations to schedule. It may be very expensive to consider each one separately, and so we try to group them according to characteristics of some kind.

In a steel company, the weekly production programme may involve several hundred jobs with several operations on each, and it is first of all required to get a general balance of work load on all the equipment.

Each job i requires a certain production time per unit, t_{ij}, on rolling mill j, and an equivalent production time per unit, T_{ik}, in annealing furnace k.

Figure 94 indicates the situation. In this case there was a correlation between, not only the time factors on different mills for a given job, but also between the times on mills and in furnaces. Individual jobs might deviate considerably from this, but, taken over many jobs, this correlation did exist. This correlation was useful in deriving a crude overall loading procedure.

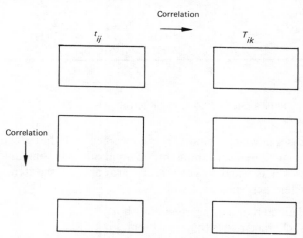

Figure 94. Rolling and annealing configuration

Let us assume we have three mills and three furnaces.
The capacity balance equations are then:

$$\sum_i x_{ij} t_{ij} \leqslant t_j \quad \text{for all } j \qquad\qquad \textbf{1}$$

$$\sum_i x_{ik} T_{ik} \leqslant T_k \quad \text{for all } k \qquad\qquad \textbf{2}$$

where:

t_j = available time on mill j;
T_i = available time in furnace i;
x_{ij} = amount of job i done on mill j;
x_{ik} = amount of job i done in furnace k.

Let us group the jobs and let I be the symbol for a group. Now suppose, approximately:

$$
\begin{aligned}
T_{ik} &\simeq \lambda_{Ik} T_{i1}, & i \in I \\
t_{ij} &\simeq \lambda_{Ij} t_{i1}, & i \in I \\
T_{i1} &\simeq \lambda_I t_{i1}, & i \in I \\
t_{i1} &\simeq Z_I, & i \in I
\end{aligned}
$$

We neglect the possibility that some jobs cannot be done on certain equipment, but the same applies in principle, with modifications.

This is only a best statistical relationship taken over all $i \in I$; thus we expect that some $i \in I$ will require three rolling reductions and some will require four, etc.

Then the above equations **1** and **2** become

$$\sum_I \sum_{i \in I} x_{ij} \lambda_{Ij} Z_I \leqslant t_j \quad \text{for all } j \qquad\qquad \textbf{1}^{\text{i}}$$

$$\sum_I \sum_{i \in I} x_{ik} \lambda_{Ik} \lambda_I Z_I \leqslant T_k \quad \text{for all } k \qquad\qquad \textbf{2}^{\text{i}}$$

i.e.

$$\sum_I (\lambda_{Ij} Z_I) \sum_{i \in I} x_{ij} \leqslant t_j \quad \text{for all } j \qquad\qquad \textbf{1}^{\text{ii}}$$

$$\sum_I (\lambda_{Ik} \lambda_I Z_I) \sum_{i \in I} x_{ik} \leqslant T_k \quad \text{for all } k \qquad\qquad \textbf{2}^{\text{ii}}$$

If $\sum_{i \in I} x_{ij} = X_{Ij}$, $\sum_{i \in I} x_{ik} = X_{Ik}$ and $\lambda_{Ik} Z_I \lambda_I = V_{Ik}$, $\lambda_{Ij} Z_I = U_{Ij}$, we have

$$\sum_I X_{Ij} U_{Ij} \leqslant t_j \quad \text{for all } j \qquad\qquad \textbf{1}^{\text{iii}}$$

$$\sum_I X_{Ik} V_{Ik} \leqslant T_k \quad \text{for all } k \qquad\qquad \textbf{2}^{\text{iii}}$$

If, further

$$
\begin{aligned}
U_{Ij} &= \gamma_j U_{I1} & \text{for all } I \\
V_{Ik} &= \eta_k V_{I1} & \text{for all } I
\end{aligned}
$$

we have

$$\sum_I X_{Ij} U_{I1} \leqslant t_j/\gamma_j \quad \text{for all } j \qquad\qquad \mathbf{1^{iv}}$$

$$\sum_I X_{Ik} V_{I1} \leqslant T_k/\eta_k \quad \text{for all } k \qquad\qquad \mathbf{2^{iv}}$$

If X_{Ij}, X_{Ik} are continuous variables, approximately, then this is equivalent to:

$$\sum_I X_I U_{I1} \leqslant \sum_j t_j/\gamma_j \quad \text{for all } j \qquad\qquad \mathbf{1^v}$$

$$\sum_I X_I V_{I1} \leqslant \sum_k T_k/\eta_k \quad \text{for all } k \qquad\qquad \mathbf{2^v}$$

This follows since, if $\{X_I\}$ satisfies $\mathbf{1^v}$, $\mathbf{2^v}$, then $\{X_{Ij}\} = (t_j/\gamma_j)/\sum_j (t_j/\gamma_j) X_I$ satisfies $\mathbf{1^{iv}}$ and $\mathbf{2^{iv}}$ and, clearly, any solution satisfying $\mathbf{1^{iv}}$, $\mathbf{2^{iv}}$ satisfies $\mathbf{1^v}$ and $\mathbf{2^v}$.

We thus see that we can have various degrees of simplicity depending on the extent to which we can make use of correlations. In the best position we have only $\mathbf{1^v}$ and $\mathbf{2^v}$. In the next best position we have $\mathbf{1^{iii}}$ and $\mathbf{2^{iii}}$. Failing these, we have to revert to $\mathbf{1}$ and $\mathbf{2}$, which can be time consuming to handle on a repetitive basis if very large numbers of jobs and machines are involved.

The validity of the approach must depend on the extent of the correlation. When the approximate solution has been obtained, possible errors must be considered.

If certain jobs cannot be done on certain machines then we make $\{t_j\}$, $\{T_k\}$ conditional on the allocations of these jobs, provisionally.

Many jobs can only be done on one machine, and this simplifies the problem.

The problem may be considerably reduced and allow a manual balancing of loads, although there is still the problem of finding a schedule sequence.

D GROUPING OF DECISIONS

In some problems the decisions concerned are combinations of decisions. For example, in routing problems, a route is a combination of moves from one location to another; in timetabling, a timetable for a class may be a specific set of subjects taken at specific times of the week; in a materials problem, a materials mix might be a combination of various lengths and widths to be taken from a specific material. By considering specified combinations as the basic components of decisions, the magnitude of the number of alternatives can be reduced, thus reducing the p. /blem to an integer programming problem, in which x_j is the number of times the specific combination is included in the total solution. Naturally there will be the need to specify the ways in which the combinations of contributions make up a total solution.

Example

If we have a materials problem, and if n_{ji} is the contribution of combination j to the ith requirement, and if the ith requirement is n_i we have

$$\sum_j n_{ji} x_j = n_i$$

As with all our grouping problems, we face the secondary problem of choosing the groups. This is done on an intuitive basis to a large extent, the premise being that certain groupings are likely to contribute more to the improvement of costs, for example, than others.

Example

If we are concerned with depot location, the grouping of locations to be served by a specific depot may be chosen intuitively. Admittedly this can be treated as a decision, but can complicate an otherwise reasonably quick study.

E   GROUPING VIA THE PARETO LAW

It is worth while noting that, when we are dealing with groups of elements, there are rough laws which describe the 'proportion of the total work, information, . . ., etc., . . . contributed by the first n items', where items are ranked according to their contribution.

Examples

(1) In a study of the frequency of references to various journals the following curve was obtained, where journals are numbered in an appropriate manner (see Figure 95).

If we take an article and determine the number of times it is referenced in various journals, then R_n represents the proportion of times it is referenced in the first n journals, ordered in a certain manner.

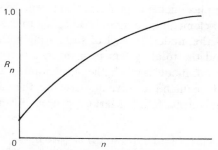

Figure 95. Reference frequency Pareto curve

This takes the form:

$$R_n = 1 - e^{-n}$$

where R_n is total contribution by the first n items.

(2) In layman's terms, in inventory control, it is often stated in something of the form:

'10% of the items account for 80% of the throughput'.
(See Figure 96.)

These 'laws' are useful in deciding on the nature of the study being carried out. Thus, in the inventory control case, if 100 items contribute 90% of the through-

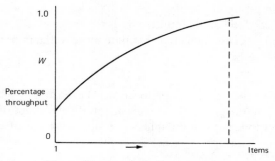

Figure 96. Inventory Pareto curve

put, it may, in general, be better to concentrate one's effort on these 100, rather than disperse the effort over, say, 1000. Hence such laws are useful when making the secondary decisions relating to allocation of effort.

2.3.6 Choice of Model and Solution Method

We must stress again that the method of solution will depend on the form of the model which has been constructed, and, although we talk about 'building' and 'solving' models as if they were distinct, they are very much interrelated, and the building of the model may proceed with a method of solution in mind.

Examples

(1) If we have a complex queueing problem and intend to solve by simulation, then our model is very elemental, going only so far as to describe the behaviour of each component of the model; the act of simulating is the process by which they are integrated and the total system behaviour is derived. If we intend to solve analytically, then our model is of a higher level, joining together the elements by sets of equations. If we intend to solve numerically, then the analytic model is converted into an equivalent 'finite' Markov process, using some method of truncation.

(2) Even within the class of analytic solutions, we may have different models. Thus, if we think in terms of transitions from one group of states to another, at successive intervals of time, we have one model, and look for an appropriate method of solution; if we think of epochs in time when certain states are assumed, then another model will result and another method of solution becomes appropriate.

Thus if: $[p_{ij}]$ is the probability transition matrix for the system on hand; $[p_{ij}^m]$ is the corresponding m-stage transition matrix; $\{q_i\}$ is the single-stage expected return; $\{q_i^m\}$ is the m-stage expected return; $\{r_i(m)\}$ is the probability distribution of time interval m between successive realizations of state i; then we may use one of two models (in certain circumstances) where 'g' is the gain per unit time:

$$v(i) + g = q_i + \sum_j p_{ij} v(j) \qquad \textbf{M.1}$$

$$\left(\sum_m m r_i(m)\right) g = \sum_m q_i{}^m r_i(m), \quad i = 1, 2, \ldots, n \qquad \textbf{M.2}$$

$$\mathbf{q}^m = T\mathbf{q}$$

$$T = \left(\sum_{s=0}^{m-1} P^s\right)$$

The calculation of $\{r_i(m)\}$ in **M.2** is, in general, difficult, and model **M.1** may be preferable. However, for some i, in some instances $\{r_i(m)\}$ is easy to calculate. Thus if 'i' is the age of equipment, and '$i = 0$' is equivalent to the equipment being in a failed state, then the distribution of times between failed states may be easy to obtain. If 'i' is stock level, and '$i = s$' is the reorder level, it may be easy to calculate the distribution of times between reorder points.

(3) If we have an allocation problem, we may model and solve it in different ways.

Thus, the model,

$$\text{maximize } \sum_{i=1}^{n} g_i(x_i), \text{ subject to } \sum a_i x_i \leqslant c, \; x_i \geqslant 0 \qquad \textbf{M.1}$$

may be replaced by the sequential models

$$f_n(c) = \max_{0 \leqslant x_n \leqslant c/a_n} [g_n(x_n) + f_{n-1}(c - a_n x_n)] \qquad \textbf{M.2}$$

Models **M.1** and **M.2** are different models of the same problem, since they use entirely different space representations. **M.2** is a dynamic programming model, which may be solved in different ways; **M.1** is, in general, a non-linear programming model, which may also be solved in many ways.

(4) Kuipers[70] gives an example of three models of the earth, *viz.*, point, ellipsoid and fluid models. The first one is useful when only the motion of the centre of gravity is required; the second is useful when rotation around the centre of gravity is to be studied; the third one is to be used when the deformation of the earth is to be studied. All are related and can be seen as sub-models of a more comprehensive model.

2.3.7 Uncertainties and Choice of Solution Procedure

It is often held that, since we are, in many instances, uncertain about features of our model, we should not apply elaborate solution procedures. There can be several different situations, *viz.*,:

(a) all uncertainties understood and incorporated in the model, and the solution procedure known to produce the correct solution for the model;

(b) some uncertainties not understood and not incorporated in the model, and the solution procedure known to produce the correct solution for the model assumed;

(c) all uncertainties understood and incorporated in the model, and the solution procedure not known to produce the correct solution for the model;

(d) some uncertainties not understood and not incorporated in the model, and the solution procedure not known to produce the correct solution for the model assumed.

Now in case (a) the solution procedure may require considerable effort. We can, of course, choose other solution procedures and remain in situation (a), but possibly reduce the number of alternatives considered. Thus we may shy off a numerical algorithm and try a limited enumeration. However, if we accept some philosophy by which a decision is accepted as being appropriate under uncertain conditions, we can equally well accept the use of solution procedures whose ability to identify appropriate solutions is uncertain. Thus, for example, one might deliberately distort the model so that an available less limited approach

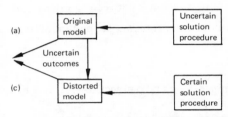

Figure 97. Distorting the model

might be used. Thus, in many queueing problems, analytic and computational methods available depend heavily on particular model structures which the model may have. One might use one of these and distort the original model to make it work, but one would be uncertain about its effect on the final solution. Pictorially we can present it as in Figure 97 where we have converted a situation of type (a) to a situation of type (c).

We are repeatedly warned about fitting the model to the procedure, and indeed this is dangerous. However, logically speaking, there is no difference between uncertainties inherent in the model and those inherent in the validity of the solution procedure. In situations of type (b) and (d), which are usually in the minds of people with respect to the opening statement of this section, there is even less ground to accept this dogma. However, this dilemma, as a methodological issue, has not been studied as yet.

Example

In a certain military problem the question of on-board-ship maintenance policy arose. In principle, the problem is a multi-equipment one involving queueing problems not amenable to existing analytic techniques. On the other hand there was considerable uncertainty about failure rates, repair rates, criteria, and about the future. Should one use a solution procedure which needed either considerable effort to give adequate coverage of alternatives, or one which gave a small coverage, but both of which were known to work for a given model, or should one use an unsure procedure which would be inexpensive and give wide coverage of the alternatives? Naturally, if the cost and effort of the procedures were small with respect to the factors involved in the primary problem, the answer would be clear. But this is not always the case.

The above point is not an argument for fitting problems to procedures. The point is being made that there is sometimes a definite decision to be made in the light of the existing circumstances.

We have, to a minimal extent, touched upon the secondary problems involved in modelling and in getting solutions. Let us now consider this problem more fully and the central problem of suboptimization from which it stems.

CHAPTER 3

Methodological Decisions and Suboptimization

3.1 The Nature of Suboptimization

3.1.1 Introductory Remarks

Decision Analysis is often identified with 'the total approach to systems investigation' in that the models constructed allow for all significant factors and interactions of subsystems. While none of us would dispute that this is an ideal which is useful, in that it urges us on to better attainments, we ultimately reach the stage when we 'judge' that further analysis cannot be justified in terms of solution improvement. We have put 'judge' in inverted commas, for, by and large, this is what is done in a rather subjective manner, whereas it would be desirable to find ways of rationalizing this secondary decision. Indeed this is one area in which Decision Methodology could make significant future general progress, and to which this chapter addresses itself.

In what follows it will be seen that, in the end analysis, the appropriateness of the methodological decisions, and hence the models developed, depends on the manner in which one outcome performance pattern is to be judged better than another. In the situation in which a value function can be established for such preferences we can begin to consider the problem. As we have seen, however, in Chapter 2, unresolved difficulties arise when it comes to ascertaining such functions for a group rather than for an individual. In such situations, although the same basic sources of suboptimization are relevant, it is not possible to consider them in this text. The replacement of the notion of an 'optimal' solution by an 'efficient' solution can take us part of the way, but only part of the way (see Ackoff,[1] Raiffa[104]).

In turning our attention to the secondary decisions it will be noted that such decisions have been mentioned in previous chapters. For example, the decision concerned with the selection of alternatives to study has been mentioned in problem formulation, and the decision concerning choice of techniques has been mentioned when discussing problem solutions. This was inevitable if these factors were to be recognized as clear decision problems, and lead naturally into a discussion of the more general methodological problems.

Before discussing specific aspects of the methodological decisions we need to discuss some aspects of modelling in relationship to the concept of 'suboptimization'.

3.1.2 Faithfulness, Insight and Suboptimality

In Decision Analysis we often hear the comment 'but that is in an ideal situation', thus inferring that the model is unrealistic. However, a glance at, for example, physics, will indicate that 'idealistic' models have been developed to some purpose. Thus the Kinetic Theory of Gases is idealistic, in relationship to the assumptions made about molecular behaviour, but it has nonetheless resulted in useful behavioural concepts which have then led to empirical estimation and verification. The same may be expected to be true in Decision Analysis. For example, in brand switching in marketing, and in traffic problems, idealistic explanatory models can generate useful behavioural constructs for total behaviour.

One must accept that one can never capture 'reality'. When we compare two alternatives via a model, the model will never be real, but at least we shall be providing a balanced comparison in the belief that the real system, which we shall never know, would rank the alternatives in the same way. It is in the belief that comparison on the basis of a common model, rather than comparison on the basis of no model, that Decision Analysis proceeds. In the end, the acceptability of our model depends on the ultimate agreement of the sponsors concerned that the model is adequate, this adequacy being as objectively studied as seems necessary.

Ball[5] stresses that models used do not have the objectives of describing reality but of providing a base for decisionmaking. He goes further:

'In one sense the more realistic the model the less we have abstracted from the complex process we are trying to control.'

Kendall[68] supports the first viewpoint and states:

'Model building should start with a simple and modest model, and work towards more complex systems by integration, rather than start with comprehensive models.'

Views on modelling are not restricted to modern times. Bacon and Mill state:

'Collect facts, facts and facts. Finally some kind of rule will become evident. When it does, use the rule to predict what will happen in the future.'

In applied research we do, however, face a dilemma, since it takes time and effort to collect facts, a point we raise in Chapter 4 in connection with data. Nonetheless, enough facts have to be collected to suggest possible rules (models).

In partial support of Kendall, Descartes and Popper state:

'Invent a model, no matter how low, deduce some consequences and design an experiment to see if they really do occur. If they do, keep the model on the books; if not, dream up a new model and test it likewise.'

There are dangers in simplifying, of course, but the dangers in overcomplication are thought to be worse. Naturally some general overview of the whole area will help the selection of the appropriate starting model.

Wallace[140] discusses the problem of determining the best design of a time-sharing computer. Basically the computer acts as a complex multiqueueing problem. The alternative ways of studying the problem are:

(i) simulation;
(ii) closed form queueing theory;
(iii) Markov numerical methods.

He says it is more important to get insight than to try for faithfulness. Nonetheless, one must have a requisite degree of faithfulness, and one does not know what the real effect of departure from 'more' to 'less' faithfulness means in terms of the effectiveness of the solution derived. In the end analysis some check is needed, and simulation as a means of testing the implied behaviour of the abstracted system against the behaviour of a more faithful system would be needed.

Table 8 is taken from his paper.

Table 8: Technique attributes

Method	Faithfulness	Insight	Cost
1. Simulation	High	None	Very high
2. Closed form Q. theory	Low	Very high	High
3. Numerical Q. analysis	Moderate	Very high	Moderate
Required of method	High	High	Low

Simulation has low insight since it gives no real explanation of the reason for the observed effects. Usually simulation is a local exploration and gives little indication of the real functional forms in areas removed from the local parameters studied.

Thus we see that, because of the non-real nature of our models, suboptimizations must arise. Our task is to try to understand the nature of these suboptimizations so that the solutions we ultimately derive are in some way 'good', rather than 'optimal' solutions. As has been indicated, not only will the model itself constitute possible sources of suboptimization, but the process of getting the solution must be made a very relevant part of the total consideration.

3.1.3 A Framework

In the context of the primary problem confronting the decisionmaker, the solution settled for is suboptimum in that it is conceivable that better solutions exist, although it may be thought not worthwhile to search for such solutions. Suboptimality is always to be considered in the context of the primary problem.

McKean[81] distinguishes between 'restricted optimization' and 'suboptimization' in the following way: if we consider a limited set of alternatives, then this is 'restricted optimization' if the true criterion function is known; if we use a lower-level criterion, such as unit production costs for a given machine, this is 'suboptimization' in that it may not be consistent with an overall criterion such as profit. The latter refers to the usual statement that optimizing component systems separately may not result in optimal overall performance. Both of these cases will be subsumed, in this text, under the heading of 'suboptimization' since they both result, effectively, in solutions which can, in principle, be improved upon.

We are concerned with the determination of solutions which are, in some sense, better than others, and we need to consider the prior and posterior evaluation of such solutions. Let us try to formalize this.

Let a be an alternative solution being considered in a given set A; let θ_p be the perceived outcomes as a result of a and other events; let θ_u be the set of, then unperceived, outcomes; let θ be the combination of θ_p, θ_u; let T_p be the perceived transformation of a into θ_p, where T_p may be deterministic, stochastic or uncertain. We then have:

$$\theta_p = T_p(a)$$

We now need a way of assessing whether or not, given two alternatives a, a^*, a is at least as good as a^*. We write this:

$$a R a^*$$

We shall, in this book, restrict ourselves to situations which are transitive and which satisfy the irrelevance of alternatives property (see White[143]).

These requirements are that:

$$a R a^*, \quad a^* R a^{**} \to a R a^{**}$$

and

if a^* is one of the preferred solutions in A^*, and $a^* \in A \subseteq A^*$, then a^* is one of the preferred solutions in A.

These requirements are needed to be able to talk in terms of improved decision-making and avoid certain difficulties in Decision Theory. However, it must be stated that, in principle, the whole of this book could be reoriented to include the wider aspects of Decision Theory.

3.1.3.1 INCOMPLETE CONSEQUENCES

Let us first of all mention one important case, i.e. the case when θ_u becomes evident after the decision. For example: we may find the most economic routings for buses and forget about certain types of public reaction; we may find the optimal economic replacement period for some equipment, but forget about the feedback effects on the manufacturer. We will deal more fully with this type later on, but, for the moment, make the point that any such concept of sub-optimality is likely to be difficult to develop from a prior point of view. Nonetheless, empirical evidence may exist which will give an idea of the frequency and importance of such omissions under certain conditions. In addition, as has been indicated in the context of problem formulation, the development of the subject matter of Decision Analysis is likely to lead to reduced probabilities of pertinent consequences being overlooked.

3.1.3.2 PRIOR AND POSTERIOR EVALUATIONS

Let us assume that θ_u is empty for the present and examine the prior/posterior conflict. Ideally we would like to know for definite what θ would be for each a and to say:

$$a\mathrm{R}a^* \text{ if } \theta \text{ is at least as good as } \theta^*$$

In such a case there is no difference between the prior and posterior evaluations. In many instances this is neither economically practicable nor scientifically possible, and we must then base our comparisons on a prior evaluation. Thus, if we follow von Neumann and Morgenstern[138] we may use:

$$a\mathrm{R}a^* \quad \text{if} \quad E_{\theta/a}(v(\theta)) \geqslant E_{\theta/a^*}(v(\theta))$$

where $v(\theta)$ is some value function for θ.

It is then possible that the actual θ, for a given a, might have been improved upon if a^* had been chosen. However, suboptimality is strictly a prior concept here, and has little to do with any retrospect assessment. We can, of course, include a decision to get more information before taking a terminal decision (see Raiffa[104]). a would then be replaced by a combination of a and a policy decision, based on any findings. The decision is still prior evaluated.

If the primary decision is based on prior valuations, in cases of uncertainty, then the secondary decision must be fitted into an extended framework of the same kind. In the case of situations of primary decision certainty, which will entail a specific A, θ, V (or v), the framework for the secondary decision will generally be a prior uncertainty one, which will be an extension of the primary decision framework.

3.1.3.3 DEGREE OF SUBOPTIMALITY

Now, as with all sensible approaches to resolving our secondary problem (i.e. what solution to settle for without further investigation), we tend to try to estimate degrees of suboptimality. Thus, in general, we try to think in terms of the closeness of solution a to solution a^*. This, however, also has its difficulties, for a value function is not unique.

Let us take the von Neumann valuation and let

$$V(a) = E_{\theta/a}v(\theta)$$

Then if $V(a)$ is a value function, so is $V^2(a)$ a value function, although not compatible with von Neumann theory. If $\Delta V(a)$ is any error in $V(a)$, the error in $V^2(a)$ is $2V(a)\Delta V(a)$ and the ratios

$$\Delta V(a)/V(a), \; \Delta V^2(a)/V^2(a) = 2\Delta V(a)/V(a)$$

are not equal.

Even if we restrict ourselves to value functions which satisfy the von Neumann and Morgenstern expected value rule (i.e. $V(apb) = pV(a) + (1 - p)V(b)$, where '$apb$' means '$a$ with probability p and b with probability $(1 - p)$'), we meet the same problem, for if $V(a)$ is an admissible value function, then any other admissible value function, $W(a)$, is of the form $\lambda V(a) + \mu$, $\lambda > 0$ and then $\Delta W(a)/W(a) \neq \Delta V(a)/V(a)$ in general.

We will not pursue this deeply here, since it is a difficult one, but mention it solely to indicate methodological difficulties which can arise if one pursues the subject far enough. The important point is that, if we formulate the secondary problem properly, then the fact that a value function is not unique causes no trouble. Let us, for example, assume that we have a von Neumann and Morgenstern situation with alternatives $a \in A$ and probabilities $p(\theta/a)$ of outcomes θ given a.

Let us assume that we have identified $\hat{a} \in A$ which is optimum within A, i.e.

$$\underset{a \in A}{\text{maximizes}}\left\{\sum_\theta p(\theta/a)\, v(\theta)\right\} = V(\hat{a})$$

In this expression $v(\theta)$ will be calculated according to some admissible procedure, although by no means unique.

Let us also assume that we have reason to believe that an alternative $a^* \notin A$ exists with $V(\hat{a}) < V(a^*)$, but that it might be expensive, say at a cost c, to locate a^*. We have already indicated the dangers of solving this problem by comparing $V(a^*) - V(\hat{a})$ with $V(\hat{a})$. If, however, we formulate the secondary problem, we have two alternatives:

α: accept $\hat{a}$
β: find a^*

We have:

$$V(\alpha) = V(\hat{a}), \quad V(\beta) = \sum_\theta p(\theta/a^*)\, v(\theta - c)$$

We choose α, providing

$$V(\alpha) > V(\beta)$$

and the non-uniqueness of $v(\theta)$ and $V(\alpha)$, $V(\beta)$ do not create problems.

Admittedly there may still be difficulties since we have to face the problem of finding whether a better solution exists without knowing what it is. Some form of bound analysis of the $p(\theta/a)$ may be needed. However, we do have to make such decisions and hence we do have a secondary problem, and the sensitivity analysis hinted at is methodologically invalid in general.

Naturally we have an even higher-order problem, since we have to decide whether the analysis of the methodological problem is worthwhile, and, indeed, we have an infinite regress. We content ourselves, for the purposes of this book, with the fact that things are difficult enough in considering the secondary decisions without having to consider n-ary decisions, but that this may lead to subsequent developments at the higher level.

Let us now make a brief review of the ways in which suboptimization arises and may be tackled.

3.2 Sources of, and Approaches to, Suboptimization

Supplementary material to the following will be found in Ackoff.[1] Also see Chernoff and Moses[23] for a discussion of some pitfalls in modelling.

Let us restate the general Decision Analysis model for the primary problem, once it has been formulated. We have: a set, A, of alternatives; a set, θ, of outcomes; a transformation, T, of $a \in A$ into a subset of θ (we allow for stochastic systems); and value functions V, on A, and v on θ.

The two alternative end products of a Decision Analysis investigation are, as has been indicated in Chapter 1:

(a) for each $a \in A$, find $\theta = T(a)$ (T may be stochastic);
(b) find $\max_{a \in A} [V(a)]$.

The first approach permits no analysis of degree of suboptimization; the latter approach is not without its difficulties in this respect.

Let us now consider how suboptimization enters into our investigations via A, θ, T, V (or v) respectively.

These have been considered for different purposes in previous discussions. Thus, in the section on problem formulation, constraints were considered as part of problem formulation; in the section on computational methods, constraints were considered in relationship to their contribution to computational effort; in this section they are considered because of their contribution to suboptimization, which involves both aspects.

There is, inevitably, some duplication of material appearing in previous chapters.

3.2.1 Suboptimization via Alternatives

A is the set of alternatives which we eventually evaluate, and this will generally be a subset of the totality of all possible alternatives. The set A is restricted both in number and type. Quite clearly, limiting the types will also limit the numbers.

Let us consider three factors which have an important bearing on the choice of A, *viz.*:

(a) constraints;
(b) sequential decisions;
(c) multiple decisions.

(a) Constraints

A will be partly defined by a set of constraints. Constraints may be directly imposed on A, or may arise indirectly by imposing constraints on the admissible consequences θ.

Such constraints may be physically inviolable or represent value judgements concerning the effect of such violation.

An example of physically inviolable constraints arises when we have to select a daily production schedule which is constrained by the resources existing at that time, and which cannot be increased within the time span of the decision. Examples of constraints reflecting value judgements arise when: we have to select a daily production schedule allowing certain machines to be taken down for maintenance or not involving more than an hour's overtime; we have a choice of a production schedule which conforms with technological rolling restrictions when producing steel strip; we have to operate a maintenance department within its budget specification; we have the choice of an inventory reorder rule which does not give a probability of more than 0·05 of running out of stock; we have the choice of an inspection policy which will meet certain risk constraints on outgoing product. There are many more.

Again, as we have seen in Chapter 1, these latter constraints are not inviolable since we can, and do, violate them. They represent value judgements that, if they are violated, the consequences will be unacceptable. However, it is all a matter of degree, and it may well be that the benefits obtained by allowing violations may affect the penalties to be paid for violation.

In the context of this chapter the important point is that the effect of such constraints is to produce, in some cases, suboptimal solutions since only the admissible solutions, A (i.e. those satisfying the constraints), will be effectively evaluated.

The computational costs may or may not decrease as we include more constraints.

Example

If we were using a daily linear programming production scheduling procedure, whether or not an alternative was admissible would be determined by the programme. The addition of constraints tends to increase the computations.

On the other hand, good value judgements can serve to reduce the range of alternatives, which is particularly useful when an enumerative solution procedure is used.

Examples

(1) If we are evaluating inspection policies, it may be judged that the minimal cost solution, which allows a 10% poor quality output, simply would not be tolerated by the customer whatever the terms which may be reasonably offered in the light of this saving. This may then rule out certain policies almost automatically prior to the major investigation, and enable a likely area of investigation to be chosen.

(2) Similar problems arise when long-term investment in capital equipment is being investigated. The possible alternatives which are investigated have to be selected somehow, and it may well be judged that certain types of equipment just would not be profitable, or would be unreliable and hence give rise to poor customer service.

One secondary problem concerning constraints is whether or not to accept the constraints in determining a solution. There may be a better solution outside

202

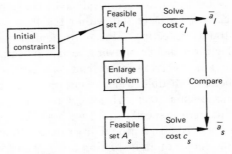

Figure 98. Constraint relaxation decision

the constraints but it will take some cost and effort to carry out the analysis. Schematically the situation is as in Figure 98.

$\bar{a}_I$ is the optimal solution relative to A_I;

A_s is the set of feasible alternatives for constraint set $C_s \subseteq C_I$;

$\bar{a}_s$ is the optimal solution relative to A_s.

Examples

(1) Suppose we have a problem in which cost and customer service are the consequences of concern. We may be given an initial customer service s_I and be asked to find the minimal cost solution. C_s is then identical with constraining the service level to s (see Figure 99).

We have already discussed constraints in previous chapters. However, the problem here is a special one, *viz.*, do we accept the solution obtained relative to any constraints at a given stage, or do we pursue the study further?

One way of approaching this would be to carry out a pilot study with customer service as a discrete variable, $s = 0, \Delta, 2\Delta, \ldots, n\Delta$. For each level of service, $r\Delta$, we would have an optimal cost $c(r)$, and let us assume that $c(n + 1)$ is estimated on the basis of these calculations. If k is the cost of a single set of computations, and if $v(c, s)$ is the value function of the decisionmaker for total cost and service, then we would proceed to calculate for the next level of service if

$$v(c(n + 1) + k, (n + 1)\, \Delta) > v(c(n), n\Delta)$$

In this case $c(n + 1)$ is only an estimate, given $c(0), c(1), \ldots, c(n)$. Once $c(n + 1)$

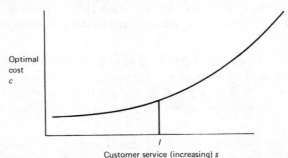

Figure 99. Customer constraint relaxation

has been obtained, we can estimate $c(n + 2)$ and repeat the process. If, of course, the first n calculations can be used to estimate all $c(r)$, $r > n$, then the problem is that much easier. We then have an estimate of the optimal value, $viz.$, $v(c(t), t)$ for some t. However, we still have to find the decision which will give this and it is a question of whether the computational cost is acceptable in the light of the anticipated gain in value.

If we have other information about the influence of s on optimal costs, we may have a probabilistic model in much the same way as described in Section 3.1.3.3.

If we do not have the value function then the decisionmaker must determine whether to proceed or stop at each stage, in the light of the results obtained so far.

(2) The problem of restrictions on overtime has already been discussed. One way of ascertaining whether it is worthwhile pursuing the constraints problem is to determine the difference between the effects of the optimal constrained and

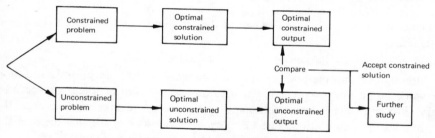

Figure 100. Overtime constraint relaxation

unconstrained problems. If this is large then it can be determined whether the extra effort to find a better solution, and then sell the solution, is worthwhile.

Schematically we have Figure 100.

In Figure 100 it is assumed that it has been decided to solve the unconstrained problem, and that the purpose of this is to enable one to decide whether gains may be made from relaxing constraints at all. This still leaves us with the secondary decision as to which constraint levels will now be considered. Naturally, the original decision to solve the unconstrained problem could be considered, and this would be done in the light of anticipated computational load and anticipated reductions in costs. Again a probabilistic model may apply. On the other hand this is not essential, for some criterion based on bounds on cost reductions, treated as a problem under uncertainty, may apply.

Reference should be made to Chapter 2, which also discusses the decisions on constraint handling. The emphasis was essentially on the computational side, aiming at solutions of roughly the same value, whereas, here, the emphasis is on the possibility of having suboptimal solutions. However, the two aspects are clearly related in a secondary problem framework, for, if the cost of computation were not important, we would deal with all constraint modifications which were felt to be relevant to the suboptimization issue.

204

Another aspect of alternatives arises when the set A is fixed, and known, perhaps implicitly or explicitly defined by constraints, and in which we have to decide, at any point in time, whether to accept the solution we have, or to search further, with the same constraints operating all the time.

We consider several possibilities.

One such approach is referred to as the Las Vegas approach, which will now be described. This approach is referred to in Ackoff.[1]

The classical optimization problem is:

$$\underset{x_1, x_2, \ldots, x_n}{\text{minimize}} \ [\phi(x_1, x_2, \ldots, x_n)]$$

subject to

$$g_i(x_1, x_2, \ldots, x_n) \leqslant 0, \quad i = 1, 2, \ldots, m$$

Some of these inequalities are equalities, but we assume them removed by expressing one variable as a function of the others, and substituting in the other inequalities, e.g. if $g_k(x_1, \ldots, x_n) = 0$, then $x_n = r_k(x_1, x_2, \ldots, x_{k-1})$, which may be multiple-valued.

Doing it this way, if $-x_n \leqslant 0$ is one of the original inequalities, we have a new one, $viz.$,

$$-r_k(x_1, x_2, \ldots, x_{n-1}) \leqslant 0$$

Although certain methods exist which either guarantee an optimal solution, or work on an improvement basis, with no such guarantee, these can become very time-consuming computationally and we need to take into account the economics of computation. The Las Vegas method is one which works on the basis of a sample procedure and is essentially a suboptimizing procedure.

The inequalities given above can be represented by a region in E_n as given in Figure 101.

A sampling procedure, π, is developed which chooses, on a random basis, a sequence of points $[x_1, x_2, \ldots, x_n]$, as follows:

(i) each point $[x_1, x_2, \ldots, x_n] \in S$ (sampling region);
(ii) if $[x_1, x_2, \ldots, x_n] \notin R$, it is discarded;
(iii) if $[x_1, x_2, \ldots, x_n] \in R$, then $\phi(x_1, \ldots, x_n)$ is computed;
(iv) for each effective sample $[x_1, x_2, \ldots, x_n] \in R$, a record is kept of the trend of values, thus:

if m_n is the minimum value to date, after n effective samples, then

$$m_{n+1} = \min [m_n, \phi(x_1, x_2, \ldots, x_n)], \quad ([x_1, x_2, \ldots, x_n] \in R)$$

Figure 102 shows this

(v) The process is terminated at some 'appropriate' point, usually when 'it is felt that the chances of getting lower values are small'. However, even if this is so, the actual minimum may yet be some distance below the stopping point (see Figure 103).

There is no 'Theory of Termination' as yet, although we will suggest some possibilities, as yet undeveloped.

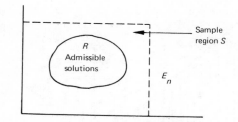

Figure 101. Sample and solution regions

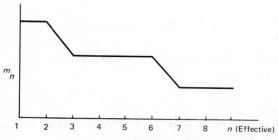

Figure 102. Sampling results

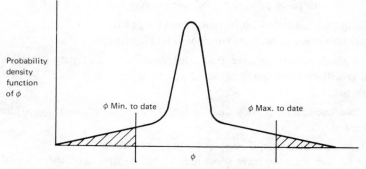

Figure 103. Probability density function of solution values

Example

Suppose we wish to minimize $\phi(x_1, x_2, \ldots, x_n)$ subject to

$$\sum_j \alpha_{ij} x_j \leqslant b_i, \quad i = 1, 2, \ldots, m$$

$$\{\alpha_{ij}\} \geqslant 0$$
$$\{x_i\} \geqslant 0$$

S may be chosen as follows:

$$S \equiv \{[x_1, x_2, \ldots, x_n] : x_k \leqslant \min_i [b_i/\alpha_{ik}] = \bar{x}_k\}$$

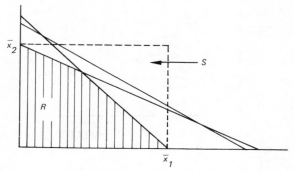

Figure 104. Sample and solution

In two dimensions we would have Figure 104.

The steps are as follows:

(i) choose N;
(ii) let $\delta_k = \bar{x}_k/N$;
(iii) choose a sequence of integers, $\{I_1, I_2, \ldots, I_n\}$, I_k being drawn randomly from the set $0 \leqslant I_k \leqslant N$;
(iv) the $[x_1, x_2, \ldots, x_n]$ sample corresponding to this is $[I_1\delta_1, I_2\delta_2, \ldots, I_k\delta_k, \ldots, I_n\delta_n]$.

Under the sampling policy, π, and sample region, S, there will be:

(a) a frequency distribution for values ϕ (say $p(\phi)$);
(b) a probability, q, that the sample will be effective.

Let us approximate the frequency distribution by a density function $g(\phi)$. In general ϕ will be bounded, and hence $g(\phi) = 0$ for $\underline{\phi} \leqslant \phi \leqslant \bar{\phi}$. The two possible methods are:

(i) We can use the frequency distribution to date to estimate $\{g(\phi)\}$ and $\underline{\phi}$ (say $(\hat{g}(\phi), \hat{\underline{\phi}})$).

(a) Once we have this, if $m_n \sim \hat{\underline{\phi}}$ we may terminate;
(b) if $m_n \nsim \hat{\underline{\phi}}$, then we have some idea of the sampling distribution of number of samples to achieve a given closeness to $\hat{\underline{\phi}}$ and can then balance expected sampling costs against the gain.

If we define $f(z)$ to be the minimum expected net cost to termination if z is our minimum value to date, we have:

$$f(z) = \min \left[\begin{array}{l} \text{Terminate}: z \\ \text{Further sample}: c + q \int_\phi f(\min(z, \phi))\,\hat{g}(\phi)\,d\phi + (1-q)f(z) \end{array} \right]$$

(ii) For a given $\{\hat{g}(\phi)\}$, π and S, we can find the distribution of m for a given sample size (effective and ineffective). This is simply the distribution of the maximum of a random number of identically distributed variables. If we are prepared to assume that $\{g(\phi)\}$ is a Beta distribution of the kind $c(\phi - \underline{\phi})^\alpha(\bar{\phi} - \phi)^\beta$ we can find the distribution function of the observed minimum for a given actual

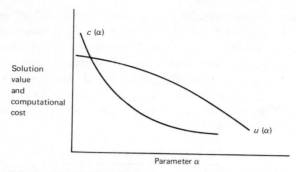

Figure 105. Parametrization of solution value and computational cost

minimum, maximum and pair of parameters (α, β). The sample number could then be chosen, as in normal sampling theory, to give specific probabilities of error.

The above approaches are only suggestions and considerable improvement may be possible. The purpose has been to show how the secondary decision problem might be formulated and solved.

There is another way of handling some secondary decision processes of the above kind.

Find a parametrization of subsets of A $(A_\alpha \subseteq A)$ such that $A_\alpha \to A$ as $\alpha \to \alpha_0$: e.g. if A is a vector space, let α be the grid size of any component, so

$$A_\alpha \equiv \{[n_1 \alpha, n_2 \alpha, n_3 \alpha, \ldots, n_k \alpha]\}$$

with $\underline{x}_i \leqslant n_i \alpha \leqslant \bar{x}_i$.

We can then plot

$$\max_{a \in A_\alpha} [V(a)] = u(\alpha) \text{ against } \alpha$$

and computational cost $c(\alpha)$ against α (see Figure 105).

$u(\alpha)$ will level out as α decreases;

$c(\alpha)$ will increase exponentially as α decreases.

We can then extrapolate at a suitable point to find out which α gives the optimal combination; and then find the optimal x_α from

$$\max_\alpha [u(\alpha) - c(\alpha)]$$

In a similar, but more detailed manner, Schmidt and Taylor[112] show how a compromise between simulation costs and gain in the value of a solution may be obtained. In this instance the learning process is somewhat different and the study is more related to hill-climbing techniques.

In situations of uncertainty it is often stated that it is a waste of time to use refined techniques. However, this is an unsubstantiated judgement and this problem can be handled in a manner similar to that of the primary problem in principle. There may be difficulties, but some framework for such judgements can be constructed.

Let us suppose we were considering a complex interactive investment problem, using present worth calculations, but with an uncertain discount factor α.

One technique, which we will label T_1, might be enumerative, and cover alternatives $q_1, q_2, \ldots, q_m$, at a cost c_1. An alternative technique, which we will label T_2, might be a sophisticated algorithm and, implicitly (not necessarily explicitly) cover additional alternatives $q_{m+1}, \ldots, q_M$ at a cost c_2. If θ_{ij} is the performance of alternative q_i when the true value of α is α_j, we can represent our secondary problem by Table 9.

Table 9: Techniques decisions

	$\alpha_1\ \alpha_2\ \ldots\ \alpha_N$
(T_1, q_1)	
(T_1, q_2)	
$\vdots$	$(\theta_{ij} - c_1)$
(T_1, q_m)	
(T_2, q_1)	
(T_2, q_2)	
$\vdots$	$(\theta_{ij} - c_2)$
(T_2, q_M)	

Now, if we are prepared to put probabilities to α_j, say p_j, and if expected net outcome is the criterion, we have the values of the alternatives as follows:

$$v(T_1, q_i) = \sum_{j=1}^{N} p_j(\theta_{ij} - c_1)$$

$$v(T_2, q_i) = \sum_{j=1}^{N} p_j(\theta_{ij} - c_2)$$

$$v(T_1) = \max_{i=1,2,\ldots,m} [v(T_1, q_i)]$$

$$v(T_2) = \max_{i=1,2,\ldots,m} [v(T_2, q_i)]$$

Therefore:

$$v(T_2) - v(T_1) = c_1 - c_2 + \max_{i=1,2,\ldots,M} \left[\sum_j p_j \theta_{ij}\right] - \max_{i=1,2,\ldots,m} \left[\sum_j p_j \theta_{ij}\right]$$

To make the choice between T_2 and T_1 requires some statement about the outcomes θ_{ij}. These in themselves may be probabilistic statements. It is to be noted that T_2 has only been used implicitly and would be used explicitly to carry out the first maximization operation.

If probabilistic ideas are not accepted, then a similar approach applies with the corresponding uncertainty criteria.

It is a modern development that a set of algorithms, which individually can solve a problem, shall be compared with each other with respect to the efficiency of solution, say, measured in terms of the amount of computation required to get the same optimal solution. This then poses the analyst with the problem of choosing between the algorithms. Such a situation exists, for example, in the area of zero–one programming (see Balas,[3] Hammer[51]).

In principle, the secondary problem can be resolved as follows. Let us assume that we can characterize the possible problem space by splitting it into n classes $Q_1, Q_2, \ldots, Q_n$. Let us assume that each class is characterized with respect to certain attributes, e.g. number of variables, constraints, etc. Let us assume that numerical testing has indicated that the expected time taken to get a solution for class i using algorithm j is t_{ij}, and that expected time is the only criterion.

Then, if we know we are in class i, we simply choose j to minimize t_{ij}. If not, however, and we know the frequency, f_i, with which class i arises, we choose j to minimize $\sum_i f_i t_{ij}$.

An example of the latter solution arises in tests of feasibility in linear programming, in which Q_1 is the set of problems which have a feasible solution, and Q_2 is the set of problems which have an infeasible solution, and we are trying to determine whether a particular problem has a feasible solution.

(b) Sequentiality

In reality, all decisions are connected over time in a variety of ways (each one influences the conditions for others). Hence, instead of considering an action, a_t, at time t, we should be considering a policy $\pi[t_0, t_1]$ over some time interval $[t_0, t_1]$.

Eventually a_t, at all t in $[t_0, t_1]$, will be taken, but separately rather than together.

The difficulties in considering π are relational and computational. Let us concentrate on the computational ones.

In many cases where π is considered, in which R is assumed correct, simulation is used for the various policies selected. To do this, a finite characterization of such policies is needed. This can result in an extremely small coverage of $\{\pi\}$.

Example

In a single item inventory control problem, with m possible inventory levels, x, and N possible alternatives, there are N^m possible policies.

A linear decision rule, of the form, $\alpha - \beta x$, taken to the nearest mark in N, will give at most $N^2 2^{m-2}$ possible policies, if $\alpha, \beta \geqslant 0$.

The efficiency of coverage, ε, then satisfies:

$$\varepsilon \leqslant (2/N)^{m-2}.$$

$N = m = 10$ gives $\varepsilon \leqslant 5^{-8}$.

The calculations given assume that we use the same decision rule at each point in time. If we allow for the fact that decision rules may vary at each point in time, then the coverage factor gets even smaller.

The reduction of $\{\pi\}$ to $\{\pi^*\} \subset \{\pi\}$ so that, although ε is still small, suboptimization is small, is not, as yet, formalized. It relies on 'experience' and 'intuition', the latter being operationally undefinable. The optimal $V(\bar{\pi})$ is seldom known, thus making rational judgements of suboptimization difficult.

An alternative to sequential suboptimization is to find optimal single-stage decision rules and to simulate these dynamically. Then to find optimal two-stage decision rules and to simulate these dynamically. After simulating optimal k-stage decision rules, the rate of improvement can be balanced against extra computation costs to determine whether extra calculations are worthwhile. A learning approach, in much the same way as mentioned in Section 3.2.1, might apply.

It might be possible to so modify R that the suboptimal problem becomes feasible with the full $\{\pi\}$, e.g. by modifying characteristics (such as arrival patterns, general probability characteristics, etc.). The suboptimal policy thus suggested may give a starting point in determining $\{\pi^*\}$, which can be made foolproof by including the present policy, if it can be determined.

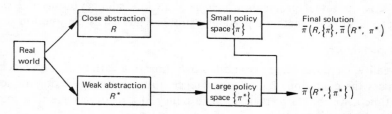

Figure 106. Increased coverage of alternatives via model distortion

In the above approach we exchange one form of suboptimization for another. By distorting R, we reduce the suboptimization arising from our inability to cover enough alternatives, but increase the suboptimization arising because of misranking alternatives because the new R is incorrect.

In Chapter 2 the possibility of getting solutions by distorting the model was mentioned, with a subsequent check that such distortion did not result in significant suboptimality. However, this cannot be guaranteed and the general secondary decisions have to allow for eventual suboptimality. The decision to distort the model will have a cost and the secondary problem may again be cast as one of decisionmaking under uncertainty, using whatever evidence and judgement as is available on the potential, or probable, improvements which $\bar{\pi}(R^*, \{\pi^*\})$ might add to the small policy space approach. Figure 106 depicts the secondary problem.

(c) Multiple Decisions

At any point in time we can partition A into $A_1 \times A_2 \times \ldots \times A_k$ if there are k decision centres within the company. This is effectively so; in actual fact there will be time intervals, but these may be too small for one centre to be aware of another centre's decision; if it is large enough then this reverts to the time characterization above.

Example

$A_1 \equiv$ production department;
$A_2 \equiv$ sales department.

We may further have:

$A_1 = A_{11} \times A_{12}$,
$A_{11} =$ production manager,
$A_{12} =$ shop foreman.

If we had: $V(a) = \sum_i \sum_j u_{ij}(a_{ij})$, and a_{ij} unconstrained by a_{rs}, $(i,j) \neq (r,s)$ then we could treat them separately.

However, in general this is not so.

Example

The engineering department may plan their maintenance activities without knowing fully the production schedule decision, i.e. that part of the decision which is not made impossible by the other decision; thus taking off a machine may still allow the required production, but overtime may now be needed.

Let:

a_m, a_p be maintenance and production decisions;
equipment availability $= A(a_m)$;
production cost $= P(a_p, A(a_m))$;
maintenance cost $= M(a_m)$;
total cost $= P(a_p, A(a_m)) + M(a_m)$, which is not separable.

Sometimes one decision area assumes more importance than another, and the decision decomposition results in one area being given priority and the other having to do its best in the face of circumstances imposed by the other.

Examples

(1) In the above example the production department may decide their work programme irrespective of maintenance schedules. The maintenance department will then have to ensure the equipment is available at the required times to meet the production requirements, and this may be at a high cost.

In solving this problem, one way is to optimize the total cost given above, and, if this were easy, this would be the thing to do. However, such problems can be quite complex and it may be much easier to optimize for production, including the choice of availability, and leave the maintenance department to provide the availability at minimum cost, if it can. There is a possible loss of total cost performance and this has to be weighed against the cost of a more integrated analysis. It might be possible to say something about the minimal costs possibly achievable under each approach, and the secondary problem then becomes one of decisionmaking under uncertainty in much the same way as others have been formulated, again depending on evidence and judgements about the costs involved. As with the other problems, it may well be that the suboptimal solution is preferable when viewed against heavy computational costs of optimal solutions.

(2) A_1: patient appointments;
    A_2: ambulance scheduling.

Hospitals would almost certainly be unlikely to schedule the appointments to give any consideration to efficiency of ambulance scheduling. However, the result of this is that, in a given day, a widely dispersed geographical pick-up pattern arises, thus making the ambulances travel considerably to pick up patients.

Whether an attempt to schedule to improve effectiveness of the ambulance operations should be made, depends on the potential savings from doing so.

(3) Consider the problem of determining both what work will be scheduled in a week and how it will be scheduled. This is the sort of situation in which the first decision may be chosen quite 'loosely', and the second quite 'critically'. In this case they are connected in that the first one conditions the second.

Clearly, the problem of choosing both the jobs to be done and the detailed schedule can be quite complex and require considerable effort to resolve optimally. One way of justifying this is to see how present costs and service behave. For the comprehensive method, estimates of bounds for costs and services may be

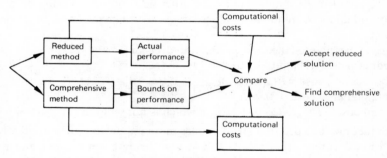

Figure 107. Integrated scheduling decisions

available, and actual performance can then be seen relative to these, and to computational costs, which the combined method would involve (see Figure 107).

The secondary decision being tackled here is that of which primary alternatives to consider and, as with the previous decisions, may be tackled within a framework of decisionmaking under uncertainty.

(4) Consider a problem of providing spare parts for a process.

An examination of the statistical demand for spares will provide us with information about the demand as it is now. Let us assume that the life of a component has a distribution function $F(t, \alpha)$ with $\alpha = \alpha_0$, now.

On the assumption that, indeed, this will remain the distribution, we can calculate the optimal spares replenishment policy.

However, we may examine the way in which decisions are made about the use of spares.

They may depend on:

 (i) the condition of the spares;
 (ii) an interpretation of this condition in the context of production losses or quality, etc.;
(iii) the economics of changing components.

To consider both the spares replenishment policy decision and the component changing policy decision can be quite complex.

If x relates to the spares policy, and y to replacement policy, we may be able to represent the problem thus:

$$\min_{x,y} [\theta(x,\alpha) + \phi(y,x)]$$

where $\alpha = X(y) = $ demand level for policy y; $\theta(x,\alpha)$ is the spares purchasing and storing cost; $\phi(y,x)$ is the spares usage cost.

It needs to be stressed that x, y are policies and not single decisions, and that α can be a complex function of y, which might prevent an integral evaluation of both x, y together.

On the assumption that there will be no changes in the spares policy, then we have reduced difficulties.

However, if we wish to do this, the results will be suboptimal. We may be able to assess the computational and other costs in covering both policies and their interaction. We may also be able to assess lower bounds on the combined replacement and spares costs. In addition, we may be able to determine the actual best replacement policy, using the present spares policy. If so, we can assess the net potential gains, which will be one measure on the basis of which we may be able to determine whether the combined analysis should be done, this being the secondary decision of concern.

(5) Labour policies (intake, training) in the light of absenteeism and wastage have an interaction with labour utilization decisions. It would be computationally expensive to look at the latter alternatives and, in the first instance, one would try to determine the needs for labour as they are seen in the light of present production patterns. As a second stage, one could then examine the ability of the chosen labour programme to meet changes in production pattern.

The rationalizing of the suboptimizing process can be approached in much the same way as in the other instances.

(6) In organizing the inspection and replacement of street lighting, the ways in which vehicles are routed will influence the policy costs. It is possible that, in determining the optimal frequency of maintenance, this policy is not too dependent on the precise routing, but more on the frequency. If, however, this were not the case, we would have a similar suboptimization problem to those discussed previously.

3.2.2 Suboptimization via Consequences

There are several ways in which suboptimization can arise through θ.

(a) when θ is not known completely in principle;
(b) when θ contains 'non-ultimate' variables;
(c) when some elements of θ are not measured and incorporated into the decision model directly;
(d) when the measurements are erroneous.

214

These aspects have each been mentioned in Chapter 2 in the context of problem formulation or general model building.

(a) θ Incomplete

Clearly, in this sort of suboptimization, we may infer that one alternative, X, is better than another, Y, but in effect the reverse may apply in the light of the complete θ.

Example

In the medical field, certain forms of treatment seem to be better than others when based upon things we perceive as relevant to the decision. But who knows what hidden consequences may eventually arise?

This problem is common to all scientific investigation. We hope that, even if we do not get our decisions ordered perfectly, our ignorance will not prevent us from at least distinguishing between good and bad decisions.

In Figure 108, A is the initial set of alternatives and Y is the optimal solution in A relative to perceived outcomes θ_p. If Y is implemented and, later on, the

Figure 108. Suboptimization via incomplete consequences

initially unperceived θ_u is identified, Y may not be optimal. It may be hoped that, whatever θ_u turns out to be, there is a sufficiently small region, $\mathscr{A}$, with $Y \in \mathscr{A} \subseteq A$, such that the optimal $X \in A$, relative to $\theta = (\theta_p, \theta_u)$ is also in $\mathscr{A}$, so that if $\mathscr{A}$ is small enough the errors in using Y are also small.

Note that we have to be careful how we define A. If we are dealing with a sequential situation, A would refer only to the decisions which have to be made at the time, and the fact that choices still remain open for subsequent decisions does not destroy the need for $Y \in A$ to be chosen on some appropriate basis. For example, a dynamic programming approach (see White[146] and Chapter 2, Section 2.3 of this text) would enable such appropriateness to be examined.

The secondary decision in this case is whether to search for further effects, or to evaluate relative to those established. Such a decision might be made on the basis of empirical knowledge about the relative incidence rate of projects which have been invalidated by further factors turning up later on. We may also need some idea of the relationship between search effort and the extent of identification of such factors. Finally, we may need to know the extent to which the recognition of new factors would improve the solutions. Clearly any such approach is in its infancy and the above comments only identify some relevant components.

If one tries to cast this in a framework of decisionmaking under uncertainty, as with the other situations studied, some difficulties arise. First of all the problem of ascertaining the complete θ is the same as identifying a 'state' in the usual format, and this has not been tackled. Secondly, although we may determine the best Y relative to each θ, it is difficult to determine what is the best Y with respect to a set of uncertain θ.

Note that if X is the present solution and Y is preferred to X relative to θ_p, we might still have Y preferred to X relative to θ. Empirical evidence on the likelihood of reversal of preferences would be useful to such decisions.

Hanssmann[54] draws our attention to the suboptimization of the above type in the context of unknown 'spill-over' effects.

(b) θ Non-ultimate

In many instances θ contains outcomes which ideally we might wish to trace through to cash terms. Thus 'customer service', 'financial liquidity', 'flexibility', 'quality', may all, ideally, be viewed as producers of cash. The reasons for not tracing them through are a mixture of scientific and economic considerations, which we will not pursue here. The fact is that value judgements are made in terms of non-ultimate variables.

In such instances we have the same sort of suboptimality discussed in section (a), and we at present rely on the expertise of the decisionmaker (or his advisers) to establish the 'correct order of magnitude' for the values of the outcomes concerned.

A rational approach to the secondary decision to accept or further decompose consequences may be considered along the empirical lines suggested for (a). In essence, the problem is one of whether the values attached to certain consequences would be changed if they were traced further. Experimentation would give some idea, in certain cases, of the risks of non-ultimate valuations misrepresenting true valuations. If we then know the costs of further decomposition we can determine when further effort is worthwhile or not.

Example

Suppose we determined a subjective valuation for combinations of cost and time to respond to an emergency in an ambulance fleet problem. We might find a value function:

$$v(t, c) = v_0 - \alpha c - \beta e^{\lambda t} \qquad \textbf{1}$$

Suppose we now examine the straight economic effects of t in respect to future expected costs for the Health Services. Thus a minor operation may become a major operation if t is too large. Let $E(t)$ be the economic effects of t, which we assume for our purposes is deterministic. If we can separate, additively, the economic effects of t, from the life value judgements of t, then we can derive a value function:

$$u(t, c) = u_0 - a(c + E(t)) - bF(t) \qquad \textbf{2}$$

Clearly, unless $E(t) = pe^{\lambda t} + r = qF(t) + s$, expressions **1** and **2** will produce different rankings of pairs (t, c).

We still have to make the secondary decision as to whether the determination of expression $u(t, c)$ is worthwhile, when we do not know this in advance. This problem does not suffer from the first difficulty that incomplete consequences suffers from, since we can always conceive of the spectrum of $E(t)$, $F(t)$ functions in principle. However, it does suffer from the difficulty of comparing different value systems. This latter point serves once again to stress the dangers in misusing value theory. One way out of this is to state the problem in terms of unknowns $\{E(t)\}$ and treat it directly as a problem of decisionmaking under uncertainty. For example, suppose that one can assume that $E(t) = e.t$, but e is unknown. If x is the decision variable and if $\theta = (c,t,e)$, we might have the expected value approach where

$$V(x) = \sum_e p(e)\,v(c(x), t(x), e)$$

where $c(x)$ is the operational cost and $t(x)$ is the response time (assumed to be the average in this case) for decision x, and v is a suitable value function.

If C were the cost of the investigation, then this would be undertaken if

$$\sum_e p(e) \max_x \{v(C + c(x), t(x), e\} > \max_x \left\{\sum_e p(e)\,v(c(x), t(x), e)\right\}$$

Other criteria may apply, but some formulation of the secondary problem seems possible. Judgements about e may be implicit in the original valuation $v(t, c)$.

(c) Representation of θ

Even if the outcomes are identified in concept, they may not be measured and incorporated directly in the model. The interplay between the partial model constructed, and other important factors of this kind, is a subtle one, and we cannot discuss this here, but point out that the situation is a common one. Thus distinctions are made between proposed solutions, using concepts of 'flexibility', without measuring it; distinctions are made between proposed types of insurance policy, using concepts of 'attraction of undesirable buyers' without measuring the 'undesirability' factor; distinctions are made between investment opportunities, using 'probability' concepts, but without measuring them.

We are not arguing about the appropriateness or otherwise of such measurement or non-measurement, which was discussed in Chapter 2. However, it is clear that suboptimization 'can' arise in the same sense as in the previous section.

The secondary problem is one of whether to measure specific variables, or not to measure these variables. As we have seen, the penalties for non-measurement are partly that the scope of the analysis is reduced and hence, even if the non-measured factors are incorporated subjectively at the end, the range of alternatives we can cover may be reduced. This then reduces to a secondary problem already covered under the heading of 'alternatives'.

In addition, the process of measurement allows a higher discrimination between realizations of a variable, which will clearly influence the final solution (see White[143]).

Other penalties arise because the way in which such subjective judgements are made may not reflect the true significance of the variable, and may be tackled in a manner analogous to that of (b).

Example

In problems involving the concept of 'quality', a subjective assessment may not really represent quality as a codeterminant of future contingencies such as high failure rates, poor performance, etc. The processes of defining and measuring quality will do so in such a context, and the results may differ radically from any subjective assessment.

As with the other secondary problems, a rational resolution may require empirical evidence on the incidence rate of misjudgements and the level of their effects, in addition to which we need evidence relating further research effort to the likelihood of uncovering such misjudgements.

(*d*) *Erroneous Measurements*

This is the obvious situation in which errors in technique, or its application, can arise. The latter fault is obvious.

Typical of this situation is the case of incorrect costs.

Examples

(1) Situations arise in which historical costs are used, but the true values of which are dependent on the decisions to be taken now and in future. Thus the reduction of vehicle fleet depends on the cost of vehicles, but these depend on the work they have to do, which may change as a result of the new decision.

(2) Similar problems arise when 'minimal cost production schedules' are sought, and when long-term subcontracting is considered, involving consideration of overhead costs, which depend on future decisions to be made about the facilities concerned.

In this sort of situation the same sort of secondary problem arises as in the previous section, and similar points apply. The secondary decision is whether to accept the costs given, without a detailed study of their appropriateness, or to determine the costs with the aid of further study.

3.2.3 Suboptimization via Relations

When dealing with T we need to recognize different situations, *viz.*:

(a) situations of certainty;
(b) situations of probability (known);
(c) situations of probability (unknown, but can be learnt);
(d) situations of probability (unknown, conflict);
(e) situations of uncertainty (conflict and non-conflict).

Bellman[9] refers to situations of types (a), (b), (c) as level 0, 1, 2 respectively. In situation type (d) we include Savage's[111] subjective probability, since such probabilities are not given *a priori*, and the theory is within the general framework of uncertainty as discussed by Milnor.[86]

In each case, it is required to determine a set of uncontrolled (by the primary decisionmaker) variables, U, such that, for each $a \in A$, $u \in U$.

$$\theta = T(a, u).$$

218

The suboptimization which then arises can arise in three ways:

(A) if T is not correct;
(B) if U is not complete;
(C) by virtue of information content, relative to U.

A INCORRECT T

T can be incorrect either with respect to its form or to the parameters involved.

Example

In the latter case, incorrect costing procedures are fairly common. The failure to recognize that historical costs are not valid in some cases, since the true costs depend on the decision being considered, can arise. Thus if we can find a feasible way of collecting refuse with less vehicles, the load on each vehicle may increase and historical maintenance and capital costs may be invalid. The failure in such cases arises from not recognizing the correct basic model.

In essence this is a fault in measurement, a point already discussed. The point is, however, that it will result in an incorrect T.

Problems of form arise when T is being determined on the basis of historical data. The question of whether T is, in principle, with the proper U, deterministic, arises. A discussion of all the salient aspects has been given in Chapter 2.

The secondary problem here is one of whether to accept a specific set $\{T_i\}$, or, whether to spend more effort in finding a 'better' set, assuming we determine 'better' in the context of the uses of $\{T_i\}$ for decisionmaking.

In Chapter 2 a discussion of the ways in which T can be erroneous is given, and empirical evidence on the level of incidence of such errors would be relevant to the secondary decision, as would the eventual effects of such errors, and the costs of further study, plus the likelihood of finding better Ts.

An analysis of the effect of T on the decision, and on the effects of the decision, would provide an assessment of the risks involved and hence provide a framework within which the secondary decision might be made. Figure 109 indicates this secondary problem.

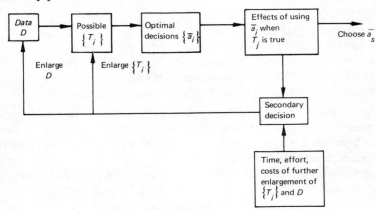

Figure 109. Rational decisions

In Figure 109 the decision not to enlarge the study may be taken even when the errors in using the wrong T_js are large, since it is always relative to the time, effort and costs of further study. This is not the usual sensitivity analysis on its own, referred to in Chapter 2, since we have no reason to believe, in many cases, that the possible errors within a specific set $\{T_i\}$ will be small.

In the end analysis, whether or not a particular T_i is accepted depends solely on the errors in the consequences, and the problem can be cast as one of decision-making under uncertainty. Since it is the values of such consequences, and not just the consequences, which matter, the errors in T_i express themselves as errors in the values of the alternatives, a point to which we return later on.

As an example of a secondary decision problem of this kind consider the following.

Example

In a certain military problem, decisions were being considered as to what the mix and level of particular forces should be. One of the contributory factors was

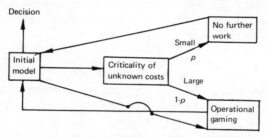

Figure 110. Maintenance costing decisions

maintenance support services. These were known for particular levels of operation within existing experience. It was not known what the resources required would be for situations outside experience. It was thought that operational gaming might help. However, this was expensive and its worth was in doubt. One way of looking at the problem was to determine the range of resource variation within which not much influence on the force mix solution would arise, and then to assess, perhaps subjectively, whether or not the maintenance support was likely to be within this region. The costs of doing this were small, since a normal linear programming parametric analysis was possible, when compared with operational gaming costs, although there was the possibility that the simple approach would be inconclusive. Pictorially we can present it thus in Figure 110.

Assuming that we end up with the same degree of confidence in our final solution, if p is the probability that the criticality method will result in a small assessment, if c is the cost of the criticality method and o is the cost of the operational gaming, we carry out the criticality method, if expected costs are the basis of this decision, if

$$c + (1-p)o < 0$$

i.e.

$$c < p.o$$

This is, of course, very simple minded, but the nature of the general approach remains valid. This, of course, raises the question of whether p is empirically derivable, or based on the opinion of experts.

In Chapter 2 we have made reference to aspects which might be called 'structural' features of a model, and to aspects which might be called 'parametric' features. The former are concerned with the nature of the relationships between groups of variables. The latter are concerned with particular numerical levels within this framework. It is known that changes in structure can radically alter the behaviour of a model. For example, the conversion of an ordinary functional relationship to a differential functional relationship can radically alter the behaviour. It is felt by many (see Forrester[46]) that it is much more important to ascertain structure precisely than it is to ascertain parameters precisely. There is no measure of 'closeness' of structures, and hence it is difficult to give this empirical validity in terms of 'precision'. In addition, if a model has a very large number of parameters, small errors in each could lead to large scale overall error. The point must, however, be borne in mind, but left for further rigorous study as to its meaning and validity. It will clearly have considerable relevance to the formulation of the secondary problem.

B INCOMPLETE U

In some circumstances, it may not be possible to specify U completely. Thus, in situations of type (d) or (e), involving conflict, U may contain variables relating to opponents' strategies in business, or enemies' strategies in the military sphere. It is thought that it is not possible, in general, to enumerate all the possible strategies, and, even if we could, there could be an enormous number.

The secondary problem is then one of determining what policies of competitors, or enemies, to evaluate. Clearly the costs of each inclusion will be evaluated. If, empirically, evidence exists that the coverage has been inadequate, in other problems, the extent and incidence level of such inadequacies has a bearing on the decision.

If the best policy, relative to a given U, is determined, a search for a competitor's, or enemy's, policy, which could make this policy a poor one, seems plausible, stopping if no such policy can be conjectured, and re-evaluating the whole problem if one is found, repeating the cycle. However, the justification of this approach still depends on some assessment of the likelihood of a search for best counter policies being effective for a given amount of effort.

In some circumstances, we may wish to determine, on a historical basis, the effects of the alternatives being considered. U would then contain variables, some of which are themselves controllable, some of which are not. There would be a residual unidentified set, resulting in a T form partly in terms of known elements of U, and partly in terms of unknown elements.

In Chapter 2 it has already been stated that T can be made perfectly fitting by including enough U variables. Hence, since this is clearly not an acceptable philosophy, the role of U as a true predictor contributor must depend on an understanding of the situation on hand, to the extent that each $u \in U$ is accepted as being a causal variable, the only question being one of degree.

The secondary problem is then one of deciding whether the 'predictive' content is adequate for the decision on hand, or whether the implied risks are unacceptable.

It is rather like the problem of Statistical Decision Theory, but, in this case, it is the identification of new variables, not new observations on a known variable, which gives rise to the secondary decision. The same difficulties which applied to formalizing the secondary problem of incomplete consequences apply here.

In looking for sources of suboptimization it has been noted that true relations may be a function of decisions yet to be made either by the decisionmaker or other parties. Since these are essentially free (to some extent) the relation obtained may depend on what assumptions one makes about these other decisions. One may not consider them, and simply look at past events and see how y varied with x, the danger being that decisions based on this relationship may alter it.

Examples

(1) A spares solution may depend on the component replacement decision, or on production decisions, influencing load and, hence, maintenance needs. The relationships used depend on assumptions about such factors. The actual assumption may depend on the decisions about the spares in the first instance.

(2) An insurance company's branch location and size decision may depend on cost relationships which are functions of bonus scheme, the effects of which may depend on the general economic condition of the company and, hence, on the location and size decisions.

From the foregoing, it is clear that the formulation and resolution of the secondary decision problems, when T is not known, will depend on the nature of the assumptions we can make about T. Later on we will treat the simplest one (i.e. when T is known except for a specific parameter), but the more general one, when the structure of T is unknown, is left for further research.

C THE INFORMATION PROBLEM RELATIVE TO U

U may be presented in varying informational environments.

Thus, suppose we consider a problem in which the consequence θ depends, among other things, on the demand for a product in the next year.

U might be identical with a set of possible demands, and the decisionmaker may have to subjectively assess the situation in the light of his own, implicit, experience (case (e)). Alternatively, some sophisticated mathematical approach may produce probability information (case (b) or (c)). On the other hand, the actual data relating to historical demand for similar products may be presented prior to processing to obtain such probabilities (case (e)).

Each of these situations differs in informational presentation. It is not meaningful to compare alternatives, in A, under different informational conditions, but it is meaningful to compare the information systems themselves by comparing the resulting performance when each system is used in an optimal manner.

In order to compare information systems we have to realize that such systems will be related, and that some overall model of the information systems, such that each system is seen as some projection of the overall model, is needed to compare such systems.

Example

In weather forecasting, we may simply use the climatological frequencies of various weather states $s_1, s_2, \ldots, s_n$. However, if we use certain meteorological information, with states $m_1, m_2, \ldots, m_N$, we have a relationship between:

$p(s_k)$: probability of s_k;
$q(m_l)$: probability of m_l;
$r(s_k/m_l)$: probability of s_k given m_l;

viz.:

$$p(s_k) = \sum_l r(s_k/m_l)q(m_l)$$

Nelson and Winter[95] use the above approach to study the economic information requirements of a builder, whose work is influenced by the weather.

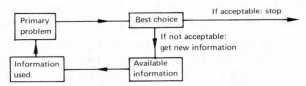

Figure 111. Information decisions

From a prior point of view we may have one alternative preferred to another, but the reverse may apply on a posterior basis, once other relevant information becomes available. As we have already pointed out, it is the prior valuation which must concern us.

The secondary decision, as to whether to get further information, can be included in the initial formulation of the problem, in the context of the informational system used.

Pictorially we represent this in Figure 111.

This secondary decision is whether to get more information or to make the decision without it. Clearly the costs of getting the information are relevant. There remains the question of determining its worth. Also, since we can only determine the procedure and not the actual information, there remains the question of relating the actual information to the procedure.

Where the information system is fixed, but one can choose, within this system, to get particular pieces of information, the optimal choice of such informational decisions is well covered in Statistical Decision Theory, in which, although a suboptimal terminal decision is made, the combination of secondary and primary decisions is optimal (see Raiffa and Schlaiffer[105]).

This is a different secondary problem to that in which one has a choice of the informational system itself.

It has been pointed out that decisions are optimal relative to specific information systems, and additional information may simply change the ranking, and this poses the difficult question of whether the decision is actually improved. In the case when we consider the information problem as a policy problem in the context of many situations, the 'long run' argument may be invoked to establish that the policy may be better although individual decisions may not be.

As examples of the dependence of optimality on information, consider the following.

Examples

(1) If a builder decides his building operations on the basis that rain has occurred a certain proportion of times in the past on a given day, he will get one optimal solution. If he uses a weather forecast and bases his decision on the fact that weather forecasts have been right a certain proportion of times, he will get another optimal solution. If the forecast is to have value the latter solution must be better.

(2) In inventory control problems it can happen that production programmes are made without knowing exactly what stock is available at any point in time. This raises the question of the value of such information. The values of different frequencies of monitoring can be demonstrated.

(3) In a study of production of greetings cards, each card has a sales profile. An initial production run is made, and a second production run is made after so many months. The information available for assessing the second production run requirements will depend on the point in time at which the second decision is made. The optimality of any solution depends on the information period specified and the value of the latter can be demonstrated.

(4) In a study concerned with ordering supplies, it was known that the supply was irregular and not always geared to quantities asked for, at least in respect to recent quantities. When ordering, we can make this dependent on:

(a) present stock level;
(b) present stock level, last order quantity and last quantity supplied;
(c) present stock level, all previous order quantities and supplies.

(a) is the simplest, (c) the most complicated.

However, one could experiment and find out how (a), (b), (c) would perform, although in (c) many different decision rules would be possible. We can still talk about the best policy in (a), in (b) and in (c), but the best in (c) would be at least as good as the best in (b) and in (a).

The basic reason for bringing in more information arises from the belief that the probability distribution of amounts supplied depends, not only on present quantity ordered, but also on past supplies and existing backlogs. The value of the new information system can be demonstrated.

(5) We often meet the problem of finding ways of estimating certain variables where the reliability of the estimate needs to be examined in the context of the

decisions for which it is to be used. Some means of assessing the value of such reliability in relationship to its cost should be made.

In the fabrication shop of a shipyard they were issued with an erection programme and constrained the fabrication programme to follow the same sequence, with weekly programmes being scheduled when detailed times and work content were known at the beginning of the week. The question arose as to whether a quick and inexpensive method of estimating times and work content could be used for loading the fabrication shop over a few weeks, rather than a week at a time. The advantage is that better work mixes can be planned to improve throughput. The disadvantage is that, in order to achieve this better utilization, some units may be planned later in the programme and may be late for the erection schedule. By simulating the present system and the proposed system, knowing the reliability of the estimating procedure, throughput sales and erection requirement effectiveness can be compared to determine whether the crude estimating is worthwhile.

(6) In the same company the reliability of estimating work content, times and costs, can be valued in the context of the tendering problem.

In its very simplest form, suppose only costs matter and we have two methods of estimating, each giving conditional distributions of actual costs given estimated costs, say $p_1(c/e)$, $p_2(c/e)$. Let $q(c)$ be the distribution of actual costs. We then have the relationships for the probability distributions of estimated costs using either system, viz.:

$$q(c) = \sum_e p_1(e) . p_1(c/e)$$

$$= \sum_e p_2(e) . p_2(c/e)$$

From these we find $p_1(e)$, $p_2(e)$.

Now for a given situation, if $r(b/c)$ is the distribution for the winning bid given c, the expected profit from each estimating method is as follows:

$$E_1 = \sum_e p_1(e) \max_x \left[\sum_{b>x} \sum_c p_1(c/e) r(b/c)(x-c) \right]$$

$$E_2 = \sum_e p_2(e) \max_x \left[\sum_{b>x} \sum_c p_2(c/e) r(b/c)(x-c) \right]$$

For a perfect forecast of costs, $p_1(c/e) = 0$ if $c \neq e$, $p_1(c/e) = 1$ if $c = e$, and E gives its maximal value.

In the above problem we have made use of probabilistic ideas. However, the problem can be approached in a similar manner if we have different approaches to uncertainty, for example if we could not give probabilities to the events, but made our choice in terms of minimax solutions. The important point is that the information decision can be added to the initial primary decisions to form an extended problem, but within the same uncertain framework of the primary decision problem. There may be difficulties in setting up such models, but if the information decision is to be justified, one way or another, some model of the secondary decision process is needed. (See White[143] and Szaniawski.[132])

3.2.4 Suboptimization via Values

As has been indicated, we need to distinguish between prior and posterior evaluations of a solution.

Quite clearly, any solution may, in retrospect, be seen to be worse than an alternative solution which may or may not have been considered at the analysis stage, and hence suboptimality in retrospect will undoubtedly arise.

In the context of this discussion, suboptimality is taken to be in the prior sense. The value function for alternatives will then range from the deterministic (as it is thought to be at the time of assessment) to the uncertain. In the latter case we will not discuss the obvious case of prior unforeseen outcomes and events, to which reference has already been made, and assume that the problem is formulated in its standard form, *viz.*,

$$\theta = T(a, u)$$

where T is a deterministic transformation, θ are the outcomes, a is an alternative and u are the other, specified, events (or states of nature) which, together with a, determine θ, in suitable terms.

Prior suboptimization could apparently then arise when a value function, V, on a exists, but: either (a) we do not know this; or (b) we use the wrong one.

We have already pointed out the methodological difficulties which arise because value functions are not unique, when considering deviations of value. We also need to consider the possible sources of variations in values. In Section 3.2.2 the possibility that inappropriate value functions arose, not because of the measurement process, but because the decisionmaker was uninformed about further consequences ensuing from his effective consequences. In that case it was shown that one might avoid the use of values altogether, at least directly, by an appropriate formulation of the secondary problem. There is, however, the possibility that the measurement process is at fault, and that the value function finally obtained does not represent the true ranking of the alternatives. There are reasons for this, and, as has been pointed out in Chapter 2, normally an error modification theory is needed. However, this may be difficult to determine, and hence some approach to uncertainty in values may be needed.

(a) Unknown V

In this case the decisionmaker is presented with the outcomes θ relating to a chosen set A, in terms of $T(a, u)$, and he then makes his choice. It is then not meaningful to talk about suboptimization, since we are not, in principle, able to test it. The principles of ontological relativism requires that constructs be testable if we wish to give them meaning.

In this case, the search for further alternatives, for example, can only stem from the decisionmaker, since the Decision Analyst has no way of judging whether a solution could or could not, economically, be improved upon.

(b) Incorrect V

In this case we have a value function V but it may be incorrect. Clearly this is the same as in case (a) unless (α): we assume that V is, in some sense, 'close' to the true value function; or, alternatively, (β): we assume that V is one of a given set.

(α) V *'Close' to True* $\hat{V}$. There are two types of closeness, *viz.*, closeness of V to $\hat{V}$, and closeness of one alternative a to another alternative $\hat{a}$. The latter case is not, in itself, meaningful since, in the end, it is the closeness of the effects of a and $\hat{a}$ which is important.

Example

Thus if we have an inventory control procedure of the standard (S, Q) form and $S \sim \hat{S}$, $Q \sim \hat{Q}$, this in itself is not evidence that (S, Q) and $(\hat{S}, \hat{Q})$ will have relatively close effects; and even if the effects were similar, the acceptability of these may be radically different, particularly if θ included run-out effects with high penalty costs. Thus we come back to the problem of closeness of V, $\hat{V}$.

The fact that V, $\hat{V}$ may result in high-rank correlation coefficients for a given set of alternatives A, says nothing about the 'magnitude' of errors involved in the occasional reversed ranking. If the ranking were the same, no problem arises, of course, for a given A. Problems could arise if we had to decide whether or not to extend A.

In view of the fact that value functions are not unique, we need to be careful when discussing 'closeness'. We need to stipulate enough about the situation to ensure that the true value function is unique in a specified sense. Thus, for example, if we are using von Neumann and Morgenstern's theory of value, if we can choose some $\bar{\theta}$, $\underline{\theta}$, with $\bar{\theta}$ preferred to $\underline{\theta}$, we set $v(\bar{\theta}) = 1$, $v(\underline{\theta}) = 0$. Let us assume this for all competing value functions, if we assume the stated theory. Now let V be the present value function and let $\hat{V}$ be a potential value function. Let a^* be optimum relative to V, $\hat{a}^*$ be optimum relative to $\hat{V}$. The secondary decision is whether to accept V, and hence a^*, or to search further for a more realistic $\hat{V}$.

To make the problem specific, suppose we have a fixed amount of money, x, to invest between certain activities. We then have value functions $V(a, x)$, $\hat{V}(a, x)$. If $\hat{V}$ turns out to be true, and the cost of finding this is c, then the value is $\hat{V}(\hat{a}^*, x - c)$, where $\hat{a}^*$ depends on $x - c$. If we can assume that differences in value are meaningful, then the loss in value by using the solution a^*, without search, is $\hat{V}(\hat{a}^*, x - c) - \hat{V}(a^*, x)$ (which may be negative). Now one definition of closeness of two value functions is that

$$|V(b, y) - V(b', y')| \sim |\hat{V}(b, y) - \hat{V}(b', y')|,$$

for all relevant b, y, b', y'. In this case

$$|\hat{V}(\hat{a}^*, x - c) - \hat{V}(a^*, x)| \sim |V(\hat{a}^*, x - c) - V(a^*, x)|,$$

and, under certain conditions, $\hat{a}^*(x-c) \sim a^*(x-c)$. Hence

$$|V(a^*(x-c), x-c) - V(a^*(x), x)|$$

will give some idea of potential losses if further search is not pursued.

The above approach is only rudimentary and there are clear difficulties in formulating this problem. We need evidence that the real $\hat{V}$ is close to V in some sense. We also need to accept that differences in value are usable as an indicator for the secondary decision. If there were only one $\hat{V}$, then this point could be avoided, since we only need determine whether or not $(\hat{a}^*(x-c), x-c)$ is preferred to (a^*, x) relative to $\hat{V}$.

It is to be noted that the above argument is related to the usual sensitivity analysis and, if c is not too large, then the potential differences in value, under suitable conditions are

$$-c \frac{\partial V(a^*, x)}{\partial x} + O(c^2)$$

This differs from the usual sensitivity analysis in that the search cost c is directly included in the secondary problem. At the same time, we have not expressed the differences between $V(a,x)$ and $\hat{V}(a,x)$. If the V, $\hat{V}$ were the same, except for some parameter $\alpha(\hat{\alpha})$, then the above expression would be corrected by a term $O(\alpha - \hat{\alpha})^2$, occurring in the usual sensitivity analysis, providing $\alpha \sim \hat{\alpha}$.

Part of the preceding discussion relates to the popular 'sensitivity analysis'. It must be pointed out that such an analysis has a limited usefulness.

If it results that the changes in value are small within a range of parameter variation, for this to be useful, we must know that the parameters lie in this range, for if they were not so limited, the analysis would be useless.

If the analysis results in demonstrating that the change in value is very sensitive to changes of parameter within a range which might contain the true value, then this is useful and may lead to further effort in precise location of the parameter.

The oft-quoted 'flatness' characteristic is concerned with sensitivity of value to solution for a given parameter, and is not identical with the usual 'sensitivity of parameter' concept.

Example

The function

$$f(x, \alpha) = k/(1 - \alpha)$$

is flat with respect to x, for a given $\alpha \neq 1$, but is highly sensitive to changes of α in the region of $\alpha = 1$. In this case it would not matter what the chosen x was.

(β) *V One of a Given Set.* Typical of this type of situation is the capital investment situation in which various criteria have been discussed very widely in the literature, such as: $V_1 = $ present worth of a; $V_2 = $ pay-back period of a; $V_3 = $ internal rate of return of a; $V_4 = $ some function of V_1, V_2, V_3, ...

In this situation the decisionmaker may be so unsure of his criteria that either we have to set up a very sophisticated experiment to determine whether his values are based on a proper representation of the problem anyhow (see White[144, 146] where an investigation of long-term objectives casts light on the problem of valuing individual investments), or we have to investigate the robustness of solution to criteria.

Unfortunately, in the latter case, we are back to our problem in (α), since, unless the same optimal choice is made for each criterion, we really have to go back to the errors in criterion values. One way of doing this is to calculate the value error ratios when the optimal decision relating to one criterion is used, but another criterion is true. Thus if a_i^* is an optimal decision according to V_i, we calculate

$$\varepsilon_{ij} = |V_i(a_i^*) - V_i(a_j^*)|/V_i(a_i^*) \quad (V_i(a_i^*) \neq 0)$$

The fact that value functions are not unique still raises its head. Even if V_1, V_2, V_3 are uniquely defined, if V_4 is some subjectively derived function, then it need not be unique. The suggestion above is no more than a statement of what is done in some cases, but it clearly requires considerable examination as to its validity. The use of the error ratio, rather than the errors, is simply a device to get some normalized comparison between different value schemes, but even this is questionable.

Although situation (α) may give some results in the sense that a^* may be a good solution within the admissible V set, and situation (β) may give some results in the sense that a^* may be optimum whatever the true V in the specified set, it does not seem possible to proceed further. In the end analysis, if we set up the secondary decision problem of whether or not to determine the true criterion, we see that the decisions have to be related to the consequences of an action, for which a definite criterion is needed.

Let us consider a problem in which each primary alternative, a, results in a time series of cash returns, say $(r_1(a), r_2(a), \ldots, r_t(a), \ldots) = \mathbf{r}(a)$.

Let c be the cost of determining the true V_i, for the sake of simplification. Then Table 10 describes the secondary problem.

We cannot solve this problem without knowing the true criterion, except in the cases where we can invoke the closeness ideas of case (α) or the domination ideas of case (β).

Oportel[99] takes a very formal view on modelling and considers six ways in which model approximations can be introduced, which overlap with the previous possibilities discussed.

Table 10: Criteria decisions

		V_1	V_2	$\ldots$	V_n
	a_1	$\mathbf{r}(a_1)$	$\mathbf{r}(a_1)$	$\ldots$	$\mathbf{r}(a_1)$
Primary alternatives	a_2	$\mathbf{r}(a_2)$	$\mathbf{r}(a_2)$	$\ldots$	$\mathbf{r}(a_2)$
	$\vdots$	$\vdots$			
	a_m	$\mathbf{r}(a_m)$	$\mathbf{r}(a_m)$	$\ldots$	$\mathbf{r}(a_m)$
Find true V_i	f	$\mathbf{r}(a_1^*) - \mathbf{c}$	$\mathbf{r}(a_2^*) - \mathbf{c}$	$\ldots$	$\mathbf{r}(a_m^*) - \mathbf{c}$

3.3 Suboptimizing as a Decision Problem

We see that suboptimization, therefore, arises out of a limited consideration of
A, and difficulties in the derivations of θ, T and V.

Some of the difficulties arise because of:

(i) insufficient information;
(ii) insufficient theory allowing us to determine θ, T, V;
(iii) the time and cost associated with each phase of the analysis.

We know that there are bound to be suboptimizations, and that the time and
cost of more rigorous analyses may outweigh the gains, measured in better
primary decisions. The central question is: 'can we construct a suboptimizing
procedure which provides the correct compromise between choice of problem
formulation, the choice of model, the choice of method of solution, and the
benefits from analysis?'

In Section 3.2 some, very limited, approaches have been discussed to some
secondary decisions governing the suboptimization process. These are only
suggestions put forward in the belief that something may be done in some cases,
and that, in all cases, secondary decisions have to be taken. It has often been
said that it is more important to formulate the primary problem than to solve
some problem with sophisticated techniques. Equally well one might say that
the secondary decisions problem should be studied properly, rather than not
formulate it at all.

Minas[87] puts forward four popular views on the secondary problem:

(1) the problem is meaningless, it cannot be formulated or we cannot get data;
(2) the problem is meaningful, has no general solution, but common sense
dictates the special solution;
(3) the problem is meaningful and can be resolved by group participation—
socialized common sense;
(4) the problem is meaningful and is open to scientific enquiry.

He believes the last. If so, then we generate a much more complex requirement
than for the primary problem, which is itself subject to suboptimality considerations. Thus, since we are concerned with suboptimality arising from a study of
the primary decision using the scientific method, then so should we be concerned
with suboptimality arising in the secondary decision because the scientific method
applied to the secondary problem will influence the primary decision suboptimality. We may, for example, equally well ask ourselves how we should test
a model of the secondary problem, as the secondary problem asks how we should
test a model of the primary problem. In principle we have an infinite regress, but
the dependence of the suboptimality of the primary decision on higher-order
decisions may become less as we move further away from the primary decision
itself. Although we have an infinite regress, there are only two sorts of problem.
For let Q be a problem area at a certain level, and let $T(Q)$ be the set of immediate
higher-order decisions needed to analyse and resolve Q. Let P be the primary

230

decision area, S the immediate secondary decision area. Then $S = TP$; $S = TS$. Figure 112 illustrates the interrelationship.

The condensation of secondary and higher-order problems in Figure 112 arises from the fact that decisions at these levels are of a similar kind, e.g. get further information, seek for further alternatives, etc., although, naturally, the specific content of these decisions will differ.

It can be seen from Figure 112 that the resolution of the secondary and higher-order problems has to be through the primary problem representation in principle, if a solution is to exist. However, whereas we have managed to do this in some cases, difficulties appear when the primary criteria are not certain, as indicated by Table 10. The possibility of having higher-order criteria not stemming from lower-order criteria does not appear to be valid, but further study may show otherwise (see Mitroff and Betz[89]).

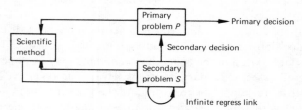

Figure 112. Primary, secondary and higher-order problems

Whichever way we view Minas's problem, we do have to face these secondary decision problems and, if we wish to justify our choices, we do need some model on which to base these. Otherwise the choice is unsupported. If we are able to construct such a model, the suboptimization may no longer exist in the primary problem and may be transferred to the secondary problem. What is appropriate for the primary problem has to be viewed in light of the problems faced in arriving at that solution. It is the net effect of the combined secondary and primary decisions which have to be evaluated.

The general secondary problem is very much tied up with a dilemma facing most Decision Analysts, *viz.*, 'should one begin with small models and work up to the larger one, terminating the construction at a suitable stage, or should one go for the full model and cut it down to meet capabilities of handling?'

Solandt,[125] based on his wartime experience, firmly believes the former. The advantage of this approach is that we can guide ourselves to a model in which the realistic characteristics have been incorporated. The procedure is to make certain broad assumptions for the purpose of producing an analysable model, without which grave complications would arise. If subsequent conflicts arise, we must then resolve them.

3.4 Bounded Computational Rates

When considering the suboptimization problem we face problems of data existence and collection, and computational problems. It is important to realize that, even if the resources existed to model and solve a primary problem situation to any degree of sophistication, there may be reasons why we could not do this in any case. There are, on the basis of certain physical laws of nature, limitations on the ability to produce fine measurements and on the ability to process information at more than a given rate.

Bremermann[18] conjectures such limitations on the basis of Einstein's mass–energy equation and Heisenberg's principle of uncertainty. He reasons that all information processing needs energy for transmitting and recording information. From Einstein's equation there is a maximum amount of energy available for processing and recording. He postulates that, for a given time limit Δt, there is a smallest energy interval, ΔE, within which one can locate, with reasonable certainty, the level of any variable. This means there is a maximal amount of information which can be recorded at any instant in time. Using Heisenberg's principle of uncertainty, he postulates that, for a given ΔE, there is a smallest time interval needed to locate a variable in a given energy level. Combining these, he arrives at a maximal rate of transmitting information per gram of its mass. This figure is 2×10^{47} and even this is an overestimate.

As an example, consider the time taken to explore the alternatives in the following problem.

Suppose we had an N variable state description of a system with each variable having m discrimination levels, and with D alternative actions possible for each state. Suppose we wish to find an optimal policy over n periods of time.

There are m^N states, D^{m^N} possible rules at each stage, and $(D^{m^N})^n$ possible overall policies.

With $m = N = 3$, $D = n = 10$, we have 10^{90} policies.

Allowing only for the presentation of the values of each policy (not considering all forms of transmission and operations necessary for arithmetical calculations), and assuming all the mass of the computer is needed in this presentation, it would take a milion-ton computer $1 \cdot 6 \times 10^{23}$ years to do this, even if every value were 0 or 1, which it is not. To k binary places this would require $k \times 1 \cdot 6 \times 10^{23}$ years.

Heisenberg's principle might look a little strange in the context of the output of a computer, e.g. on tape. However, it has to be realized that some energized mechanism is required to punch the hole and if we reduce the energy impulses below a certain level (in order to get more holes punched, instantaneously or over time) then there may result a non-zero probability of non-triggering of the mechanism and hence producing erroneous information.

We can see that, if we insist on accuracy of calculation, even assuming the input is accurate, then we are severely limited in our ability to analyse problems of more than a very limited complexity. Bearing in mind the fact that many of our input variables (e.g. parameters, etc.) are not perfectly accurate, we might be prepared to drop a certain amount of our restrictions on 'perfect computations' and accept a machine which may, say, treat 10111 as 10110, arising out of probabilistic triggering of mechanism. This way we can carry out far more calculations, at a risk of miscalculation, however, this risk being the compound of a succession of risks.

It is also essential to note that although the binary form is the most efficient for information storage purposes, it is also the least reliable in the event of incorrect triggering of computing mechanism, the reason being that a misfiring on the first digit is a serious calculation error.

The following gives an outline of Bremermann's argument as interpreted by this author.

Conjecture

No data processing system, whether artificial or living, can process more than 2×10^{47} bits per second per gram of its mass.

If this is true it places an upper bound on our computational rates.

Let us first of all outline his 'proof'.

Proof

(i) All information is represented by observations on one, or several, markers or reception of signals (impulses, etc.), at one or several points in time, e.g. if it is represented in paper-tape form we may have:

(a) two holes together: (0, 0) or (0, 1) or (1, 0) or (1, 1), or
(b) a single hole at different points in time: 0 or 1 at t_1, 0 or 1 at t_2.

(ii) Such a representation is called a state.

(iii) If a state is represented in binary notation, with n components, then to determine the state is equivalent to processing n bits of information.

(iv) For each component an equivalent energy level is required, say ΔE_i.

(v) For a given time limit Δt there is a lowest energy interval, ΔE, which can be measured and hence $\Delta E_i \geqslant \Delta E$ (if not we could measure $\Delta E_i < \Delta E$ by observing the component value 0 or 1).

(vi) If $E(\max)$ is the maximum available energy, then the maximum number of components we can effectively use in a given time interval Δt is $\leqslant E(\max)/\Delta E$ and hence:

'Maximal information (bits) transmissible in a given time interval Δt is $\leqslant E(\max)/\Delta E$.'

(vii) Hence the maximal rate at which information can be transmitted is $R \leqslant E(\max)/\Delta E \, \Delta t$.

(viii) Heisenberg's Principle of Uncertainty states that, given two variables, p, q, then any attempt to measure one with a better degree of accuracy will increase the inaccuracy in the measurement of the other, dependent on the nature of the variables. Basically the reason is that measuring entails an operation, and an operation on one variable can influence the other. An industrial example is given by Hampson,[52] who states that, in cost benefit analysis, it is likely that efforts to estimate, accurately, costs and benefits at the same time, will fall foul of Heisenberg's principle; we can preset the costs and we have a lower limit on the uncertainty in the benefits; or we can preset benefits to be accrued over time and have a lower limit on the uncertainty in the costs needed to achieve this benefit.

If σp, σq are the standard errors of variation of p, q, respectively, then a more concise statement is $\sigma p \, \sigma q \geqslant C(p,q)$.

In Bremermann's case, where we are trying to measure E and t, this reduces to $\sigma E \sigma t \geqslant h$, where h is Planck's constant.

Now, if we are concerned with deductive calculations, we need to make sure ΔE is large enough to make the probability of either erroneous output or erroneous perception extremely small (zero, if possible). In such a case $\Delta E \geqslant \sigma E$ almost certainly.

Since Δt is the actual elapsed time while E is being measured, we have $\sigma t \leqslant \Delta t$ on the same grounds, if Δt is to be measured with high confidence.

Whence $\Delta E \, \Delta t \geqslant h$.

(ix) Einstein's mass–energy equation gives

$$E(\max) = mc^2$$

where m = mass and c = velocity of light. Hence we get

$$R \leqslant m(c^2/h) \sim 2 \times 10^{47} m.$$

CHAPTER 4

Further Aspects of Decision Methodology

4.1 Introduction

As a prelude to this very limited chapter, we requote Ackoff,[1] on 'Implementation and Organisation of Research'.

'When we discuss implementation of research results and organisation of research effort this (the building of models to facilitate their analysis) is no longer possible. Although an increasing amount of effort is being put into the study of these aspects of research and even more into writing about them, they are very poorly understood . . . In the meantime discussions of implementation and organisation of research are more likely to be based on opinion, experience and wishful thinking, than on analysis, experimentation and systematic observation.'

The previous chapters have made an attempt to cast some structure on the methodological aspects and to identify the methodological decisions involved in any study. Nonetheless, as Ackoff says, the situation is still poorly understood.

A search of the literature will show that many people have thought about the problems which Ackoff raises.

Morris[92] raises the issues already discussed in the context of Minas[87] in the previous chapter.

He queries the stand taken by some that the Decision Analysis process must remain an art and believes that some useful guidelines can be given on the sort of problems mentioned in the main body of this text. He suggests several maxims, which he applies to the complete analysis of a transport problem. The maxims are: factor the system problem into simpler problems (this is treated as 'synthesizing' in this text); establish a clear statement of the deductive objectives of the model (in this text there are only two relevant objectives, *viz.*, to establish the decision–effects relationship and to produce a recommended decision); seek an analogue (the ability to take other models as starting points has been discussed in the first chapter); consider a specific numerical instance of the problem (this helps the process of modelling and verification and may help the solution procedure; however, in a given context numerical inputs would be needed anyway); establish some symbols (this is the first stage in producing the basic mathematical model); write down the obvious (this is simply a mechanism to get the model under way);

if a tractable model is obtained, enrich it, otherwise simplify (in other words we expand or contract a model within the constraints placed upon us in getting a solution in an effort to compromise between these and the faithfulness of the model).

Selig,[115] to whom reference has also been made, raises questions directly relevant to the implementation issue, which we have not discussed to date. He discusses factors influencing the ultimate acceptability of a solution including: experience, familiarity and special training in subject matter, creativity, pattern recognition capabilities, ability to define the nature of an acceptable solution, ingenuity in asking pertinent questions.

If one looks back at the general range of points which have arisen in the preceding chapters it will be clearly seen that the manner of handling, and capacity to handle these intuitively, depends considerably on the attributes mentioned by Selig. To take but one example, we see that the determination of what constitutes an acceptable solution has its origins in the nature of an optimal, or suboptimal solution, involving many considerations discussed in the preceding chapter.

Despite these views, little conclusive research has been carried out whereby 'opinions' may become accepted scientific conclusions.

There seem to be three key issues which permeate any Decision Analysis situation. These are as follows:

(a) the data problem and the choice of problem area;
(b) communication with and, involvement of, affected parties;
(c) implementation of results.

The first one has been indirectly tackled by looking at the component decisions involved. Certain key issues arise here, and, at the risk of duplication, it is worthwhile revisiting this area.

The second and third have not been discussed, but it is clear that methodological issues and decisions abound in these areas as well. For example, the extent of sophistication may influence the acceptability of the results (see Selig[115]) and we have a clear choice before us, which, in principle, may be formalized. However, we will not do so, but simply make reference to the factors at play. They will be of practical use in themselves.

4.2 Data Problem and Choice of Problem Area

Where do we start? Getting data? Getting objectives? Identifying decisions?

The previous discussions will have indicated a subtle interplay between all of these.

Initial data will help a useful study to be determined.

On the other hand one can collect too much data, much of which may not be useful. It may be erroneous or it may be irrelevant.

In an article on Guidelines for the Practice of Operations Research[43] reference is made to the questionable origin of sources of data.

In addition, Baylis[7] quotes Josiah Stamp (taken from Kane[65]):

'The Government are very keen in amassing statistics. They collect them, add them, raise them to the nth power, take the cube root and make wonderful diagrams. But what you must never forget is that every one of these figures comes in the first instance from the village watchman who just puts down what he damn pleases.'

Clearly this statement is a little extreme but nonetheless emphasizes the need to consider the origins of data carefully in one's studies.

If one wished to determine the ideal data one would determine the decisions for which it was to be used. But this may mean too early a commitment to decision areas. The process is clearly cyclic, as Figure 113 illustrates.

Figure 113. Problem formulation and data

Examples

(1) In the medical field, documents include a variety of data about a patient. To suspect that we have a problem at all requires knowledge of some of this data and once an apparent problem has been recognized it may lead to consideration of other data. The precise decisions to consider are part of this cycle.

(2) In the areas of police patrol or ambulance services there is a variety of data which could be collected, such as running costs, demand patterns. A similar cycle to that in the previous example exists.

There are dangers of trying to formulate the problem too quickly in the investigation if the problem is relatively complex. If this process is costly and time consuming, adequate thought must be given to what data is needed, how much, and how it is going to be used. We can collect too much or we can collect too little. Very often it is much easier to collect several types of data at the same time rather than at different times, but the danger is that we ask for more than we need.

Strauss[129] points out that once the problem has been identified the study should be oriented towards solving this particular problem. This is by no means trivial. There have been many occasions when data has been collected which has turned out to have little bearing on the original problem. Searching should be influenced by the problem on hand and not in the hope that its findings will be useful. If people have to put effort into providing data and one does not eventually demonstrate its relevance, this can be a setback for future cooperation. We can quote two examples in which this danger arose.

Examples

(1) In a study of hospital emergency beds, the researcher wanted to find out as much as he could about operations in a unit, historically, which had little bearing, at the stage of the initial problem, although it did enable later problems

to be identified. In this case the sponsor specifically requested that the stated problem be looked at.

(2) In a recent study of the provision of spares, the researcher collected a lot of dubious data and ended up by discussing a myriad of problems, whereas some answer to the original problem was possible, but not forthcoming.

We have superficially studied the general problem of the relationship between 'model', 'theory' and 'data', in particular the problem of the relevance of data. When discussing measurement, it was pointed out that such measurements presupposed a theory, e.g. cost measurements. To know that data might be relevant is to see the data in the light of some theoretical framework. Suppes[131] says:

'. . . exact analysis of the relation between empirical theories and relevant data calls for a hierarchy of models of different logical types.'

Example

Suppes[131] gives an example in the area of learning in a sequential experiment. With one of two responses at each stage of a four-hundred stage sequence, we really require notions of probability distributions of responses over all possible sequences, and this is not tractable. In addition, much other data is not included such as expressions, movements, or time taken to operate keys. Thus we have no model of the data which is known to be complete.

We will not pursue, in this book, the highly sophisticated discussions which surround this topic, but simply emphasize the real need to consider the nature of data in relationship to the analysis for which it is to be used, and to be aware of some of the models of data implicitly assumed, such as the homogeneity and stationarity of the data generating processes.

The need to consider effort in collecting data does not mean that high capital investment problems should be concentrated on, since many small problems take little time to solve and involve little effort in implementation, and many large problems do not result in a satisfactory solution and involve large uncertainties.

On the other hand the fact that an area made up of many small problems may involve high costs, in total, need not mean that the area is worth tackling.

Example

It has been stated that the amount spent on maintenance is £2,000,000,000 per annum and that it is worthwhile to study such problems because of the potential savings. However, the number of possible problems to tackle is very large, and it is possible that the savings from any one problem tackled might be small with respect to effort involved.

When selecting projects there are additional criteria which need to be considered. Some are as follows, including the two mentioned:

(i) how important is the project to the company?
(ii) what human problems might arise in carrying out, and implementing the results of the project?

(iii) what are the methodologies which might be used in carrying out the study; for example: will experimentation be needed and for how long? will a synthetic model be derived and what data will be needed? will questionnaires be needed? will the end analysis rely on judgements of any type?

(iv) what data exists, or might exist in time, for the project, and in what form?

(v) what computational effort will be required to effect a solution?

(vi) what reason is there to believe that there might be a net pay-off from the study?

(vii) what form will the end results take?

These points are fundamental in considering projects.

In (iii), for example, if we are going to have to experiment we need to consider the implications very carefully, to ensure that it is properly designed and can be executed under control. If we are to use judgements, then it is important that the sponsors know this, since a totally objective result might have been anticipated, thus negating the impact of the study.

In (vii), for example, if the end result is of the form 'if the demand for the product is d, and if you adopt policy π, your profit will be $P(d,\pi)$', it might not be acceptable to sponsors who might anticipate a definite recommendation on π. It is worth trying to get agreement on the nature of the end results as early as possible.

Mitchell,[88] writing on Operational Research, states three requirements in project selection, *viz.*:

(a) need to be aware of the contributions Operational Research can make to the various projects;

(b) need to assess likelihood of the results of the study causing change in the organization;

(c) need to ascertain that project forms part of a strategic plan for the development of Operational Research in the organization.

The great difficulty with (a) is that little quantitative evidence exists on which to base project selection decisions.

Example

When considering problems in the maintenance area, one possible subset is spares control. Let us suppose we viewed the problem in terms of the minimum directly ascertainable cost, $c(r)$, subject to a run-out probability r, and let us suppose the company wishes to assess the worth of doing a project in this area. Naturally the results of previous studies of similar problems in other organizations would be useful. Figures 114 and 115 indicate potential results.

Figure 114 indicates the curves which organizations A, B, C, D might have obtained. Figure 115 indicates, for a given $r = r^*$, the probability distribution of $c(r^*)$, based on a cut in Figure 113 at $r = r^*$, shown by the broken line.

It may well be that the company considers itself closer to A than to the rest, in which case it may take A's curve to determine whether the project is worthwhile. Alternatively, the subjective probability of it being similar to A, B, C, D might

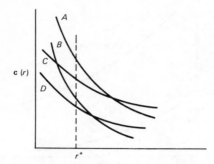

Figure 114. Minimal cost for specified
probability of run-out

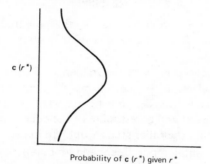

Probability of c (r*) given r*

Figure 115. Probability of minimal
cost

be used. The actual mechanism for resolving the project selection problem is not important here. It is the data base which is important.

Failing the knowledge of this data, some other method is needed to justify the choice of project. One possibility is that a crude study might give some bounds on the levels of achievement of certain variables.

Example

In the above maintenance problem a crude method may exist to determine an upper and lower curve for $c(r)$ as illustrated by Figure 116.

Such an analysis might be relatively inexpensive and give some idea of whether the project should be pursued. The point P in Figure 116 represents the present position, and any decision must be relative to this.

Failing any quantitative analysis, one can only fall back on the argument that 'logical analysis will have a payoff', but this is unconvincing.

The part that pilot studies play in any investigation should be emphasized. Such studies are sometimes essential to determine the worth of the full study.

Examples

(1) In an inventory control problem, we were concerned with controlling several thousand commodities. The work involved in this, even allowing for

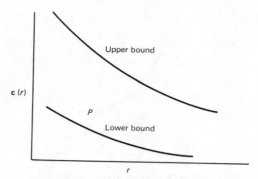

Figure 116. Cost bounds for specified reliability

aggregation, was large. In order to find out the potential savings, a sample of items was investigated. From the results of this sample the value of a major study could be assessed.

(2) In a problem concerned with the influence of crew size on economics of operating a refuse collection service, ultimately a complete rearrangement of rounds may be involved. In order to estimate what the total benefit might be, sample rounds were taken and an estimate of the effects on these was made. On this basis the decision on the fuller study would be made.

(3) In a study of hospital appointment and ambulance systems, it was felt that no real gains could be obtained in integrating these two systems more closely, and that a study was of little value. Rather than carry out an extensive integrative study, it was decided to carry out a pilot study to determine what would be the potential gains if patients who were geographically close were given suitable appointment times. On the basis of the increased performance of the ambulance fleet, it was then possible to examine the real difficulties of achieving some integration against the potential economic and service factor gains so established. To have tackled the whole problem, without this, might not only have resulted in no theoretical gains, but also in unsympathetic collaboration during the project.

We have been discussing project initiation. However, it must be borne in mind that we have equally important decisions to take in project termination. As a project unfurls itself, both the research effort and the nature of the final results become clearer or less clear, and it may be that, in the light of this, the decision to terminate a project may be made.

It is tempting to think in terms of organizational diagnostics as a procedure for identifying what projects are worth undertaking. We have examples of diagnostic procedures in the medical and engineering fields in which symptoms of behaviour are linked probabilistically to causes, and in which diagnoses of causes are followed up by remedial action. We have a limited form of this in business already, arising through the collection of statistics on costs at various cost centres, both for the purpose of ascertaining that things are normal within the organization, and for the purpose of ascertaining that the organization is normal within a wider group of organizations. No analysis exists which relates such symptoms to ultimate identification of malfunction and corrective action, but such an analysis is conceivable. If this were possible it might be useful in aiding the selection of projects. It clearly has differences to the diagnostic areas cited; for example, a system does not have to be malfunctioning (even if we could define this) before projects become worthwhile. Nonetheless the ideas may well be pertinent.

In reality the problem is not necessarily one of doing or not doing a particular project, but of choosing a subset of projects from a given set. The problem is also a dynamic one involving the curtailment of some projects. Project effort also needs to be estimated as an investment input. Considerable study has been made of the resource allocation problem as part of the general problem of research and development and it is not proposed to cover this here. Much of it has a substantial subjective input and the discussion of subjectivity in this book is relevant to this. Dean[32] covers many aspects of the subject.

Finally, but not least, one should consider any time constraints on the study. Sometimes these constraints are inviolable, but, in other cases, a constraint does no more than reflect the possibility of losses of some kind arising from delays in the results of the study. The secondary problem constraints are subject to similar points made about primary problem constraints.

In the NATO publication on Operational Research in Practice, Cole[26] stresses that there is a great danger in 'fighting the problem', we are never satisfied with our model, we particularly suspect criteria given to us, maybe because we see people acting in a contradictory manner. We can never answer all the questions we would like answers to. We cannot answer this dilemma but can only point out that, in Strauss's[129] opinion, such an attitude has prevented useful studies from materializing.

4.3 Communication and Involvement

By communication we mean transmission of information by all parties during each stage of the study.

During the progress of the project the relationships of the researcher with the decisionmaker and with those who are to operate the scheme may have a definite bearing on the validity of the results and on their utilization.

This relationship is a two-way one. Those nearest to the problem will know much about it, but not have the time or ability to formulate it; the researcher fills this gap.

The researcher must allow for limited perception by himself, the decision-makers, and operators. A mutual understanding of the purpose of the research and of the difficulties is desirable as early as possible.

Hankin[53] deals with some of the technicalities of communication by means of reports, which reflect some of the difficulties one has to cater for in establishing the common language of analysis.

It is particularly important that the decisionmaker and operators understand something about the researcher's methods, and how it is that they may be of

242

help. Thus the intuitive aspects of the decisionmaker, in particular, are not subject to analysis as per the researcher's method (see Digby,[36] Charnes[22]).

Vice versa, the researcher should understand the attitudes and motives of the decisionmakers and operators.

The attitudes of the operators may make the study difficult.

When considering attitudes, it is very often useful to try to carry out the study, with their knowledge, to see what the potential gains are. This then provides a useful platform on which to bargain.

Example

There may be resistance to overtime which may be involved in a certain study. If one can determine what the potential savings are if overtime is allowed, then some of this saving can be used as a bargaining instrument.

The technique of persuasion has been insufficiently considered (see Shelley[117]). We quote:

'. . .is that persuading someone to accept the reasonableness of a decision must sometimes consist of more than convincing the recipient of the rationality of choice'.

We must recognize that our logical reasoning may in many circumstances lack persuasive powers and we may have to use other methods as well.

Example

Ruderman[110] states that it is sometimes difficult to convince medical administrators about the general usefulness of Decision Analysis studies. Practical illustrations are useful. He cites a problem concerning the value of good physical condition to the community. A Pan-American highway crew were fed three regular meals per day and it resulted in double the original amount of dirt being shifted. A convincing argument.

Blackett[12] states:

'To convince an executive that some new course of action is to be preferred to some old one, it is essential to understand why the old one was adopted'.

In many instances people have prejudicial estimates of certain facts of life, and the persuasive value of simple analyses aimed at presenting the true state of affairs is high. For example, it might be thought that equipment utilization was 95% when it was 75%; it might be thought that clients were happy with service, when they were not; it might be thought that 90% of materials were supplied within 12 weeks of request, when the figure was 50%. The effect of establishing that these beliefs are not valid can be quite remarkable and can lead to the initial acceptance of Decision Analysis studies.

As Ackoff[1] points out, involvement of the decisionmaker at an early stage may not only safeguard against errors of omission or oversimplification, but may reduce the effort needed to sell the solution later on. Also, since the operational people will be involved later on, they should be brought in early on in the study.

The manner in which the discussions are conducted is important. On one extreme we wish to avoid too pointed questioning (initially at least) since this can offend people. On the other hand, the Decision Analyst needs to be inquisitive and would not be wise to accept too much without some effort to question it.

Examples

(1) Typically one gets statements about amortization periods of life of equipment which are strongly believed. A recent study in a Water Department brought this up. Kazanowski[66] raises this as a common fallacy. However, to conduct a productive discussion of this, in the circumstances when this is strongly ingrained, can require considerable diplomacy.

(2) Getting a compromise between reasonable curiosity and reasonable risk of inhibiting the project by virtue of intensive questioning, is very important. What cannot be pressed at a particular point should be allowed for in the final report.

When the final report is produced certain points must be observed. We take the following from Strauss:[129]

(α) conclusions should be consistent with study; by this he means that the conclusions should follow from the study.

Example

In a recent study one conclusion was that a certain problem should be computerized, when this had never been discussed in the main body of the study.

It is also possible to come up with a prejudicial conclusion not implied by the main study; thus the study might be scant and only loosely support the 'biased' conclusion.

Eventually a sponsor of Decision Analysis will accept conclusions because of his belief in the analyst's integrity, and one could inhibit this by such an approach.

(β) Conditions which might change conclusions must be stated. Quite clearly these will be in the report, but this is not always read. Those conditions to which you feel you ought to draw the attention of the sponsor should be stated separately (e.g. assumption about range of market demand).

Example

In a recent study it was difficult to determine whether certain costs of steel making were dependent upon the input mix. It was assumed that the costs did not depend upon the mix, but this assumption had to be stated in the report.

(γ) Subjective judgements should be specially identified. By this he means 'highly subjective', since all judgements are subjective. This is particularly important since a study does not end when a report is produced; a re-examination of aspects of this kind may be specifically called for.

Example

In an innovating intensive care unit study, initial subjective judgements of durations of stay were made. These were clearly stated in the final results. The medics concerned had, on further consideration, changed their minds by this time, but the risk of incorrect application was minimized by the clear statement of these assumptions.

To these we add one by Reitman,[107] *viz.*,

(δ) Particular attention should be given to open constraints.

Examples

(1) Thus the range of alternatives to be considered may be so ill-defined initially that those on which the study rests may not be at all appropriate. On reading the report someone may take up this issue.

(2) When there is the risk of certain contingencies (run-out of stock, breakdown of machine), the Decision Analyst may not be able to pinpoint the constraint levels for these and is more than likely to fix them himself.

4.4 Implementation

Ackoff states:

'... implementation is often the only real test of validity of research conclusions and as such should be part of the research.'

We have already discussed some of the difficulties of such a testing procedure and note that here Ackoff's emphasis is on the need to consider the problems of implementation as an integral part of the process of research itself.

It must be noted that the acceptance of a solution and its implementation is not an adequate test in itself and, as Huysmanns[63] says, quoting Churchman and Ratoosh, such an acceptance must be accompanied by an understanding of the process of analysis itself. We make but four points in this section, *viz.*:

(α) the likelihood of implementation will depend on how the project was carried out;

(β) the ability to persuade people to implement is very important;

(γ) the resources needed to implement a solution should be considered as early on in the study as is feasible;

(δ) the participation of the researcher in the implementation is advisable because only he really understands when the model is valid and when changes should take place because of changing conditions.

We include salient aspects from a paper by Radnor, Rubenstein and Tansik,[103] who studied implementation problems in Decision Analysis and other innovative functions.

Table 11 summarizes the factors found in the above research.

The listing of factors in Table 11 does not vary significantly from the listing which has been generated by the R & D management group at Northwestern with respect to that environment. Variables there identified have included:

1. recognition of the need for an item;
2. willingness of the individuals in the receiving unit to interrupt on-going work to handle something new;

Table 11: Factors underlying implementation problems as described in 15 literature sources

Literature source

Factor number	Description	Ackoff	Ackoff	Churchman and Schainblatt	Crane	Hahn	Heiman	Hicks	Hitch	Huysmanns	Malcolm	Pennycuick	Stillson	Swager	Swan	Turban	Total of authors mentioning the factor
1	Need by OR to define results					×	×		×	×	×			×		×	7
2	Impact on users' goals					×	×			×	×			×	×		6
3	Communications (understanding, timeliness, etc.)	×			×							×			×	×	5
4	Client involved (time, money, participation)				×		×	×				×					4
5	Implementation costs and time		×								×		×				3
6	Low-level resistance to change (failure to participate)												×		×		2
7	Client requests for help		×										×				2
8	Urgency of results		×														1
9	Measurable savings		×														1
10	Improved information	×															1
11	Availability of trained people to implement						×										1
12	Reporting level of OR/MS						×										1
13	Availability of detailed implementation plan						×										1
14	Complexity of computations needed to implement and use						×										1
15	Changes in management structure	×															1
16	'Mutual understanding'			×													1
17	Cognitive style of managers									×							1

3. technical mismatch in the understanding of the specifications of the item;
4. mismatch in the understanding of the objectives of the project or task;
5. pre-existing relations of trust or confidence between the parties to an implementation transaction;
6. degree of involvement in the stages of a project;
7. self-interest;
8. urgency;
9. perceived threat;
10. level of managerial support;
11. point in time at which a management commitment is made to the project, i.e. the decision to set up a formal project mechanism.

The general model shown in Table 11 of factors influencing implementation activity is their attempt to describe and relate the significant variables in this process. All the factors noted above are included in this model either as separate variables or subsummed under another variable.

When discussing project success or failure, Moody[91] discusses five projects and examines the reasons for success or failure. His conclusions are that success depends upon:

  (i) some convincing quantifiable results being achieved;
 (ii) active support and involvement by top management;
(iii) cooperation by middle management;
 (iv) existence of adequate internal technical competence;
  (v) ability to computerize burdensome clerical tasks;
 (vi) existence of a member of the industry as part of the Operational Research team;
(vii) existence of adequate dialogue between managers involved.

This is clearly geared to the implementation activity and points (ii), (iii), (iv), (vii) are covered by Radnor et al.

The five projects covered by Moody are in the areas of: distribution of automative parts (no one familiar with inventory control, no time to spare, scepticism of scientific method, unsuccessful); mail-order fashion merchandising (lateness in bringing in middle management, difficulty in recruiting personnel to operate and monitor system, unsuccessful); beet sugar manufacturing (conflict between parts of organization, chief executive enthusiastic, no one qualified to do scientific programming, changes in staff and conditions, partly successful); telephone utility (simplified inventory control to meet environmental conditions, senior executive pushed project, successful); plywood manufacture (OR workers had extensive experience in the industry, senior executive took a keen interest, successful).

Hankin[53] deals with some factors influencing the acceptance of Operational Research results (which apply equally well to any research oriented group) by management, stressing the reputation of the research group, confidence in methods used, involvement of parties prior to the final results, and special attention to presenting the results.

In an article on Guidelines for the Practice of Operations Research[43] a study is made of the manner in which evidence for the Anti-Ballistic-Missile programme was presented. It sets down suggested steps to follow relevant to the practice of Decision Analysis. In addition, it lists certain failures arising from this study, some of which have already been mentioned.

In the previous chapters we have concentrated on the technicalities of the Decision Analysis process itself, and not on the problems discussed here, such as choice of problem, and implementation. The factors discussed in this chapter are clearly important. All projects have to be carried out in specific environments and the impact of this environment could be significant in achieving successful results. Nonetheless, we have little quantitative evidence on how the right compromises between environment and the Decision Analysis should be reached. For example, it is often stated that simple mechanisms should be used, in many instances, even if there is a loss in potential gains from a more rigorous study, in the belief that the net pay-off is positive. However, this can only remain a belief until appropriate research evidence is available. All we can do for the moment is to be aware that there are specific procedural decisions to be made, with subsequent consequences, and make our judgement at the time.

Huysmanns[63] considers the possibilities of developing a secondary decision model for the implementation decision, where a central factor is that of different degrees of implementation, which will arise as a result of different solutions and effort put into the implementation aspect itself, and will influence the ultimate profitability of the study. Despite the difficulties in getting the appropriate data, this is clearly an essential step towards setting implementation in its proper context as a contributor to overall performance.

Ratoosh[106] provides further material on the implementation issue.

CHAPTER 5

Exercises

1. If you were Operational Research Manager for Celtic football club, how would you set about devising a strategy of play for a given match?

2. A police authority is responsible for a city region in which, on certain evenings of the week, disturbances requiring police intervention occur at widely scattered points. Information about such disturbances may come from a member of the public or policeman on the beat, and the action taken by the authority is to send a police-car to the scene of the disturbance.

The authority has a central headquarters which is able to keep in constant touch by radio with its cars. Assuming the number of cars is fixed, how would you compare the following policies for controlling these cars:

policy (a) cars remain at headquarters until called out;
policy (b) all cars are out on patrol with a fixed beat;
policy (c) a compromise between (a) and (b)?

Are there still other policies which might in some sense yield better results?

3. An individual travels by public transport and may reach his destination on either of two buses, route numbers 1 and 2, say, which pass with equal frequency along a certain length of street where there are two request stops, A and B, 50 yards apart. Buses on route 1 stop at stop A only and buses on route 2 at stop B, but will do so only if they contain a passenger wanting to alight or if flagged by a person standing within 5 yards of the appropriate stop who makes this signal before the bus is 50 yards from the stop. Where should the individual stand to maximize his probability of catching the next bus? Assume that he cannot make out the route number of a bus until it is d yards from him (consider the case where $d > 45$ only) and that no other persons are waiting. Make what assumptions seem reasonable to you about the speed of buses and the bus catcher.

Start with a simple model of the situation and develop it as seems most relevant to take into account:

(1) others waiting at these stops, perhaps for buses on routes other than routes 1 and 2,
(2) the complication that one route may be less convenient to the traveller's destination than the other.

4. You are opening a filling station supplying three different grades of petrol. Assuming that your profit is proportional to selling price how would you determine the relative capacity of storage tanks to be installed?

5. The press officer of a large organization has to optimize the use of money spent on recruiting staff. What should he do?

6. Comment on the problems of developing an actuarial measurement of house life. How might such measurements be used in the context of the problem of allocation of resources between new house building and various forms of improvement to older houses? Develop models where you can.

7. How would you set about determining the number of taxi-cab licences to be issued in a large city?

8. How would you set about determining a labour policy for a company whose labour force fluctuates through absenteeism and leaving, and when it takes three months to train an employee?

9. A fourteen-storey block in a university building has four lifts. The building is used for lecturing, staff accommodation and canteen facilities. How should the lift system be programmed?

10. How would you set about determining priorities for jobs coming into a maintenance workshop?

11. How would you set about deciding what sizes of packing box a cigarette manufacturer, who supplies direct to retailers, should stock?

12. How would you set about determining the size of a local police force?

13. How would you set about determining the size of an evening newspaper?

14. A university is split into two different geographical locations with staff and student movement between them. It is proposed to introduce a means of transport between the two for either, or both, staff and students, for lecture purposes only. How would you set about evaluating the proposals, giving consideration to the mode of operation?

15. Engineering shops are traditionally laid out with rows of similar types of machine tool grouped together, i.e. all lathes are grouped together, all drills together, etc. If the shop is a jobbing shop (i.e. produces small batches of many varieties of parts) the progress of individual batches through the shop is erratic, involves substantial stocks of work in progress and is not readily subject to management control.

It is suggested that examination of shop records will indicate that particular groups of machines can be formed such that particular types of part can be processed from start to finish within one of these groups. How would you set about establishing such groups?

16. It is intended to establish a number (to be determined) of production units to supply hospitals with sterile infusion fluids such as normal saline, dextrose, etc. A number of feasible solutions exist ranging from one large central unit to a unit at Inverness, Aberdeen, Dundee, Edinburgh, Glasgow and Dumfries. Demand is variable from any hospital and the appropriate probability distribution can be determined. Planners wish to establish the 'optimal' number of units, taking the following factors into account:

(1) each unit built incurs only running costs;

(2) each unit is intended to have some excess capacity to cover peaks in demand and breakdowns of other units;

(3) it is feasible for any unit to supply the area served by its immediate neighbours (or neighbour) on the list given, i.e. Inverness could supply Aberdeen, Aberdeen could supply Inverness or Dundee, Dundee could supply Aberdeen or Edinburgh;

(4) a more remote area could be served by the formation of a depot at the corresponding location and the running costs of such a depot are 10% of the running costs of a production unit;

(5) it is assumed that mean demand for each area is proportional to the populations of the town or city named as the site, and that demand is normally distributed with standard deviation equal to 10% of the mean;

(6) the number of days of production lost per month is Poisson distributed with mean 1 day;

(7) running costs are proportional to the square root of production capacity;

(8) shortages of supply can be made good from commercial sources at ten times the cost of supply from the envisaged units.

Formulate a general model to enable the 'optimal' number and location of production units with their production capacities to be established.

17. A company has decided to open a new department store in a city centre. What size of floor area should the new store have?

18. A road haulage company has a fleet of vehicles with carrying capacities of 8, 11, 16 or 21 tons. The 8- and 11-ton lorries are rigid vehicles whereas the 16- and 21-tonners are units for towing articulated trailers. Trailers may be of two types (vans and flats) and two carrying capacities (16 and 21 tons). The types of equipment owned by the company are shown in the table below:

Equipment carrying capacity (tons)	Type
8	Rigid flat
11	Rigid flat
16	Towing unit
21	Towing unit
16	Flat trailer
16	Van trailer
21	Flat trailer
21	Van trailer

A 21-ton towing unit may pull a 16-ton trailer (either a van or flat) but a 16-ton towing unit may not pull a 21-ton trailer.

For convenience when trading the company has more trailers than towing units. Journeys last from 1 to 6 days. No regular services are operated. It is not company policy to hire vehicles from other hauliers to meet peaks of demand but if no vehicles are available to take a load it may wait up to 3 days before being moved, otherwise the load is lost.

A record of demands for loads of each category is kept by the company. How many pieces of equipment of each type should the company own in order to operate efficiently?

19. Consider the following simplified problem.

A hospital has a waiting list of patients. It has a policy of calling in patients at fixed unit intervals of time, who are admitted one time unit later. Probability distributions are available for the durations of stay and arrival pattern (into the waiting list) of various categories of patient. In addition the arrival of patients (into hospital) is unreliable. Formulate the problem of determining an admissions policy and construct a simplified model, making appropriate assumptions, to illustrate how you would solve the problem.

20. A production process consists of three stages. Each stage is liable to produce defective production, the probability characteristics of which are known. Products are specifically made to customer's requirements and we may assume no substitutability at any stage. The product is inspected at each stage and the defective content determined. On the basis of this information an additional production programme for the specific product can be authorized. Assume that the product mix is such that a production phase is completed each week for any product and that this is not significantly dependent on the amount added at any stage to cater for defective production. In addition there is a lead time of three weeks before any authorized extra production at the end of each phase can actually commence. Formulate the problem of determining an initial production policy and a further production authorization policy dependent on the results of inspections and construct a simplified model, making appropriate assumptions, to illustrate how you would solve the problem.

21. A power station has the problem of stocking coal to produce electricity for future demand. Demand of electricity at any one station is highly variable; availability of coal in winter is highly variable; stocking facilities are very restricted.

What stock policy would you recommend for adoption?

22. An engineering company has a problem of determining policy with regard to the acceptance of orders for non-standard products whilst ensuring that production of standard products is not adversely affected. The company would like to develop a procedure by which a balance can be made between full production and profitability, accompanied with a policy by which customers can be discouraged from placing an order. How would you tackle this problem?

23. The intersection of two major roads is at present in the form of a roundabout. Complaints of large queues of vehicles at peak hours have forced the authorities to request a study of the problem. State how you would set about analysing this problem and what effect your results might have on future design of road intersections.

24. A competition promoter wishes to organize a series of competitions to determine the best player of a specific game. His problem is that the money he can make for a contest depends on the calibre of the contestants. If a player is relatively unknown his return is negative, but can be considered as an investment for the future. The promoter wishes to know how many players he should have in his 'pool' and the ratio of known to unknown players to maximize his long-term return. This implies a known strategy for each competition and he wishes to know the effect of various strategies such as knockout competition, or a form of league, on his return.

The game can be considered as professional tennis if desired, and any assumption about the returns for specific contests should be stated.

25. You are employed by the Automobile Association, who wish to provide, for their individual members, a computer package to enable them to make optimal decisions with regard to replacement of personally owned cars. Specify broadly the major aspects of such a package.

26. A paint manufacturer makes 50 different paints of different colours (10) and lead content (5). The paints can be arranged in a sequence, by colour, of 'darkness' and also in a sequence by amount of lead content. The paints are mixed on a single large machine whose input, mixing, and output are under automatic control. Cleaning is required between batches if either colour or lead content is changed. This cleaning is lengthy if the later batch (i) is lighter in colour or (ii) has lower lead content. Demands for the paints are stable but different. Discuss the problem of scheduling the mixing machine.

27. How would you tackle the British Standard Time versus Greenwich Mean Time problem?

28. You are organizing a twenty-mile walk by 400 participants who may withdraw from the walk at any time. The mileage walked by each participant must be checked and you have 40 checkers for this purpose. How would you organize the location of the checking points and the number of checkers at each point?

29. Ships periodically enter a drydock where maintenance work is performed. These drydocks are scattered throughout the world and the efficiency and cost of drydocking can vary from dock to dock. How would you set about determining where and when a ship should be drydocked?

30. By way of part of its function, a voluntary youth organization with limited funds provide, at county level, the means to pursue various adventure activities such as skiing, archery, canoeing, ponytrekking, go-carting, etc. How would you determine the best extent of investment in each activity?

31. Your client wishes you to advise him on the best site for a new university in Scotland. How would you set about advising him?

32. A farmer owns a 200-acre farm. Conditions are such that he can grow crops or keep animals or both. What should he do?

33. A student has the choice between taking a course for which he will receive a grant of £X p.a. or getting a job for which he will receive an initial salary of £Y p.a. ($Y > X$). He may successfully complete the course, in which case he will be able to obtain a job with a starting salary of £Z p.a. ($Z > Y$). Should he take the course?

34. A certain retail bakery employs a number of vans as mobile shops to take its goods to the housewife, instead of expecting her to come to the baker's shop.

Assuming that the marketing area is a town of 60,000 population and a rural area of radius ten miles around with a fair sprinkling of villages, how could the route pattern and size of van fleet be established to:

(a) maximize sales;
(b) maintain a certain standard of service and choice to the housewives along the route;
(c) minimize wastage?

The salesmen are paid on a salary plus commission basis. About 50% of items carried have a shelf life of one day, and there is very small chance of obtaining replenishment of these items as the day goes on, baking being done the night before.

35. A package holiday organizer is contracted to a fairly large number of hotels to fill their bedrooms throughout the season. Holidays advertised in their brochure must be organized before it is printed, hence an allocation of beds to the various types of holidays must be made. Holidays offered vary according to place, quality of hotel, and duration which can be 8, 10, 14 and 21 days. Each type of holiday will have a different profit margin depending on:

(a) constant air transport cost;
(b) a variable ground transport cost depending on distance between hotel and airport (this is a relatively small cost);
(c) variable bed cost depending on the quality of the hotel and length of stay where this cost is directly reflected in the price of the holiday.

Demand statistics are available from past seasons, and some market research can be carried out. The market is subject to a high degree of price elasticity.

How would you go about allocating beds to the various types of holiday to maximize profit?

36. An Education Committee is faced with various proposals for reducing the number of schools in its area. The aim is to conserve the use of staff, to reduce the costs of education and to increase the choice, if not of school, then of courses within a school open to pupils. It is desired to reach a solution which takes due account of problems of depopulation, industrial redevelopment, etc. How would you tackle this problem?

37. A certain city has a severe shortage of houses and a high proportion of old, unfit houses, some of which might be made fit. It wishes to determine an allocation of resources between new building and old house improvement. (The city might be Glasgow.) How would you tackle this problem?

38. In a country where universities obtain most of their funds from students' fees, the number of students attending the University of x has declined, the quality of its product has also declined, and that university now finds itself in financial difficulties. There is a proposal for amalgamation from the nearby University of y, which may take place because of pressure from x's creditors. You have been appointed by a Secretary of State to conduct an inquiry and report on the proposed amalgamation. (The country might be Britain in 10 years time.) How would you tackle this problem?

39. A chemical company is planning to launch a new product. This is a high purity form of a chemical which they already market. The demand for the first year is expected to be 4000 tons, and demand is expected to increase at 15% per annum over the succeeding two years. Beyond three years it is not known whether demand will level off, or continue to increase, but it is most unlikely that it will decrease for some years.

To manufacture the new product the company needs to import a new bulk raw material. Plant trials indicate that the yield from raw material to finished product will be 94%. Their problem is to decide what size of shipment to order, and what stocks of raw material to hold.

The raw material is to be sent to the UK by sea, and shipments may be received at any time of the year. It comes packed in bags for protection against contamination and against moisture in the atmosphere, and may be stored under cover for up to one year without deterioration. Trials suggest that if it is stored for much longer than this, moisture tends to get in, and cause the material to set solid.

Warehouse space may be rented at the quayside, from the port authorities. From the port the material is to be taken by road direct to the company's works. At the works there are three storage hoppers which were built some years previously to hold raw material for a process which has now been discontinued. The hoppers are conveniently sited at the start of the new production process, and it is therefore proposed to use them. The total nominal capacity of the hoppers is 600 tons, in terms of the new raw material, but preliminary trials on flow suggest that it may not be practicable to fill the hoppers to capacity because of the risk of jamming. It is likely that at least 300 tons may be stored in the hoppers, without risk.

Further storage space is available at the works, in the form of hard standing, exposed to the elements. An extensive area is available, which is not at present in use, and it would be possible to cover a part, or the whole, of this area.

The production process itself is continuous, and will be manned for three shifts. The first stage in the process is to crush the raw material to a uniform fine grade.

Demand for the product is expected to be non-seasonal.

How would you tackle this problem?

40. The Works General Manager has asked you to advise on the best ordering and stocking policy for the new material. What model would you construct of the situation? What data would you require as input for your model? How would you use the model to obtain a solution to the problem?

41. Sales of draught beer are found to be related to:

(a) the number of faunts (dispensers) in public houses in the sales area;
(b) the average daytime temperature;
(c) the movement of population in or out of the sales area due to holidays, etc.;
(d) annual festivities.

Explain how you might use this information to assist the decisionmaking of:

(a) the Brewery Production Manager;
(b) the Brewery Distribution Manager.

42. A motor-vehicle distributor buys spare parts from the manufacturer, stores them in his own warehouse, and sells them to the public and the motor trade. Some 20,000 items are involved with various speeds of movement ranging from no demand per annum to 1000 demands per annum.

Price ranges from 2p to £500 for an item. Lead time varies from 2 weeks to 6 months for delivery from the manufacturer.

Explain how you would set up a system to control the purchase of stock.

43. The jury for one trial in one Court of Law is chosen from a pool of jurors assigned to that court. A person called for jury service is required to be available for service for a given number of days. If he is not chosen during that time he is exempt from further jury service for several years. If he is chosen, then he is a juror for that particular trial only. Taking into consideration that a jury may require to be 'balanced' in terms of age, sex and general appearance and thus acceptable to the defence and prosecution, how would you decide the number in the pool, and which days within the given number of attendance, if you wished to minimize the cost of reimbursing those who attend, at a fixed rate, plus the cost of the Court not being able to function due to the lack of a jury.

44. Discuss the relevance of the following factors associated with the problem formulation stage of Operational Research: (a) context of the problem; (b) the decisionmakers; (c) the objectives; (d) the alternative courses of action.

45. 'Models of a *problem situation* take the form of a *functional relationship* relating the *measure of value of the decision* made to the *decision variables* and *parameters*.'

Explain what you understand by the terms underlined in the above sentence and devise a hypothetical example to illustrate the meaning of the sentence.

46. What is meant by (a) operational, (b) conceptual, (c) structural, (d) functional, (e) extensive, (f) intensive, characteristics of a definition? Give examples.

Explain why the operational/functional/intensive characteristics are relevant to Operational Research, using, as examples, any two of the following: 'defective', 'customer satisfaction', 'cost', 'profit', 'flexibility', 'illness', 'experience', 'similarity', 'difficulty'.

47. Given that the costs of a simple random sampling exercise to estimate a population mean are given by

C_1 = cost of preparing the sample;

C_2 = cost per unit of sample observed;

KS^2/n = expected cost of error of estimate;

and that these costs are additive, derive an expression for (a) the optimal sample size and (b) the minimal total expected cost.

48. Ornea classifies problems according to whether they are concerned with operational, technological or investment objectives. Commenting on the meaning and adequacy of this classification, explain the contributions, nature of solutions, and difficulties arising from the Operational Research approach to each class using appropriate examples to illustrate your points.

49. Comment on the following statement by Ackoff, by examining an appropriate problematic situation:

'It is only through implementation that many research conclusions can be tested.'

50. 'The next few years will probably see the end of the vicious circle of the past, in which poor model building justified rapid rough "solutions" and, conversely, the non-existence of methods of accurate solution justified poor model building. It is likely that both model building and solution techniques will begin to reinforce each other in a positive manner.' (Dantzig: *Linear Programming and Extension*.) Comment.

51. There are not many applications of Operational Research techniques in the general area of equipment maintenance. What applications there are have been made by only a few organizations. Discuss why this is the case. Do you think that maintenance is a worthwhile area for Operational Researchers?

52. How would you site a city airport?

53. How would you set about determining the composition of a maintenance workshop?

54. How would you set about choosing between the purchase of a kidney machine or an iron lung if you were in charge of medical finance?

55. If you were in the forestry business, how would you decide when to cut down your trees?

56. A production process consists of two stages. At the beginning of a specific time period the production requirements at the end of each of T successive periods are communicated to the first stage as requirements for the second stage. Normally the first-stage work and time factors associated with each job are not known at the first stage until production begins on a specific item and jobs are scheduled according to the sequence required at the second stage. However, this can result in underutilization of the facilities at the first stage which might be improved by mixing items out of sequence but still trying to meet time requirements at the second stage. Because of lack of knowledge of actual processing times and work content at the first stage, one cannot, in any case, guarantee to meet the second-stage requirements.

One way of improving utilization at the first stage, with due consideration being given to service requirements to the second stage, is to introduce an estimating procedure. Such a procedure may have a varying reliability dependent on how sophisticated it is. How would you set about measuring the worth of an estimating system with a specific degree of reliability, as measured by variance of proportional errors in work and time estimates, for the above problem?

57. A contractor has completed £6m worth of an estimated £7m project. Because of a dispute on payments he has ceased work and the matter has gone to arbitration, which both he and his client have agreed to accept and is expected to take 18 months to completion. However, the client, being a hospital authority, does not wish to delay the use of the building so far completed, and wishes to consider a mutual settlement before arbitration. The contractor is also losing considerable interest while payments are withheld from him.

Develop a framework within which a decision can be made either on settlement, and at what level, or to wait for arbitration.

An assessment of the probabilities of various awards by the arbitration panel is provided.

58. A certain company manufactures 800 products for a highly seasonal market. Apart from many small selling products where the demand and pattern of demand is very variable, demand for products in the last quarter of the year is, typically, three times demand in the first quarter of the year. The company has at present a permanent labour force just capable of meeting demand at its peak with the aid of overtime working and with certain of the peak demand met from a small finished goods store. It is considering building a much larger finished goods store, cutting its labour force and attempting to spread production more evenly over the year, and has asked for an Operational Research Study.

The company has fourteen production lines. The average product may be made on any one of three production lines and production rates may vary for the same product from line to line. Output is measured in cases and output rates in cases per day. The figure below shows the total sales of the N largest selling items expressed as a percentage

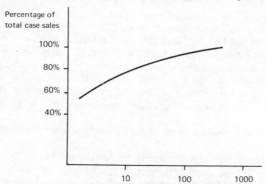

Figure 117. Number of products arranged by annual case sale

Product	Production rate %	Standard production cost %
A	25	40
B	14	42
C	2	100
D	7·5	70
E	100	20
F	40	32
G	27	28
H	7	48
J	13	31
K	16	31
L	5	51

of the total sales of all products and the table shows manufacturing rates and standard production costs for certain typical large selling items.

Develop a model which might be used to analyse the alternatives open to the company, explaining clearly what parameters you would require to estimate for the model. It should be capable of solution at reasonable cost on a moderately sized computer.

59. Assuming you are a car owner, how could you decide when to sell your private car and buy a new one? Consider the problem from the viewpoint of (a) a commercial traveller, (b) a medical practitioner, (c) a business man with an office in the City of London.

60. The Operational Research approach is often broken up into various identifiable phases. Define these and discuss the interdependence between them, giving illustrations.

61. What are the principles of optimality implicit in the following approaches to solving problems: (a) enumeration, (b) calculus, (c) dynamic programming, (d) algorithmic, (e) heuristic, (f) physical analogue. Illustrate your answers.

62. An extensive mathematical model covering all relevant aspects of a problem situation has been formulated. It is found, however, that the mathematical problem so defined is too difficult to solve exactly with available knowledge and expertise. In such a situation the initial procedure could be to:

1. obtain an approximate solution to the exact problem,
2. obtain an exact solution to an approximated problem.

Comment on the use and value of results so obtained.

Are there any alternative courses of action?

63. 'We in O.R. do not know government and industry as well as we think we do, and administrators and managers know this. Therefore, they tend to use us in restricted and highly structured ways, on specific problems on which we have propagandized them into believing that we have some competence. . . . Perhaps we should not tell administrators and managers how to use us, but rather involve them in systematic efforts to find out what we can best do and how they can best use us.' R. L. Ackoff.

Comment.

64. Operational Research is said to be 'the science of decisionmaking'. Discuss, using appropriate illustrations.

65. Define the following terms relating to measurement in Operational Research: qualitative, quantitative, nominal, counting, ordinal, restricted interval and ratio. Discuss the ways in which the various measures are used, drawing on appropriate illustrations.

66. Using appropriate illustrations, define the following methods of measuring performance in Operational Research:

(a) *a priori*, objective transformation, subjective transformation;
(b) *a posteriori*, efficiency curve method, retrospective optimization method, effectiveness curve method.

Discuss, briefly, the merits of each.

67. Explain the following methods of solution which can be used in Operational Research, explaining why each method may be better than the others in appropriately chosen instances: analytic; enumerative; logically aided; algorithmic; heuristic; simulation.

68. Explain what you understand by (a) certainty, (b) risk, and (c) uncertainty in the context of decisionmaking.

Describe the minimal and sufficient conditions for a problem to exist together with three ways in which complicating conditions can occur.

69. Explain what you understand by the following terms: iconic model, analogue model, symbolic model, sequential-decision model.

Discuss the difference between *predictive* models and *control* models using an illustrative example.

70. Distinguish between 'accuracy', 'bias' and 'precision' of sampling procedures.

Define the characteristics of the following sampling procedures and suggest situations to which each might be appropriate:

(a) systematic random sampling;
(b) stratified sampling;
(c) cluster sampling;
(d) sequential sampling;
(e) judgement sampling.

71. Discuss the general methodological problem of selection of (i) a best 'solution procedure', (ii) a best 'set of primary alternatives', commenting on the possibility of scientific study.

72. Discuss the 'criterion' problem in the health services.

73. Discuss the following quotation (V. Perry; *Precision: A Scientific Vice*): 'If you cannot count it, it does not count.'

74. You have decided to join the management services department of a local authority where you are expected to use your operational research training. How would you set about your job if the operational research approach to problems had not been used before by the department?

75. A publisher of an established quarterly journal is faced with demands for back issues from time to time, some of which arise from new subscribers, and others arise from people interested in specific issues because of their specific content. It is expensive to reprint any issue, but overproduction of issues is also costly. How would you set about solving the problem of determining when to reprint a particular issue and how many to reprint?

76. A company distributes its goods over an area using some of its own vehicles and hiring vehicles when the demand for transport exceeds their capacity, this demand fluctuating and increasing with time. Discuss the problem of determining the number of company-owned vehicles to add to the fleet at the beginning of each year.

77. A small company providing a cleaning and laundry service for industrial clothing operates a fleet of six vans. The vans are used to collect dirty garments and return clean ones, but are only partly used in the middle of each week.

The garments are owned by the company, which operates what it calls '2-garment' and '3-garment' systems. With the first system, two garments are provided for each individual, a dirty one being collected early each week and returned clean at the end of the week. With the second system, three garments are provided for each individual and one journey is made each week to deliver a clean garment and collect a dirty one (the third garment being in use).

What are the effects of the two systems described on vehicle utilization and the distribution of load on laundry and cleaning facilities? Which system is better? Take into account the fact that when a new contract is signed new garments have to be supplied and that if a contract terminates the partially used garments go into stock, usable only slowly as replacement garments in continuing contracts. Indicate clearly the assumptions you make in your analysis.

78. Describe how you would plan the sizes of parking bays associated with parking meters in a restricted zone in the centre of a large city.

79. Schumaker and Smith indicate that 30% of OR personnel, in the USA, are either mathematicians or statisticians. Rivett indicates that, in the UK, some senior OR workers are disturbed by the high proportion of mathematicians and statisticians in OR groups. Discuss the reasons why the high proportion exists now and why it should or should not exist in the future.

80. Rivett has written recently 'It is difficult to see how a university operational research group with less than say eight people who are competent practitioners in the subject, can achieve any form of critical mass'. What does he mean? How do you think he arrived at the figure of eight?

Outline any relevant arguments which might support or refute such a figure. Consider both the industrial and the academic situation.

81. The following quotation is taken from Shakespeare: 'When we mean to build we first survey the plot, then draw the model.'

Illustrate the relevance of this principle to Operational Research.

82. Comment on the need for a single 'objective' criterion in Mathematical Optimizing problems and on the difficulty in practice of finding such a criterion within an organization.

To what extent has this difficulty caused the restriction of the application of optimizing techniques to problems dealing with parts only of the activity of organizations?

83. It is stated that 'survival' is the only 'goal' of any organization. Comment on this, drawing on any examples you wish.

84. The following quotation was taken from a British Productivity Council Report—comment on it.

'The Maintenance Function—to ensure that at a minimum cost, production plant and equipment is available for productive use for the scheduled hours, operating to agreed standards and at minimum waste.'

85. In a certain academic institution, when its newest refectory accommodation comes into use, the estimated numbers of lunches that can be served in a two-hour period are as follows:

Student refectories (self service)

	Seats	Lunches served
J-hn Street Union	430	1700
R-y-l College	160	500
Sc-tt-sh College	265	420
Total	855	2620

Staff refectories

	Seats	Lunches served
L-v-ngst-n- T-w-r	200	650
L-v-ngst-n- T-w-r (Staff club)	165	400
Sc-tt-sh College (table service)	60	80
Total	425	1130

The institution has 4500 students and a staff of 1400, and plans for an expansion by 1972 to a target number of 7500 students.

Comment on the observations you might make and the techniques you might use in investigating ways of enabling the refectories listed above to cope with greater numbers of students and staff without substantial capital cost.

How might the results of this investigation affect any assessment of the need for further refectories?

Relate your remarks to your own experience in this institution if you wish.

86. A library committee has a fixed quantity of money to allocate among a group of departments who have each submitted an estimate. As an Operational Analyst how would you go about the problem of allocating such funds.

87. A large warehousing organization finds that there are errors in the data supplied to the department responsible for recording stock levels. How would you deal with this situation?

88. A political party has limited resources. How should it decide how many candidates to field in a general election?

89. You apply for a number of jobs. Offers come in over an extended period and each offer requires immediate acceptance or rejection. What is your policy?

90. A car manufacturer changes his production model. He is required to supply spare parts for the new model for a period of 20 years from completion of the production run, which will last two years. How could he set about determining how to produce the spare parts?

91. How would you set about determining the number of inspectors for a corporation transport fleet?

92. Outline four ways in which suboptimization enters into Operational Research studies, using appropriate examples. Comment on the following statement by Minas, who raises the question of whether the suboptimization problem can be scientifically studied:

   (i) the problem is meaningless;
  (ii) the problem is meaningful, but has no general solution, and common sense dictates the special solution;
 (iii) it is meaningful and can be resolved by group participation—socialized common sense;
 (iv) the problem is meaningful and is open to scientific enquiry.

93. Operational Research is only one of several well-established Management Services. If you were asked, by a layman, to explain the effective differences between Operational Research and Organization and Methods/Work Study/Industrial Engineering/Industrial Statistics/Economics, what would you say?

94. Discuss the following statement by Makower and Williamson.
   'There are no such things as Operational Research problems: there are just problems.'
   What do you think the statement means? Do you agree?

95. It is the opinion of managers in many companies, looking back on their experience when first making use of computers, that it is better for a company to have a member of its own staff (who, presumably, knows the company and its operation) trained to run a computer installation, than for it to recruit an outsider who is already a computing expert but knows nothing about the company he is joining.
   Would you expect the same opinion to be expressed about the appointment of an Operational Research Manager? Give your reasons.

96. A large area of a town has to be demolished and rebuilt. Suggest how the 'optimal' size of demolition area could be determined.

97. There are 288,700 pupils in secondary schools in Scotland and 16,900 teachers in these schools. Pupil–teacher ratios greatly differ from school to school, depending on size, locality and type of school, and are felt to be inequitable. Discuss how a quota (of teachers) in schools might be imposed and the problems associated with the imposition of such a quota. Build a model making appropriate assumptions.

98. A local authority has the task of replacing bulbs, neon tubes, etc. for street lighting. It is required to devise a replacement policy allowing for possible replacement before failure, as well as delayed replacement after failure. What data would you need to determine such a policy?
   Build a model to illustrate the basic conflicts in the problem, making **suitable** assumptions.

References

1. Ackoff, R. *Scientific Method: Optimising Applied Research Decisions*, Wiley, 1962.
2. Arrow, K. J. *Social Choice and Individual Values*, Wiley, 1963.
3. Balas, E. 'An additive algorithm for solving linear programs with zero–one variables', *O.R.S.A.* **13**, 4, 1965.
4. Baligh, H. H., and Laughlunn, D. J. 'An economic and linear model of the hospital', *Health Services Research*, Winter, 1969.
5. Ball, R. J. 'Econometric model building', in *Mathematical Model Building in Economics and Industry*, First Series, Griffin, 1969.
6. Bartee, E. M. 'On the methodology of solution synthesis', *Man. Sc.*, **17**, 6, 1971.
7. Baylis, R. *A Contribution to the Application of Systems Analysis to Manpower Planning with a Naive Model*, Department of Econometrics, Southampton University, 1970.
8. Bellman, R. *Applied Dynamic Programming*, Princeton University Press, 1962.
9. Bellman, R. *Adaptive Processes, A Guided Tour*, Princeton University Press, 1961.
10. Bellman, R., Cooke, K., and Lockett, J. *Algorithms, Graphs and Computers*, Academic Press, 1970.
11. Bettman, J. R. *Measuring Individual's Priorities for National Goals: A Methodology and Empirical Example*, Graduate School of Business Administration, University of California, Los Angeles, 1971.
12. Blackett, P. S. *Studies of War*, Oliver and Boyd, 1962.
13. Blalock, H. M. *Theory Construction*, Prentice Hall, 1969.
14. Bonder, S. 'Needs in operational research education', *27th National O.R.S.A. Meeting*, 1970.
15. Bowen, K. C. Statistical analysis of data from uncontrolled processes, *Defence Operational Analysis Establishment, Research Working Paper*, No. M8, 1972.
16. Braithwaite, R. 'Models in the empirical sciences', in *Logic, Methodology and Philosophy of Science*, Eds. Nagel, E., Suppes, P., and Tarski, A., Stanford University Press, 1962.
17. Brand, H. W. *The Fecundity of Mathematical Methods*, D. Reidel Pub. Co., Dordrecht, 1961.
18. Bremermann, H. J. 'Optimisation through evolution and recombination', in *Self Organising Systems*, Eds. Yovitts, M. C., Jacobi, G. T., and Goldstein, G. D., Spartan Books, 1962.
19. Bross, I. D. J. *Design for Decision*, MacMillan, 1953.
20. Camp, G. D. 'Approximation and bounding in operations research', in *Operations Research II*, 1957–58 Seminar in Operations Research, University of Michigan, 1958.
21. Chambers, R. 'Measurement and misrepresentation', *Man. Sc.*, **6**, 2, 1960.
22. Charnes, A. *Management Science and Management; Some Requirements for Further Development*, Carnegie Institute of Technology, 1965.

23. Chernoff, H., and Moses, L. E. *Elementary Decision Theory*, Wiley, 1959.
24. Churchman, C. W. *Prediction and Optimal Decision*, Prentice Hall, 1961.
25. Churchman, C. W., and Eisenberg, H. W. 'Deliberation and judgement', in *Human Judgements and Optimality*, Eds. Shelly, M., and Bryan, G., Wiley, 1964.
26. Cole, H. M. 'Selection and training of operations research scientists in operations research office', in *Operational Research in Practice*, Eds. Davies, M., and Verhulst, M., N.A.T.O. Conference, Pergamon Press, 1958.
27. Coleman, J. S. *Introduction to Mathematical Sociology*, Free Press, 1964.
28. Cooper, W. W., Leavitt, H. J., and Shelly, M. W. *New Perspectives in Organization Research*, Wiley, 1962.
29. Courant, R. *Differential and Integral Calculus*, Vols. I and II, Blackie and Son, 1953.
30. Damon, W., and Schramm, R. *A Simultaneous Descriptive Model for Production, Marketing and Finance*, Duke University, North Carolina, Durham, 1971.
31. Davies, O. *Statistical Methods in Research and Production*, Oliver and Boyd, 1957.
32. Dean, B. *Operations Research in Research and Development*, Wiley, 1963.
33. De Groot, M. H. *Optimal Statistical Decisions*, McGraw Hill, 1970.
34. Dewey, J. *How do we Think ?* D. Heath and Co., 1910.
35. Dick, J. B. *A Study of the Effectiveness of Some Recent Research at the Building Research Station U.K.*, Current Paper 87/68, 1968.
36. Digby, F. 'Heuristic analysis of decision situations', in *Human Judgements and Optimality*, Eds. Shelly, M., and Bryan, G., Wiley, 1964.
37. Dodson, E. N. 'Cost effectiveness in urban transportation', *O.R.S.A.*, **17**, 3, 1969.
38. Duckworth, W. E., and Wyatt, J. K. 'Rapid statistical techniques for operational research workers', *O.R.Q.*, **9**, 1958.
39. Dukes, J. A., Buckman, D. A., and Dixson, A. *Introduction to Incentive Schemes in Building Maintenance*, Department of the Environment Research and Development Paper, 69/059/1, 1971.
40. Ehrenberg, A. S. C. 'Models of fact; examples of marketing', in *Mathematical Model Building in Economics and Industry*, First Series, Griffin, 1969, also in *Man. Sc.*, **16**, 7, 1970.
41. Eilon, S. 'Prescription and management decision', *J. Man. Studies*, **6**, 2, 1969.
42. Ellis, J. W., and Greene, T. E. 'The contextual study, a structural approach to the study of political and military aspects of limited war', *O.R.S.A.*, **8**, 5, 1960.
43. Engel, J. H., Caywood, T. E., Berger, H. M., Magee, J. F., Miser, H. J., and Thrall, R. M. 'Guidelines for the practice of operations research', *O.R.S.A.*, **19**, 5, 1971.
44. Fishburn, P. *Utility Theory for Decisionmaking*, Wiley, 1970.
45. Flagle, C. 'Conference on operational research in the health services in Great Britain', *O.R.S.A.*, **9**, 3, 1961.
46. Forrester, J. S. *World Dynamics*, Wright Allen, 1971.
47. Freudenthal, H. 'Models in applied probability', in *The Concept and Role of the Model in Mathematics and Natural and Social Sciences*, Eds. Hazemier, B., and Vuysje, D., D. Reidel Publishing Company, 1961.
48. Gruenberger, F. *A Measure for Crackpots*, Rand Corp., Memo P-2678, 1962.
49. Haley, K. B. 'The siting of depots', *International Journal of Production Research*, **2**, 1, 1962.
50. Haley, K. B., and Stringer, J. *The Application of Linear Programming to a Large Scale Transportation Problem*, First International Conference on Operational Research, 1957.
51. Hammer, P. L. *A Boolean Approach for Bivalent Optimisation*, Centre de Recherches Mathematiques, University of Montreal, 1971.
52. Hampson, R. *R & D Decisions by Cost Effectiveness*, 33rd National O.R.S.A./T.I.M.S. Meeting, 1968.

262

53. Hankin, B. D. 'Communication of the results of operational research', *O.R.Q.*, **9**, 4, 1958.
54. Hanssmann, F. *Operational Research Techniques for Capital Investment*, Wiley, 1968.
55. Hayward, P. *When is a Property Measurable*, National O.R.S.A. Conference, 1970.
56. Helmer, O. 'On the epistemology of inexact sciences', *Man. Sc.*, **6**, 1, 1960.
57. Hempel, C. G. *Aspects of Scientific Explanation*, Collier MacMillan, 1965.
58. Hitch, C. 'Suboptimisation in operations research problems', *O.R.S.A.*, **1**, 3, 1953.
59. Hole, W. V. *User Needs and the Design of Houses*, Building Research Station, Current Paper 51/68, 1968.
60. Hollander, G. L. 'Synthesis of major systems, an open challenge', *O.R./S.A. Today*, **2**, 2, 1972.
61. Horwath, W. J. 'Need for estimating the influence of technological and social changes on future health facility requirements', *Health Service Research*, **3**, 1968.
62. Howard, R. A. *Dynamic Programming and Markov Processes*, Technology Press, 1960.
63. Huysmanns, J. S. *The Implementation of Operations Research*, Wiley, 1970.
64. Jennings, J. B. 'An analysis of hospital blood bank whole blood inventory control policies', *Transfusion*, **8**, 6, 1968.
65. Kane, E. J. *Economic Statistics and Econometrics*, Harper & Row, 1969.
66. Kazanowski, A. *Cost Effectiveness Fallacies and Misconceptions Revisited*, 29th O.R.S.A. National Meeting, 1966.
67. Keighley, E. C. *Acceptability Criteria for Noise in Large Offices*, Building Research Station, Current Paper 15/70, 1970.
68. Kendall, M. G. 'Introduction to model building and decision problems', in *Mathematical Model Building in Economics and Industry*, Griffin, First Series, 1969.
69. Kendrick, C. *Vehicle Component Replacement Policy*, Ph.D. Thesis, Birmingham University, 1960.
70. Kuipers, A. 'Model and insight', in *The Concept and the Role of the Model in Mathematics and Natural and Social Sciences*, Eds. Hazemier, B., and Vuysje, D., D. Reidel Pub. Co., 1961.
71. Lacey, R. E. 'Index of exposure to driving rain', *Building Research Station Digest*, Second Series, No. 127, 1971.
72. Lampkin, W., and Saalmans, P. D. 'The design of routes, service frequencies and schedules for a municipal bus undertaking', *O.R.Q.*, **18**, 4, 1967.
73. Laut, S. 'Subsystem optimisation effectiveness', *I.R.E. Trans. Systems Science and Cybernetics*, **S.S.C.-4**, 2, 1968.
74. Lawler, E. L., and Wood, D. E. 'Branch and bound methods: a survey', *O.R.S.A.*, **14**, 4, 1966.
75. Little, J. D. C. 'Models and manager, the concept of a decision calculus', *Man. Sc.*, **16**, 8, 1970.
76. Lowe, C. W. 'A report on a simplex evolutionary operation for multiple responses', *Trans. Inst. Chem. Eng.*, **45**, 1, 1967.
77. Luce, R. D., and Raiffa, H. *Games and Decisions*, Wiley, 1957.
78. Margeneau, H. 'Is the mathematical explanation of physical data unique', in *Logic, Methodology and Philosophy of Science*, Eds. Nagel, E., Suppes, P., and Tarski, A., Stanford University Press, 1962.
79. Markowitz, H. *Portfolio Analysis*, Wiley, 1959.
80. May, K. 'Intransitivity, utility and aggregation of preference patterns', *Econometrica*, **22**, 1, 1954.
81. McKean, R. N. *Suboptimisation Criteria and Operations Research*, Rand Corp., P386, 1963.
82. McNamara, R. S. *The Essence of Security*, Hodder and Stoughton, 1968.

83. Mehlberg, H. 'Theoretical and empirical aspects of science', in *Logic, Methodology and Philosophy of Science*, Eds. Nagel, E., Suppes, P., and Tarski, A., Stanford University Press, 1962.

84. Mellen, T. *Operational Research in the Gas Industry*, Research Communication G.C. 140, The Gas Council, 1967.

85. Michael, D. 'The social environment', *O.R.S.A.*, **7**, 4, 1959.

86. Milnor, J. 'Games against nature', in *Decision Processes*, Eds. Thrall, R. M., Coombs, C. H., and Davis, R. L., Wiley, 1957.

87. Minas, J. 'Formalism, realism and management science', *Man. Sc.*, **3**, 1957.

88. Mitchell, G. *Private Memorandum to Operational Research Education Committee*, 1969.

89. Mitroff, I., and Betz, F. 'Dialectical decision theory, a meta-theory of decision-making', *Man. Sc. Theory*, **19**, 1, 1972.

90. Monarchi, D., Kisiel, C. C., and Duckstein, L. *Interactive Multi-Objective Programming in Water Resources: A Case Study*, University of Arizona, Tucson, USA, 1972.

91. Moody, L. *Implementation in O.R. and in R & D in Government and Business Organisations*, National O.R.S.A. Meeting, 1969.

92. Morris, W. T. 'On the art of modelling', *Man. Sc.*, **13**, 12, 1967.

93. Morse, P. M. 'Where is the new blood', *O.R.S.A.*, **3**, 4, 1955.

94. Mulligan, J. E. 'Basic optimisation techniques, a brief survey', in *Programming for Optimal Decisions*, Eds. Moore, P. G., and Hodges, S. D., Penguin Books, 1970.

95. Nelson, R., and Winter, S. *Weather Information and Economic Decisions, A Preliminary Report*, Rand Corporation, R.M.-2620-N.A.S.A., 1960.

96. Northropp, G., Jenkins, C., and Thomasell, A. *Cost Effectiveness of Data Buoy Systems*, 38th National O.R.S.A. Meeting, 1970.

97. Northropp, G. M., Davis, E. L., Swanton, E. R., and Merlin, W. F. *Use of Quantified Expert Judgement in Cost Effectiveness Studies*, 38th National O.R.S.A. Meeting, 1970.

98. Olsen, R. M. *Allocating Sales Effort to Sales Branches and Territories*, The School of Business, The University of Kansas, Working Paper No. 11, 1968.

99. Oportel, L. 'Towards the formal study of models in the non-formal sciences', in *The Concept and the Role of the Model in Mathematics and Natural and Social Sciences*, Eds. Hazemier, B., and Vuysje, D., D. Reidel Pub. Co., 1961.

100. Ornea, J. C., and Stillson, P. 'On the optimum solution in operations research', *O.R.S.A.*, **8**, 5, 1960.

101. Pfanzagl, J. 'A general theory of measurements, applications to utility', *Naval Res. Log. Quarterly*, **6**, 1959.

102. Pfanzagl, J. *Theory of Measurement*, Physica-Verlag and Würzburg, 1968.

103. Radnor, M., Rubenstein, A., and Tansik, D. *Implementation in O.R. and R & D in Government and Business Organisations*, 34th National Meeting of O.R.S.A., 1968.

104. Raiffa, H. *Decision Analysis*, Addison Wesley, 1970.

105. Raiffa, H., and Schlaiffer, R. *Applied Statistical Decision Theory*, Harvard Business School, 1961.

106. Ratoosh, P. 'Experimental studies of implementation in *Operational Research in the Social Sciences*, Ed. Lawrence, J., Tavistock, 1966.

107. Reitman, W. R. 'Heuristic decision procedures, open constraints and the structure of ill defined problems', in *Human Judgements and Optimality*, Eds. Shelly, M., and Bryan, G., Wiley, 1964.

108. Rogosinski, W. W. *Volume and Integral*, Cambridge University Mathematical Texts, Oliver and Boyd, 1952.

109. Roy, R. H. 'An outline for research in penology', *O.R.S.A.*, **12**, 1, 1964.

110. Ruderman, A. P. 'Lessons from Latin American experience', in *Economic Benefits from Public Health Services*, U.S. Department of Health, Education and Welfare, 1967.
111. Savage, L. J. *Foundations of Statistics*, Wiley, 1954.
112. Schmitt, J. W., and Taylor, R. E. *System Optimisation Through Simulation*, O.R.S.A. Conference, 1970.
113. Schwartz, J. 'The pernicious influence of mathematics in science', in *Logic, Methodology and Philosophy of Science*, Eds. Nagel, E., Suppes, P., and Tarski, A., Stanford University Press, 1962.
114. Sciorrino, G. 'Decision theory and scientific method: present, past and future', *Management International Review*, **17**, 2, **17**, 3, 1967.
115. Selig, F. *How to Solve Ill Structured Problems*, 35th National O.R.S.A. Meeting, 1969.
116. Sells, S. B. 'Towards a taxonomy of organisations', in *New Perspectives in Organisation Research*, Eds. Cooper, W. W., Leavitt, H. J., and Shelly, M. W., Wiley, 1962.
117. Shelly, M., and Bryan, G. 'Judgements and the language of decisions', in *Human Judgements and Optimality*, Eds. Shelly, M., and Bryan, G., Wiley, 1964.
118. Simon, H. A. *Models of Man*, Wiley, 1957.
119. Simon, H. A. *The New Science of Management Decision*, Harper and Row, 1960.
120. Simon, H. A. 'On the concept of an organisational goal', *Administrative Science Quarterly*, Vol. 9, 1964.
121. Sinden, F. W. 'Mechanisms for linear programs', *O.R.S.A.*, **17**, 6, 1959.
122. Smallwood, R. 'A decision analysis of model selection', *I.E.E.E. Transactions on Systems Science and Cybernetics*, **SSC-4**, 3, 1968.
123. Smith, A. 'Defence manpower studies', *O.R.Q.*, **19**, 3, 1968.
124. Snodgrass, M. *Agricultural Economics and Growth*, Appleton Century Crofts, 1970.
125. Solandt, O. 'Observation, experiment and measurement in operations research', *O.R.S.A.*, **3**, 1, 1955.
126. Stark, R. M., and Mayer, R. H., Jnr. 'Some multi-contract decision theoretic competitive bidding models', *O.R.S.A.*, **19**, 2, 1971.
127. Steiner, J. A. *Methodology for Measures of Effectiveness*, O.R.S.A./T.I.M.S. National Meeting, 1968.
128. Stratton, A. *Measurement of Effectiveness*, Paper given to International Federation of Operational Research Societies, 1971.
129. Strauss, W. J. 'The nature and validity of operations research studies with emphasis on force composition', *O.R.S.A.*, **8**, 5, 1960.
130. Suppes, P. 'Models of data', in *Logic, Methodology and Philosophy of Science*, Eds. Nagel, E., Suppes, P., and Tarski, A., Stanford University Press, 1962.
131. Suppes, P. 'A comparison of the meaning and uses of models in the mathematical and empirical sciences', in *The Concept and Role of the Model in Mathematics and the Natural and Social Sciences*, Eds. Hazemier, B., and Vuysje, D., D. Reidel Publishing Co., 1961.
132. Szaniawski, K. 'The value of perfect information', *Synthese*, **17**, 1967.
133. Thurley, K., Hatchett, M., Henley, J., Latham, P., and Trill, J. *Structure and Operation of Selected Maintenance Organisations in the Public and Private Sectors*, 1968–70, Interim Report, 1969.
134. Tocher, K. D. 'The role of models in operational research', *J.R.S.S.*, Series A, **124**, 2, 1961.
135. Tocher, K. D. *The Role of Operational Research*, British Steel, 1961.
136. Tocher, K. D. *Control Research Seminar*, Lancaster University, 1968.
137. Thomson, J. 'Traffic restraints in Central London', *J.R.S.S.*, A, **130**, 3, 1967.
138. Von Neumann, J., and Morgenstern, O. *Theory of Games and Economic Behaviour*, Princeton University Press, 1953.

139. Wall, H., Orcutt, G., Robinson, E., Suits, D., and de Wolff, P. 'Forecasting on a scientific basis', *Proc. Int. Summer Inst. Curia, Portugal*, Centro de Economia e Financas, Lisboa, September 1966.
140. Wallace, V. *Faithfulness vs. Insight: The Economics of Computer Stochastic Models*, Paper given to the British Ship Research Association, Wallsend, 1970.
141. Weingartner, H. 'Some new views on payback period and capital budgeting decisions', *Man. Sc. Appl.*, **15**, 12, 1969.
142. Weiss, H. K. 'The distribution of urban population and an application to a servicing problem', *O.R.Q.*, **9**, 6, 1961.
143. White, D. J. *Decision Theory*, Allen & Unwin, 1969.
144. White, D. J. *The Value of an Investment Opportunity*, Centre for Business Research, Working Paper No. 14, Manchester University, 1963.
145. White, D. J. 'Optimisation techniques in technology', *International Journal of Production Research*, **9**, 1, 1971.
146. White, D. J. *Dynamic Programming*, Oliver & Boyd, 1969.
147. White D. J. *Attributes and Computational Developments in Dynamic Programming*, Paper given to South Wales Operational Research Group, 1971.
148. White, D. J. 'A critique of the paper "Research methodology in the management sciences: formalism or empiricism", by Beged-Dov, A. G., and Klein, T. A.', *O.R.Q.*, **21**, 1970.
149. White, D. J. 'Problems involving infrequent but significant contingencies', *O.R.Q.*, **20**, 1, 1969.
150. White, D. J. *Decision Theory and Operational Research*, Operational Research Society Conference, 1968.
151. White, D. J. *A Linear Programming Algorithm, a Duality Theorem and a Dynamic Algorithm*, Decision Theory Note No. 8, Department of Decision Theory, Manchester University, 1971.
152. White, D. J. 'Loosely coupled stages in dynamic programming', *Man. Sc. Theory*, **20**, 7, 1973.
153. White, D. J. 'Taxonomic difficulties in operational research', *O.R.Q.*, **17**, 1966.
154. Wold, H. O. 'Model building and scientific method, a graphic introduction', in *Mathematical Model Building in Economics and Industry*, Griffin, 1969.

Index

268

269